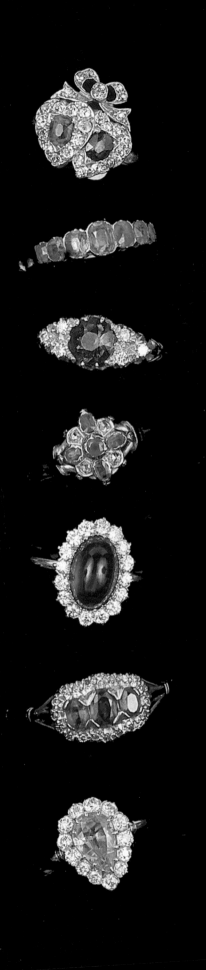
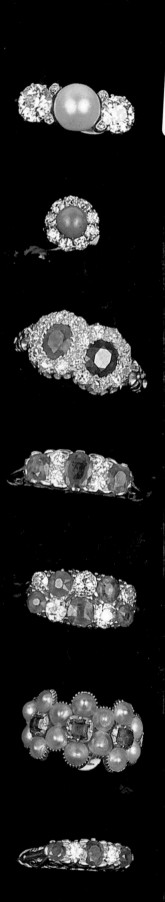
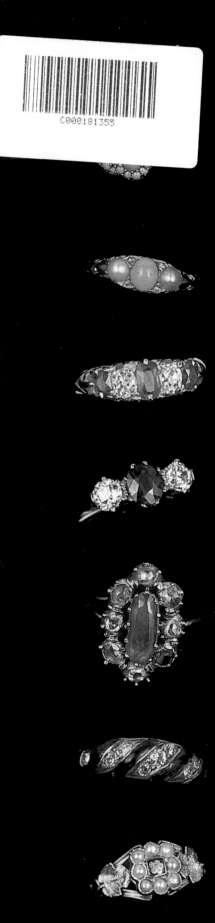

JEWELLERY
REFERENCE AND PRICE GUIDE

JEWELLERY
REFERENCE AND PRICE GUIDE

by Michael Poynder

Prices revised by Michele Rowan

ANTIQUE COLLECTORS' CLUB

First published 1976
© 1976 Michael Poynder
World copyright reserved
2nd revised edition 2000

ISBN 1 85149 309 3

British Library Cataloguing-in-Publication Data
A catalogue record for this book is available from the British Library

The Antique Collectors' Club is grateful to Geoffrey Munn of Wartski, London, for providing colour
illustrations from *Pre-Raphaelite to Arts and Crafts Jewellery*, by Charlotte Gere and Geoffrey Munn, for use
in this book

By the same author

Pi in the Sky
The Lost Magic of Christianity

FRONTISPIECE

Group of gem-set and enamelled gold jewellery by Carlo Giuliano. *Varying in price £3,000–£35,000.*
Wartski, London

TITLE PAGE

Openwork gold brooch pendant in the form of a bird on an olive branch by Giuliano, with translucent
green and red enamel and set with turquoise, coral, pearls and a ruby. *No quote.*
Wartski, London

Printed in England by the Antique Collectors' Club Ltd., Woodbridge, Suffolk IP12 1DS
on Consort Royal Satin paper supplied by the Donside Paper Company, Aberdeen, Scotland

CONTENTS

INTRODUCTION TO 1st EDITION

In compiling this book I have only been able to give an idea of the style and quality of jewellery over the centuries. The book is, after all, a reference and price guide. But, in order that readers might appreciate jewellery more, I have tried to fill in as much background information as possible in terms of origins, technical details, mounting and setting, and the sentiment that attaches to small things of great value.

Man has adorned himself and his women for thousands of years but few pieces of jewellery are ever the same, and no two single stones are identical in terms of colour, clarity and shape. Therefore, each piece of jewellery must be appreciated or rejected in its own right. Also, no two jewellers will evaluate the same piece of jewellery in the same way. Experience and knowledge will always vary with the individual, as will personal taste.

The prices quoted as a guide in this book echo the prices being asked in various retail businesses in England. None of these estimates includes or allows for Value Added Tax which is variable and all jewellery is subject to VAT in one form or another. The machinations of the tax are so complicated that it is not within the scope of this book to teach its workings. However, I would mention that non-residents of the United Kingdom do not have to pay VAT, providing the piece is exported within three months of purchase.

Prices will vary from shop to shop. Obviously if you shop in Bond Street and buy your jewellery from world-renowned firms with expensive premises and a large staff then you must expect to pay for the privilege, but rest assured that you are paying for some of the best craftsmanship in the world. However, antiques markets have sprung up serving the public and the antiques trade, with many individual stall-holders dealing in jewellery, silver and *objets d'art*. This has expanded interest and knowledge in all facets of antiques, and allows members of the public wishing to buy and sell to do so without feeling embarrassed at taking minor objects to an awe-inspiring shop. The 'trade' has therefore become much less formal and this must be a good thing for everybody.

I mention these aspects of the business at some length since they are borne out in the contents of the book, where 95% of the pieces shown are, or have been, on sale in particular shops, or have passed through the salerooms within the last few years [prior to 1976]. Many similar pieces from different shops would seem to have varying prices, and this illustrates the difference between buying from the top of the ladder in the West End and from the bottom in the market stalls. Therefore, I have shown a price against each piece relevant to the shop concerned and within the range of the price asked. Bear in mind that an item of jewellery in its original box will have a greater value.

The prices are within a bracket which the private individual might expect to pay when buying from a retail business, and should not be taken as a guide to what he might be offered when selling. Nobody is in business for charity and you, the individual, must expect a jeweller to make a profit, so the amount you will be offered will vary with the experience and personal taste of the purchaser. I remember being told by a respected member of the jewellery trade that the most important person in the business is the man who says: 'I will give you . . . ' and is prepared to put his money on the table.

Finally, a word on insurance. Every week there are hundreds of burglaries, and jewellery is the prime target. Please bring your insurance up to date every two or three years to keep in line with inflation. You should not be charged more than a nominal fee if you use the same jeweller who did your original valuation.

Michael Poynder
1976

INTRODUCTION TO 2ND EDITION

Since I wrote the original *Price Guide to Jewellery* in 1976 there have been amazing changes in the jewellery markets due to the explosion of unconventional fashion in what we wear and how we express ourselves today. The conservatism of the 1960s and 1970s has been replaced by a society that would be considered outrageous by previous generations. The style of jewellery worn today is therefore very different from the pretty items of the 1930s to 1950s. Much jewellery has been broken up and vast numbers of individual pieces exported to the Far East. Perhaps the worst aspect of the change is the everyday heat treatment of the coloured stones to enhance their colour – it is now rare to find a good blue sapphire that has not been tampered with in the laboratories of Sri Lanka and America. Pollution of the seas has meant that stocks of coral and real pearls are becoming so dangerously depleted that now real pearls are nearly extinct in a natural state.

Since I am no longer actively involved with the jewellery market (having retired to write books on metaphysics), I have been fortunate to have the expertise of Michele Rowan to do the repricing for this edition.

Michael Poynder
1999

NOTE ON PRICING – 2ND EDITION

The prices in this 2nd edition are current retail prices for the same jewellery featured in the 1st edition of Michael Poynder's book. Many individuals and establishments kindly reassessed the value of their pieces. My thanks to the following for so willingly updating their prices:

N. Bloom & Son Ltd.
Cobra & Bellamy
Richard Digby
Harvey & Gore Ltd.
Jack Ogden
Richard Ogden Ltd.
S.J. Phillips Ltd.
Tessiers Ltd.
Wartski London

Some businesses whose jewellery appeared in the 1976 edition have ceased operating. I have consulted dealers who sell similar pieces and formulated 1999 retail prices for those particular pieces.

Thank you to those listed for sharing their knowledge:

Didier
Richard Digby
Blane Thompson
Adam Nathan
Donald Edge
The National Association of Goldsmiths
Kieron Reilly
Trevor Allen
William Wain
Billy Rae
Julie Fox
And most of all Robert Raymond

A number of pieces that were on the market when the book was first published nearly twenty-five years ago are so rare today that it is impractical to put a value on them, hence they are marked 'No quote'. Even so, by showing such a vast range of jewellery periods and styles, Michael Poynder's book remains an invaluable guide to anyone interested in this subject, retailers and collectors alike.

Michele Rowan
London, 1999

Sizes: Every effort has been made to show jewellery actual size. However, in a book of this nature, both design constrictions and the use of composite photographs means this has not always been practical or possible. In such cases, jewellery is either shown as near actual size as possible, or the size or approximate size is given.

Illustrations: Time and security were against removing hundreds of individual pieces from place to place in order to create the plates; as a result, jewellery not relevant to a particular plate is occasionally included in it. All items, however, are described and priced.

MATERIALS AND PROCESSES
used in the creation of jewellery

DIAMONDS

Diamonds are pure carbon crystals and are the hardest substance known to man. The main colour is white although they occur in a variety of fancy colours, thus enabling the jeweller to produce fascinating and exciting designs. They are the most common of the four main precious stones, the other three being ruby, emerald and sapphire.

Traditionally, diamond is the emblem of love and fearlessness. The finest diamonds are graded as 'finest white' and any diamond that is not white, or is an off-shade of white, is referred to as 'coloured' or 'fancy', with the appropriate colour. Blue-white is a term used to denote a diamond with a distinct bluish tinge due to natural fluorescence. Another expression often used is 'of the first water'; this is not a gemmological term and means nothing.

Diamonds have a natural brilliance which has captivated man over the centuries, and the stone has been sought after from early times.

The earliest mining of diamonds was in India, and historically is thought to have dated from around 500B.C. The most important mining area was Golconda. Borneo and Indonesia have also produced stones since the Dark Ages, and these three places were the major sources of world supply until the discovery of diamonds in Brazil in the early 18th century. The impetus that this discovery gave to the diamond trade meant that large quantities of jewellery were produced in Europe in the 18th and 19th centuries. It was not until the discovery of diamonds in Australia in the middle of the 19th century and, far more important, the discoveries in South Africa around the turn of the century, that diamonds began to fall within the price range of ordinary people. Since then, diamonds have been found in large quantities in Africa – in Angola, south-west Africa, Zaire, Sierra Leone – and more recently in Russia. Only a minority of all stones mined throughout the world are of gem quality and the great bulk are used in industry for grinding and cutting. Diamonds are found in 'pipes' in a substance known as blue ground, or in alluvial deposits such as the beds of streams. In some cases they are mined from the sea where the sand that contains them is sucked up from the sea-bed and filtered.

The cutting of diamonds has developed in order to show the stones at their best, the 'brilliant' cut being the most effective. Diamonds have been cut in many different ways but their brilliance is sometimes sacrificed in order to produce a different shape of stone, such as baguette. See pp.331–335.

Technicalities: Chemical composition: carbon. Crystal structure: cubic, forming octahedra, dodecahedra, 24- and even 48-sided crystals. Hardness: 10. S.G.: 3.52. R.I.: 2.42. Diamonds are basically classified in terms of their worth under the headings of clarity and colour. Clarity means exactly what it says. A flawless stone is a stone that shows no inclusions at all under a 10 x magnification jeweller's glass. Diamonds are graded from 'flawless' to 'heavily spotted', i.e. including spots of carbon, flaws and discoloration. Colour is graded from 'finest white' to 'cape'. Synthetic gem diamonds are still too expensive to produce to take the place of natural stones. However, they have been imitated in jewellery by white zircons, sapphires, crystals and pastes, all of which should be easily identified by the experienced eye. Synthetically-made imitations such as strontium titanate (fabulite), YAG (cirolite, diamonair or diagem), synthetic rutile and synthetic white spinels and sapphires may fool members of the public who are not used to handling them, but they should not fool the expert!

Plate 1.

1. Georgian diamond spray brooch set in silver and gold, c.1820. *£20,000 – £30,000.*

2. Victorian diamond spray brooch, the flowerhead *en tremblant* and set with a ruby, *£15,000 – £20,000.*

3. Reproduction diamond spray brooch, set with old-cut diamonds in silver and gold, using the same methods of craftsmanship as the originals. *£10,000.*

4. Georgian diamond flower spray brooch, *en tremblant* and pavé set, c.1800. *£15,000.*

5. Small Georgian rose diamond flower brooch, closed back, c.1800. *£1,750 – £2,000.*

Wartski, London

Plate 2.

1. Mid-Victorian ruby and diamond star brooch set in silver and gold, c.1860. £6,000 – £8,000.

2. Mid-Victorian amethyst and diamond oval cluster brooch set in silver and gold, c.1860. £6,000 – £7,000.

3. Early Victorian carved cabochon garnet, diamond and pearl cluster brooch which also forms the centre and clasp of a bracelet, c.1840. £4,000 – £5,000.

4. Early Victorian emerald and diamond cluster brooch set in silver and gold, c.1850. £7,000 – £10,000.

5. Early Victorian sapphire and diamond peacock-feather brooch set in silver and gold, c.1840. £6,000 – £7,500.

6. Cabochon emerald, ruby, sapphire and diamond open-work floral brooch in early 19th century style, mounted in silver and gold. £8,000 – £10,000.

7. Late Georgian fine pink topaz and diamond rectangular cluster brooch set in silver and gold, open-backed, c.1830. £10,000+.   *S.J. Phillips*

Plate 3.

18th century diamond suite of necklace and earrings in girandole form, the linked ribbon loops and pendant sections set with rose- and cushion-cut diamonds. An elaborate and formal suite with a large weight of set stones. *No quote.*   *Christie's*

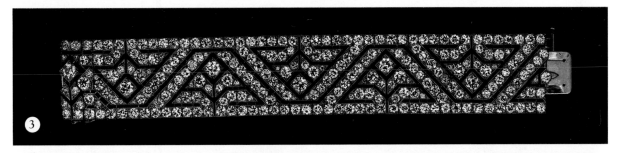

Plate 4.

1. Diamond tiara formed of twisted scrolls, c.1935. £20,000+.

2. Art deco diamond bracelet, formed of six linked sections, set in platinum, c.1920. £12,000 – £18,000.

3. Diamond bracelet of open triangular design, set in platinum, by Van Cleef & Arpels. *No quote*.

4. Art deco diamond link bracelet. £12,000 – £14,000.

5. Important emerald and brilliant-cut diamond bracelet of twelve emeralds and ten diamonds. *No quote*.

Christie's

13

RUBIES

Rubies are probably the rarest of the four main precious stones and are red in colour. They belong to the gem species called corundum which has only one other group, sapphire. They occur in mines and alluvial deposits in conjunction with various semi-precious stones.

Rubies have always had superstition attached to them because they are the colour of blood, and in the Far East where they are mainly found they are considered to enhance the wearer's divinity and protect him against force and illness. Unlike most gemstones, rubies do not occur in large sizes and stones of the finest colour and clarity seldom weigh more than a few carats. A 5ct. stone of top quality is considered of importance, and over 10cts. a great rarity.

The finest stones come from the mines in the Mogok area of Burma where they have been mined for centuries. These stones are of a beautiful bright red, often referred to as 'pigeon's blood' red. Although Thailand is next door to Burma, the rubies of that country are not of the same colour and quality, tending to be darker, often with a brownish tinge, and commonly referred to as Siam rubies, to differentiate quality. Rubies are found all over the Indian sub-continent, and Sri Lanka (Ceylon) in particular produces a large quantity from the Ratnapura area. However, they tend to be pale and pinkish, and are not used a great deal in western jewellery. Although these are the main sources, reports have appeared of gem quality rubies being found in Africa, but not of any significant size.

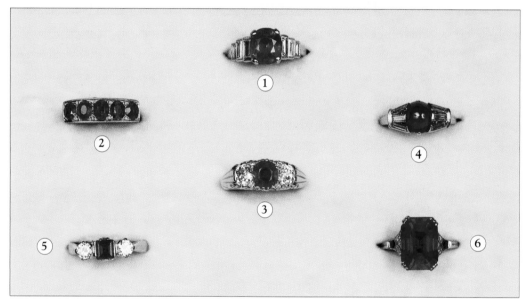

Plate 5.

1. Fine Burma ruby of 2.75cts., mounted as a ring in platinum with baguette diamond shoulders. £15,000 – £25,000.

2. Art deco ruby five stone ring with diamond points in a curved rectangular platinum mount. £4,000 – £6,000.

3. Traditional ruby and diamond three stone ring in yellow gold. £8,000 – £12,000.

4. Art deco cabochon ruby ring with baguette diamond shoulders, set in platinum. £6,000 – £9,000.

5. Ruby and diamond three stone ring set with a square-cut ruby in 18ct. yellow gold. £3,000 – £4,000.

6. Art deco red tourmaline (rubellite) ring in platinum with onyx and diamond shoulders. £ 1,500 – £2,500.

Prices vary considerably on subtle colour qualities and variation in rubies.   N. Bloom

14

The most usual cut is a combination of a brilliant-cut crown and a step-cut pavilion, and most stones are native-cut, i.e. faceted and polished by the miners at source. This is easily discernible, even to the inexperienced eye, as the facets are not uniform, and the shape of the cut stones by no means symmetrical, having been cut to give maximum weight and to show their best colour. Some rubies (and sapphires), because of their crystal formation, when cut *en cabochon* show a property known as asterism. This is a whitish, six- (sometimes twelve-) rayed star best viewed under a direct light. These stones are seldom the finer reds (or blues) and are usually translucent to opaque and paler in colour. They are known as star rubies or sapphires, and are particularly popular with Asiatics and Americans (see Plate 6).

Technicalities: Chemical composition: aluminium oxide (Al_2O_3). Crystal structure: trigonal, forming hexagonal crystals. Hardness: 9. S.G.: 3.99. R.I.: 1.76–1.77. Ruby is coloured by chromium, and the darker colour and brownish tint in Siam stones is due to traces of iron. Synthetic rubies are made in laboratories, usually by the Verneuil process, but they are distinguishable to an expert since they are too perfect, the colour too good, and they will show inclusions of minute gas bubbles rather than any of the small natural inclusions normally found in natural stones. Synthetic star-stones are also made by the Verneuil process, but their body-colour is usually much stronger than in natural star-stones, and the rays of the star much sharper. A particular inclusion in natural stones is known as 'silk', which through a jeweller's glass looks like a very fine layer of white silk strands.

'Balas ruby' is a misnomer applied to red spinel, particularly in medieval times when, gemmologically, stones were not always distinguishable one from another. Spinels are often doubled with glass or crystal in order to pass them off as rubies.

Plate 6.

1. Pair of star rubies, set as cufflinks surrounded by baguette diamonds in platinum, approximately 14cts. rubies. *No quote.*

2. Fine star ruby of good colour and showing pronounced asterism, weighing 26.66cts. This is a particularly good colour for a star stone as the background colour is normally much milkier. Although the asterism is said to be pronounced, it does not show in the photograph as well as in the cufflinks left and right. *No quote.*

3. Pair of star ruby and diamond cluster earrings, weight of the two rubies approximately 22cts., and a cabochon ruby and diamond cluster ring, the ruby weighing approximately 15cts. *No quote.*

Sotheby Parke Bernet, Hong Kong

15

EMERALDS

Emeralds are green in colour. They belong to a gem species called beryl, which also includes aquamarine (pale greenish-blue), golden beryl (yellow) and morganite (pink). Emeralds are usually found on their own whereas the other three are often mined together. (See also p.28.)

There is a certain superstition attached to emeralds because of their colour, and they are still thought to be unlucky. Although they are hard stones, they have a fracture property and nearly always show inclusions and marks to the naked eye. A 'clean' emerald should be treated with suspicion as it might well be a synthetic.

They have been mined since archaic times, originally in Egypt, although these stones were of poor quality. The most famous and lasting source is in South America (Colombia) and the original abundant supply of fine stones came to Europe for the first time after the Spanish conquest. The main Colombian mines are Muzo, Chivor and Cosquez, and all three supply top quality stones. A small number of stones are mined in Brazil, but they are generally of poor quality. Other known sources still in use today are Russia (Ural Mountains) mined from 1830 onwards, Australia 1890 onwards, and South Africa 1920 onwards. India and Pakistan produced emeralds in ancient times, but the mines were only reopened in the 1940s. Zimbabwe (Rhodesia), Tanzania, Zambia and Zaire have produced emeralds, and stones from the Sandawana mine in Zimbabwe can be of excellent quality. Other minor sources are Norway, South Carolina and Mozambique.

The finer stones are normally step-cut, also known as emerald-cut, as this shows their natural colour to best advantage. Small stones are brilliant-cut and are used extensively with other small stones in jewellery. Lesser quality stones may be cut *en cabochon* or as beads. Occasionally, emeralds are cut as cameos or intaglios, but this is difficult due to the fracture properties already mentioned.

Technicalities: Chemical composition: beryllium aluminium silicate ($Be_3Al_2(SiO_3)_6$). Crystal structure: hexagonal, forming hexagonal prisms. Hardness: 7¾ S.G.: 2.69–2.75. R.I.:1.56–1.59. Synthetics are laboratory-made in the United States (some are marketed as Chatham emeralds) and are often used in jewellery. Clear beryl and quartz doublets with a green gelatine 'sandwich' are also used but are easily discernible with a jeweller's glass. Emeralds generally show red through the Chelsea Colour Filter which may be used as a rough guide to help identification.

Plate 7.

Emerald and diamond suite in granulated gold setting, c.1820. *£15,000 – £20,000.*   *S.J. Phillips*

Plate 8.

1. Victorian emerald and diamond three stone ring in an 18ct. carved gold mount, c.1870. *£10,000 – £15,000.*

2. Large single stone, emerald (4.93cts.) ring in 18ct. white gold with baguette diamond shoulders. *£15,000 – £25,000.*

3. Victorian emerald and diamond three stone ring in an 18ct. carved gold mount, c.1880. *£8,000 – £12,000.*

4. Edwardian emerald and diamond three stone ring, the stones collet-set in platinum and yellow gold. *£7,500.*

5. Edwardian emerald and diamond rectangular double cluster ring in white and yellow gold. *£2,500–£3,000.*

Prices vary considerably on subtle colour qualities and variation in emeralds.   *N. Bloom*

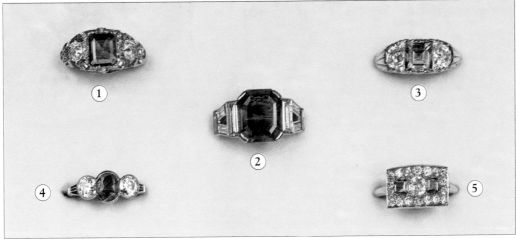

SAPPHIRES

Sapphires belong to the corundum family. They are best known as blue, but in fact occur in just about every colour possible, including a deep pink when they resemble rubies (the other member of the corundum family).

Blue sapphires are particularly popular in the western world, as they go so well with the natural colouring of northern women with their blue or grey eyes and pale skins. Amongst the peoples of the Middle and Far East the sapphire has a peculiar superstition attached to it, whereby it is supposed either to bring the wearer great luck and fortune, or great misfortune; but it is not until the owner has worn the stone that he or she will know which way fortune will swing. This superstition is only attached to the colour blue, and to blue sapphires, which is why one seldom sees blue sapphires or blue enamel in jewellery from those parts of the world. Stones of the finest quality occur in larger sizes than either rubies or emeralds and superb stones in excess of 60cts. appear on the market.

Sapphires are found in different parts of the world and vary enormously in quality and colour. The finest ones are considered to come from Burma and Kashmir. The Burma stones are a deep royal blue without any hint of mauve, and have a great deal of 'life' and brilliance. Kashmir stones are particularly fine and have their own colour range which is hard to describe: it is a royal blue, but with a very slight milky appearance due to minute inclusions of 'silk' (already mentioned in connection with rubies). They are considered by some experts to be even finer than the best Burmese stones. The mines in Kashmir are at over 14,000 feet above sea-level, and for much of the year are inaccessible due to the extremes of climate. Thailand is a major source of sapphires, but they tend to be dark and a duller blue and therefore are not nearly as costly. Sri Lanka produces probably the greatest amount of gem quality sapphires in the world, from the Ratnapura area. The characteristic colour here is known as 'cornflower' blue, and they can be beautiful stones of great brilliance and size. Sri Lanka is also the main producer of the 'fancy-coloured' sapphires: white, yellow, purple, green, pink and a very rare colour – peachy orange – known as Padparascha, which means lotus blossom. It is most unusual to find a really good blue stone showing the property of asterism. Star sapphires are translucent and have a base-colour of greyish-blue. Australia produces a large quantity of blue stones, but they tend to be inky, over-dark and usually have a greenish tinge. They are not considered to compare in quality with the Asiatic stones. The only other major source is Montana, in the United States, and these are easily recognisable for their intense steely blue. They seldom occur in large sizes, but are used in art nouveau and 20th century jewellery.

Technicalities: Chemical composition: aluminium oxide (Al_2O_3). Crystal structure: trigonal, forming bi-pyramids. Hardness: 9. S.G.: 3.99. R.I.: 1.76–1.77. Synthetic sapphires are made in laboratories by the Verneuil process, as are star sapphires. When viewed through the jeweller's glass or microscope, they normally show curved colour bands as opposed to straight

Plate 9.

Unusually large engraved and enamelled silver and gold mounted brooch set centrally with a sapphire, by Child & Child, c.1900. *No quote.*   *Wartski, London*

bands in natural stones, and minute gas bubbles may also be visible. Synthetic white sapphires are sometimes used to imitate diamonds.

The usual cuts apply to sapphires – step-cut, brilliant-cut, mixed-cut, cabochon (the only cut used for star stones), and beads. Native-cut sapphires are common, even in highly sophisticated jewellery produced by some of the great jewellery houses, since to re-cut the stone in modern terms would not necessarily enhance its colour and it would certainly lose weight. Native cutters have an instinctive eye and centuries of inherited experience in faceting stones. When cutting a parti-coloured stone, they have the ability to facet it in such a way as to show the greatest amount of colour throughout the stone. This is done by cutting it with the strongest colour at the base, so that the stone appears to have a uniform colour when viewed through the table, whereas if viewed from the side, it might be almost clear except for a small concentration of colour near the pavilion. These parti-coloured stones are described as having 'windows', which means that when tilted a clear view through a colourless part of the stone becomes visible. Naturally this detracts from the value of the stone.

Plate 10.

1. Large traditional Victorian sapphire and diamond cluster ring, the sapphire weighing 7.14cts., mounted in 18ct. gold. *£10,000 – £15,000.*

2. Edwardian sapphire (3.25cts.) and double-row diamond cluster ring set in platinum. *£5,000 – £8,000.*

3. Large Ceylon (Sri Lanka) cornflower sapphire (16.35cts.) mounted as a ring with diamonds, in gold. *£10,000 – £15,000.*

4. Square-cut sapphire (1.60cts.) and oval-shaped diamond cluster ring, mounted in platinum. *£2,500 – £3,000.*

5. Sapphire and diamond three stone ring in white gold. *£2,000 – £3,000.*

6. Large sapphire five stone ring containing approximately 6cts. of sapphires in an 18ct. yellow gold mount. *£3,000 – £5,000.*

Prices vary considerably on subtle colour qualities and variation in sapphires.　　　　　*N. Bloom*

GARNETS

There are four types of garnet used in jewellery differing in colour from red to green. They are called pyrope, almandine, hessonite and demantoid.

Pyrope garnets: Sometimes called Bohemian garnets because of their traditional source in southern Europe, these are a deep blood red colour and were popular in Victorian jewellery. They are usually small in size and rose-cut. Main source – Bohemia.

Almandine garnets: These are a lovely deep red, tinged with violet. Used in Greek, Roman and Anglo-Saxon jewellery, they were flat cut and set in brooches and pins, sword hilts and shields, as can be seen in the Sutton Hoo burial hoard in the British Museum. Almandines have been used extensively since then, in all forms. They were particularly popular in the late 18th and early 19th centuries, set in suites or as the surround for memorial and romantic brooches. Garnet jewellery was used by the middle classes of the period. In the Victorian era it was popular to cut almandines *en cabochon* and when cut in this way they are known as carbuncles. Main sources are India and Sri Lanka.

Hessonite garnets: Bright orange-brown stones, not used as much as the other types of garnet, and often mistaken for sherry-coloured citrines or precious topaz. Main source – Sri Lanka.

Demantoid garnets: These are a bright vivid green with 'fire' and are rarely found in excess of 5cts. The colour is something between an emerald and a peridot. The only source of any significance is the Ural Mountains of Russia; they were first mined in any quantity in the latter part of the 19th century, therefore seldom appearing in antique jewellery prior to 1850.

Technicalities: *Pyrope:* Chemical composition: magnesium aluminum silicate $(Mg_3Al_2(SiO_4)_3)$. Crystal structure: cubic. Hardness: 7¼. S.G.: 3.80. R.I.: 1.75.

Almandine: Chemical composition: iron aluminium silicate $(Fe_3Al_2(SiO_4)_3)$. Crystal structure: cubic. Hardness: 7½. S.G.: 3.95 and over. R.I. 1.78.

Hessonite: Chemical composition: calcium aluminium silicate $(Ca_3Al_2(SiO_4)_3)$. Crystal structure: cubic. Hardness: 7¼. S.G.: 3.65. R.I.: 1.742–1.748.

Demantoid: Chemical composition: calcium iron silicate $(Ca_2Fe_3(SiO_4)_3)$. Crystal structure: cubic. Hardness: 6½. S.G.: 3.82–3.85. R.I.: 1.89. Demantoid garnets have been imitated by paste, and a green, grossular garnet of the same composition as hessonite garnet has been used to imitate jade and is known as 'Transvaal Jade'.

Plate 11.

1. Pyrope garnet bracelet, the garnets set in hinged gold sections of four stones, c.1900. £800 – £1,200.

2. Victorian oval open circle brooch set in metal gilt. £75.

3. Cabochon garnet (carbuncle) stickpin in gold claw setting, Victorian, c.1870. £200.

4. Cabochon garnet stickpin in gold scroll setting. £200.

5. Late 18th century moss agate and flat-cut garnet brooch set in silver. £450 – £500.

6. Georgian filigree gold flat-cut garnet and Oriental pearl drop earrings, c.1820. £850 – £950.

7. Mid-Victorian flexible gold bracelet with carbuncle and gold clasp, c.1850. £1,500 – £1,800.

8. Large carbuncle set in a plain gold circular frame with gold pendant fitting and typical mid-Victorian flexible graduated fringe. £1,200.

9. 18th century Spanish flat-cut garnet pendant with cross, and earrings (below left and right) *en suite*, set in gold, c.1775. £800 – £1,200.

10. Victorian engraved gold bow with garnet set heart pendant drop, c.1870. £650 – £850.

11. Flat-cut garnet necklace of floral design set in and backed with gold, the pendant detachable, English, c.1820. £3,000.

Cameo Corner

MOONSTONES

Moonstones are a translucent bluish-white colour and belong to the feldspar family, which also includes labradorite and amazonite. Of these three best known feldspars, moonstone is the most used in jewellery. Better quality moonstones are a bluish colour, with a fine silvery sheen called adularescence, while poor quality stones are a dull, dirty grey with yellowish tinges and are almost transparent. Moonstones were popular at the end of the last century and were used in art nouveau jewellery in conjunction with garnets, turquoises, fire opals and enamels, etc.

Labradorite: A greyish feldspar with iridescent flashes of greens and blues reflected from within the stone. It has the effect of butterflies' wings. It was used in art nouveau and art deco period jewellery and first came from the coast of Labrador, hence its name.

Amazonite is little used in jewellery.

The major source, as for so many gemstones, is Sri Lanka, although moonstones also come from Madagascar, Burma, India and Tanzania. The Madagascan moonstones have a tendency to be golden yellow, as have the Burmese stones which also show a cat's eye effect, but not as strongly as the chrysoberyl cat's eye. They are always cut *en cabochon* to show their adularescence.

Technicalities: *Moonstone:* Chemical composition: potash feldspar (orthoclase), $(KA1Si_3O_8)$. Crystal structure: monoclinic. Hardness: 6. S.G.: 2.56–2.59. R.I.: 1.52–1.525.

Plate 12.

Examples of well-designed and well-made jewellery by Sybil Dunlop, showing the sensitive use of stones with silver and gold for which her work is noted. Only a few of her earlier pieces were signed, and their style is not so formed as her later unsigned pieces. Mark SD.

1. Silver pendant set with two hexagonal-cut amethysts, opals, garnets, chalcedony and tourmalines, c.1935. *£2,000.*

2. Moonstone, mother-of-pearl, crystal and silver cross. *£1,200.*

3. Amethyst and silver open circle ivy leaf brooch. *£400 – £500.*

4. Open circle, floral brooch in silver and 18ct. gold set with crystals, aquamarines, tourmalines, emeralds and chalcedony. *£2,000.*

5. 15ct. gold floral pendant and chain set with moonstones, emeralds and an amethyst. *£3,000 – £4,000.*

6. 15ct. gold and silver open circle brooch set with tourmalines, chrysoprases and moonstones, by Henry Wilson. *£2,000.* *Private Collection, The Purple Shop*

OPALS

Opals occur in four main colours: white, black and green, which throw out vivid colour flashes, and translucent red known as 'fire' opal. It was held in esteem as a gemstone until the 19th century when the influence of Sir Walter Scott's novel *Anne of Geierstein* made people think of it as unlucky. Opal contains a varying amount of water, and extreme changes of temperature will cause it to crack and sometimes break. As it is not particularly hard, it will also scratch easily. This may well have added to the superstition that opal is unlucky, as from early times it has always been considered that to break anything precious will bring bad luck. Emeralds and mirrors are also examples of this, as both also have a high fracture property. The beautiful effects of iridescence seen in opals has led to the use of the term 'opalescence'. Opal also occurs in fossilised wood, sometimes used in jewellery. This can be very attractive, with seams of brightly coloured opal veined through the dark wood. Water opals are very pale, almost clear, and have a poor play of colour.

Opals, which have been mined in Hungary and Czechoslovakia since Roman times, are characteristically a creamy colour, with small points of red, blue and green; these are referred to as 'harlequin' opals. Those mined in Mexico range in colour from yellow to deep red, and are called fire opals. They are not used in jewellery a great deal as the colour is difficult to wear, but they can look magnificent on dark-complexioned women. Australia is a major source of fine opals and they have been mined there since the 1870s. The most famous location is Lightning Ridge in New South Wales, where black opals of top gem quality are found. Other famous mines, better known for white opals, are Coober Pedy and Andamooka. Opals occur at comparatively shallow levels, and there are no great mining problems except for the extreme temperatures encountered, often as high as 130°F. This in itself can cause an opal to crack when it is brought to the surface.

Only fire opals are faceted, either brilliant- or step-cut. Other opals are cut *en cabochon* or as beads, although where they occur in strong bands of colour, they are sometimes cameo cut, or carved to form figures or animals. Wood opals may be cut *en cabochon* or flat-cut as pendants mounted in gold or silver and were very popular in art nouveau jewellery.

Technicalities: Chemical composition: a hydrated silica (SiO_2nH_2O). Crystal structure: amorphous considered to be a solidified jelly. Hardness: 5½–6½. S.G.: 1.98–2.20. R.I.: 1.44–1.46. Doublets and triplets are common. They are composed of a thin slice of opal backed with opal matrix or wood opal, and black plastic or black mother-of-pearl. When buying what purports to be a black opal, it is best to see the stone unmounted. Synthetic opals, produced in the laboratory and marketed as Gilson opals, are distinguishable from natural opal only by laboratory-testing.

Plate 13.

1. 'Peacock' opal, diamond and gold owl brooch. £4,000.

2. Carved opal set in a brooch designed as a bird, with diamonds and rubies in gold. £5,000.

3. Edwardian diamond and black opal triplet pendant. £1,800 – £2,000.

4. Opal, ruby, diamond and gold bird brooch. £3,000 – £5,000.

5. Pair of opal and diamond drop earrings. £1,800 – £2,200.

6. Opal, emerald, diamond and gold lizard brooch. £5,000.

7. Edwardian opal and diamond bar brooch, c.1900. £1,650.

8. Oval opal and diamond cluster brooch set in platinum. £3,500.

9. Late Victorian opal and diamond large shallow crescent brooch, c.1895. £1,200 – £1,500.

10. Opal and diamond traditional flower cluster brooch. £1,600 – £1,800.

11. Art nouveau opal cameo ring in traditional diamond cluster mount. £1,600 – £1,800.

B. Barnett Ltd., Michael Poynder

TURQUOISES

Turquoise is an opaque stone which can vary in colour from the blue described by its own name to a palish blue-green. It was used a great deal in early Egyptian and Persian jewellery in conjunction with coral and gold. Later it became popular with the Victorians and may be found in fine suites of jewellery, often in conjunction with pearls. The best turquoise is a bright blue, but the poorer varieties tend to be greenish and contain flecks and seams of the natural parent rock, which is known as limonite. Turquoise is porous and may discolour after a time from the acids absorbed from the human skin. Scent will also cause discoloration.

Iran, the Sinai Peninsula, Tibet, India and China are all major sources. Turquoise is also found in Mexico, where it was used in Aztec jewellery, and in Colorado and New Mexico where with silver it became the traditional jewellery of the American Indians (see pp.166–167). Russia is another source and turquoise has surprisingly been found in Cornwall, but of poor quality.

The best material is cut *en cabochon*, although it may be faceted. It is frequently pavé set. Larger pieces make fine hardstone ornaments.

Technicalities: Chemical composition: hydrous copper aluminium phosphate. Crystal structure: triclinic, although in most cases crypto-crystalline. Hardness: 6. S.G.: 2.60–2.90. R.I.1.61–1.65. Since the finest turquoise is valuable, it has been imitated by stained ivory, porcelain, vitreous glass and enamel. All of these can be recognised by the experienced eye. Turquoise itself is sometimes stained in order to improve the colour, but this colour is often only superficial and will reveal itself if the stone is cut or scratched.

Plate 14.

1. Early Victorian turquoise and gold snake necklace with garnet eyes and rose diamond markings on the head, engraved date 1844. The turquoises near the tail are partly discoloured, probably due to being in contact with scent. £4,000 – £5,000.

2. Mid-Victorian open-work necklace of turquoises and pearls set in silver and gold, c.1850. £4,000 – £5,000.

3. Victorian turquoise and gold claw stickpin, c.1870. £250.

4. Early Victorian pavé set Maltese cross in silver and backed with gold, c.1840. £500.

5. Mid-Victorian butterfly brooch set with turquoises and rose diamonds in gold, c.1870. £2,000 – £2,500.

6. Edwardian diamond bow brooch with turquoise centre and a drop turquoise, in silver and gold, c.1900. £1,200 – £1,500.

7. Unusual mid-Victorian diaper-patterned turquoise and rose diamond locket, c.1860. A lovely example of top quality setting, convex pavé set. £3,000 – £3,500.

8. Turquoise-set Halley's Comet, 1834. £200 – £300.

9. Mid-Victorian gold scroll brooch with circular pendent locket set with turquoises, c.1845. £650 – £750.

10. Victorian turquoise and silver scrolled brooch, with locket behind, c.1880, of indifferent quality. £150 – £200.

11. Late Victorian gold leaf brooch set with turquoises and rubies, c.1885. £550.

Cameo Corner

THE BERYL FAMILY

This group consists of a variety of attractive stones used in jewellery, the best known of these being emerald which, because of its importance, is treated separately. The other beryls are: aquamarine – sky-blue to pale green; morganite – pink; heliodor – yellow; and green beryl.

The Georgians and Victorians used pale greenish aquamarines mounted with gold in elaborate suites. At the turn of the century it was discovered that by treating aquamarines with controlled heat they turned sky-blue, and this type of stone is now fashionable and highly priced. Large aquamarines are usually mounted as single stone rings or pendants with baguette diamonds. Morganite is a soft pale pink, rather similar to pink sapphire or a pale tourmaline, but it is not widely used in jewellery. Heliodor, or golden beryl, has become more popular in recent years. Green beryl is found in 18th century jewellery, particularly Spanish and Portuguese, when it is often mounted with emeralds, or occasionally pastes and crystals. It tends to be a weakish green and without laboratory tests is difficult to distinguish from pale emeralds.

The main sources of aquamarine are Brazil and the Ural Mountains of Russia (the fine aquamarine illustrated in Plate 142 is probably from the Russian mines). Aquamarine is also found in the United States, Burma and Zimbabwe (Rhodesia), which all produce rather weak-coloured stones. Morganite is chiefly found in California and heliodor in Brazil, south-west Africa and Madagascar. Green beryl is normally mined in the same locations as aquamarine.

As the various beryls tend to be pale it is important that the stones are fairly large when cut. They are normally trap-cut and set as rings, brooches and pendants, although stones in the centre of brooches are sometimes mixed-cut, and earrings briolette-cut.

Technicalities: Chemical composition: beryllium aluminium silicate ($Be_3Al_2(SiO_3)_6$). Crystal structure: hexagonal forming six-sided prisms terminating in pyramids. Hardness: 7½. S.G.: 2.68–2.90, aquamarines have lower density figure and morganites higher. R.I.: 1.57–1.59, again, aquamarines lower figure and morganites higher. Aquamarine is the only stone of the four mentioned which is of sufficient value to warrant imitation, and it is simulated by synthetic spinels and pastes.

Plate 15.

Fine Georgian aquamarine and filigree gold suite of necklace and earrings, the aquamarines foiled and backed with gold, set in a filigree gold mount of *cannetille* work, English, c.1830. £10,000+.
Cameo Corner

AMBER

Amber is yellow, brown or red in colour and is a fossilised pine resin. Sometimes it includes natural insects and when found like this it is considered to be a talisman. It dates from before the Ice Age and most deposits are thought to be some 30,000,000 years old. It is soft, light, and preferably clear and can be polished and carved although it is not normally faceted in jewellery. Amber can include flies, beetles, fish-scales and sometimes vegetable seeds, and was thought to have magical properties in ancient times because it conducts electricity. It has long been popular in jewellery form, and the Victorians made use of it extensively. Long strings of beads were worn by aesthetic ladies in the art nouveau and art deco periods. Since large pieces of amber are comparatively rare, a process was developed whereby small pieces were pressed together to form a substance called ambroid. It is relatively easy to distinguish, as the pieces were fused together under heat and pressure, and it is possible to see clear fusion lines.

The main source is the Baltic coast of Russia where it is obtained from shallow mines, and red amber is washed up on the shore and out of the sand. Amber also comes from Burma, Italy, and the Black Sea. It is normally cut with a smooth polished surface as beads, rings, brooches or pendants, which are sometimes carved.

Technicalities: Hardness: about 2. S.G.: 1.08. R.I.: 1.54. Amber is often imitated, particularly by bakelite and celluloid, and more recently by polystyrene. Glass has also been used in imitation, but this is much heavier and harder. The best test for amber is to cut a minute portion away from as inconspicuous a place as possible (perhaps round a mounted ring, or from under a claw) and to place the chip in a flame. True amber will burn with a pleasant smell, whereas bakelite will char, celluloid will flare and polystyrene will smell foul.

Plate 16.

1. String of oval red plastic translucent beads, simulating amber. *£150.*

2. Good string of graduated oval orange amber beads. *£250 – £350.*

3. Pale sea-amber bead necklace. *£200.*

4. Lozenge-shaped pendant of pressed amber, with black silk tassel. It is possible to see the lines on the surface of the pendant where individual small pieces of amber have been fused or 'pressed' together under heat. *£50.*

5. Georgian translucent carved amber brooch in the form of a daisy. *£150.*

6. Yellow amber ring set in silver. *£70.*

7. Circular amber bead brooch. *£50.*

8. Large yellow/orange amber pendant. *£200.*

9. Art deco transparent amber and silver ring. *£120.*

10. Small bakelite bead necklace, the centre plaque with a ship engraved on the underside of the circular section, allowing the motif to show through the surface of the bakelite. *£100.*

11. Modern amber ring, carved from one piece of amber. *£180.*

12. Art deco yellow amber and silver brooch. *£90.*

13. Late Victorian faceted amber circular brooch. *£60.*

14. String of translucent red/orange faceted bakelite beads. *£150.*

15. Choker formed of cylindrical beads of varying colours. *£180.*

Antiquarius, Thesaurus, Tony & Sara, The Purple Shop, Bellamy

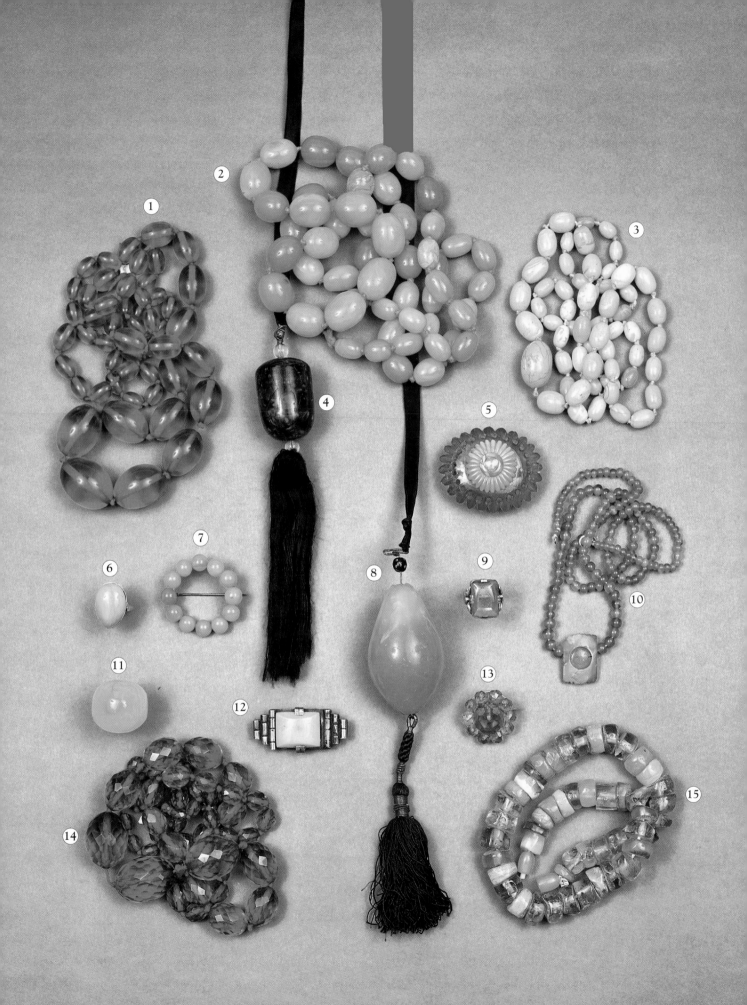

JADE

The term jade refers to two quite separate minerals, known as jadeite and nephrite. Jadeite is normally a pale to dark green, translucent material, and at best is brilliant green and almost transparent, when it is referred to as 'Imperial' jade. The finest jadeite is extremely valuable. Although green is the normally accepted colour range of jade used in jewellery, it also occurs in a variety of colours from black to mauve, red to pink, cream to white.

The coloration of nephrite is from an opaque dark green, referred to as 'spinach' jade, through browns, yellows and greys, to a dense white, referred to as 'mutton-fat' jade. The most common form of nephrite is a pale greyish-green base colour heavily flecked with dark green and it is quite easily recognised by the experienced eye. Both jadeite and nephrite are hard materials and difficult to carve; it is surprising, particularly with nephrite, that the early craftsmen were able to produce such intricate and beautiful designs using primitive tools. Something like 75 per cent of jewellery sold as jade is nephrite, and only 25 per cent the more valuable jadeite.

The main source of jadeite is in Upper Burma, in the valley of the river Uru, a tributary of the Chindwin. It does not appear to have been discovered in China itself. Jadeite from the Uru area entered China at the beginning of the 18th century and the so-called Chinese jades prior to this date, be they in jewellery or fine hardstone carving, are in fact nephrite. Nephrite is found in many parts of the world, and the main source for the Chinese carvers was Turkestan, where it is both mined and found in alluvial deposits as boulders, often of great size and weight. Other sources are Siberia, New Zealand, Silesia, Germany, Italy, Alaska, Rocky Mountains, British Columbia, Mexico, Zimbabwe and Formosa – and no doubt many other places as yet undiscovered.

Jade is cut in jewellery as beads, *en cabochon*, or carved with floral, animal or human motifs which are made into earrings or pendants.

Technicalities: *Jadeite:* Chemical composition: sodium aluminium silicate ($NaAl(SiO_3)_2$). Crystal structure: monoclinic, minute interlocking crystals. Hardness: 7. S.G.: 3.30–3.36. R.I.: 1.64–1.67. Jadeite has been imitated by such materials as green agate (Swiss jade is a misnomer for agate dyed green to simulate jade), bowenite, green grossular garnet (Transvaal jade), and even jadeite itself is sometimes stained to improve the colour, but the staining is only superficial and fades within a few years.
Nephrite: Chemical composition: magnesium calcium silicate with iron ($Ca_2(MgFe)_5(OH)_2(Si_4O_{11})_2$). Crystal structure: monoclinic, interlocking masses of fibres matted together. Hardness: 6½. S.G.: 3.00. R.I. 1.60–1.64. Nephrite has not been imitated so widely as jadeite, since at its best the value is not so high. However, materials such as bowenite and steatite or the grossular garnet may be mistaken for it.

Plate 17.

1. Dark green spinach jade beads. £600 – £800.

2. Variegated green jade beads. £1,500.

3. Circular mutton-fat jade pendant of open-carved design. £175 – £250.

4. Long carved apple-green jade pendant with gold mount. £1,500 – £1,800.

5. Pair of pale green jade and diamond earrings. £500 – £600.

6. 19th century carved jade pendant of variegated mutton-fat with brownish surface patches. £700 – £1,000.

7. String of jade beads of various colours, illustrating the wide range of possible coloration. £700.   *Cameo Corner*

Plate 18 (approx. ½ size).

1. Pale green jade bangle. £400 – £600.

2. Spinach jade (nephrite) bangle. £250 – £350.

3. Ancient jade funeral bangle. £450 – £600.

4. Bowenite bangle (an imitation of jade) with silver repair bands. £120.

5. Pale green jade ring. £150.

6. Dark green jade (nephrite) ring. £120.

7. Floral carved jade (jadeite) ring set in gold. £150.

8. Jade archer's thumb-ring. £150 – £250.

9. Rose quartz floral carving. £150.

10. Jade pendant with Indian inscription. £130.

11. Dark green jade archer's ring. £300.

12. Jade bead necklace with variegated coloured beads. £350.

13. Modern open-work carved steatite pendant imitating brownish and pale green jade. Steatite is better known as soapstone because of its soapy, greasy feel, and is soft enough to be scratched with a finger nail whereas jade is much harder. £75 – £100.

14. Cylindrical jade bead on a silver chain. £300.

15. Carved steatite pendant. £450.

Antiquarius, Stall M1, Thesaurus, The Purple Shop, Tony & Sara

AGATES

Agates are a form of mineral quartz which occur under various well-known names, depending on the colour. They are generally translucent to opaque. They are semi-precious and have been extensively used in jewellery, occurring in many cameos, seals and intaglios. They have always been popular and are still much used today, since they are colourful and inexpensive.

Cornelian, the most common form of agate, is a light orange to deep and clear red. Bloodstone is a dark opaque green flecked with red. One of the rarer agates, chrysoprase, is an attractive translucent pale apple-green. Pale varieties have been stained artificially to simulate the better greens, particularly favoured in Georgian and Victorian times. Onyx is a dark or reddish-brown; this is often banded with white when it is referred to as sardonyx. It may also be stained black and is then known as black onyx. Jasper is either an opaque rich reddish-brown or a pale bluish-mauve; the two colours are sometimes found banded together and such stones were popular in signet rings.

Agates may also be blue, green and translucent white; they sometimes contain inclusions of other materials which form in beautiful patterns, and can look like growing moss, bushes, trees or even landscapes. These are known as moss agates and were cut and mounted extensively in the late 18th and 19th centuries, with borders of flat-cut garnets or with simple gold frames. Flat-cut plaques of the finest agates were used by the great snuffbox makers of this period, including Fabergé.

Australia produced many fine agates, although they are found worldwide. Scottish agates are still mounted today in Scottish Pebble Jewellery (see pp.40–41). This jewellery, the finest of which was made in the Victorian era, is in the form of mosaics of various coloured agates, mounted in silver or gold. Moss agate occurs mainly in the Deccan region of India

Agates are normally cut *en cabochon* or plaque-cut since they are extremely popular for engraving initials or cutting seals and intaglios. If they are evenly banded they may be cut as cameos using layers in the design. However, in Victorian times, cheaper cameos cut from conch shells to achieve the same effect became more popular. Because they are not of sufficient quality, and they are nearly always opaque, agates are not normally faceted, except as beads.

Technicalities: Chemical composition: crypto-crystalline quartz (SiO_2). Crystal structure: trigonal, minute crystals. Hardness: 7. S.G.: 2.58–2.64. R.I.: 1.53–1.54. Agates are often stained.

CHRYSOBERYLS

This group consists of three stones, known as yellow chrysoberyl, a transparent greenish-yellow to brown; alexandrite, green in daylight, changing to red in artificial light; and cat's eye – the chatoyant variety of chrysoberyl.

Chrysoberyl is a hard, bright and attractive stone. In its transparent form it ranges from pale greenish-yellow to brown, although the best known colour is yellow. Pale yellow chrysoberyls from Brazil were popular with the Spanish and Portuguese, and during the 18th century they were mounted in gold to form 'chrysolite' jewellery.

The most valuable of the chrysoberyls is alexandrite, named after the Tsar Alexander II, since it was first discovered in Russia in the 1830s. As mentioned above, alexandrite has a unique quality in that it changes from a grassy-green colour in daylight to a deep red under artificial light. Large alexandrites found in Sri Lanka do not have such a strong colour change, the green appearing more grey, and the red more brown. Because of their rarity, alexandrites have been widely imitated.

Chrysoberyl cat's eyes are the best of their kind and the most highly priced. Their basic colour is greenish-yellow, with a sharp but milky cat's eye reflection across the stone. Quartz and tourmaline cat's eyes are not of the same colour or quality. The best specimens are found in Sri Lanka.

Chrysoberyls are usually flat-cut in Spanish and Portuguese jewellery, though they may be of mixed cut in the 19th century. Cat's eyes are cut *en cabochon* to show the chatoyant effect.

Technicalities: Chemical composition: a double oxide of aluminium ($BeAl_2O_4$). Crystal structure: orthorhombic. Hardness: 8½. S.G.: 3.71–3.72. R.I.: 1.75–1.76. Since alexandrite is rare and good pieces are very expensive, it has been imitated. Synthetic spinel and corundum have been made in the laboratory and show the colour change, although the colours are more subdued than in the natural alexandrite. They are sometimes sold as 'synthetic' alexandrite and have led people to believe that they own a rare stone, whereas in fact the simulant is of little value.

LAPIS LAZULI

Lapis lazuli, also known as lapis, derives from an old Persian word meaning blue, and the colour ranges from the deepest royal blue to pale greyish-blue, speckled with white. It is an opaque rock rather than a true mineral.

Iron pyrites occurs in lapis lazuli and gives the effect of fine gold flecks in the stone. The best lapis is a deep royal blue of continuous even colour without any flecks of pale material. Powdered lapis was used by artists for centuries to produce the fine colours seen in Persian art and in Italian religious painting.

The major source of the best lapis is Afghanistan where it has been mined for over six thousand years. Other sources are South America (Andes), and Colorado, but the quality is not as good. Surprisingly, the Mogok region of Upper Burma, best known for its rubies, also produces lapis.

Since lapis is opaque, there is little point in faceting it. In jewellery it is usually cut *en cabochon* or carved, particularly in Far Eastern jewellery. It is also cut as seals.

Technicalities: Chemical composition: aggregate of sodalite, hauynite, noselite and lazurite. Hardness: 5½. S.G.: 2.5–2.9. R.I.: 1.50. Since the finest lapis is valuable it is considered worth staining jasper blue to imitate it. This is known as Swiss lapis. Paste imitations containing spangles of copper crystals have also been made. Pale lapis itself has been stained a deeper blue, but this will wash out in time.

MALACHITE

Malachite is a copper conglomerate, and a by-product of the copper-mines, hence its strong green colour. It varies in colour from a pale creamy-green to an intense almost black green, usually colour-banded. These bands form attractive irregular curved patterns.

Because of its vivid colour, and the fact that it is found in large lumps, malachite has been used for objets d'art as well as in jewellery. It has been cut into fine flat pieces and used as a stone-veneer on ornamental pillars and vases, as in the Malachite Room at the Hermitage Museum in St. Petersburg. It was used for the bodies of snuffboxes and by ébénistes as an inlay for furniture and for the cases of clocks. Only the finest colours and forms were cut for use in 19th century mosaic jewellery where its unusual natural patterns can give shape and movement to a design.

The main source is the Ural Mountains of Russia, but it is also found in South Australia, and, in particular, the Zaire copper-mines.

It is usually flat-cut for plaque brooches, or in small pieces for mosaic work, and cabochons and beads were popular in the late 19th century.

Technicalities: Chemical composition: hydrated copper carbonate $(Cu_2(OH_2)CO_3)$. Crystal structure: monoclinic, usually minute crystals. Hardness: 4. S.G.: 3.8. R.I.: 1.85. Malachite is not hard, and can be broken and chipped quite easily

PERIDOT

Peridot is a bright green stone, but of a different shade of green from any other stone, which could best be described as 'oily'. It belongs to the family known as olivine.

Peridot is classed as a semi-precious stone, although it is becoming rarer, and therefore more expensive. Fine specimens of unusually large size of the deeper green colour have been found in excess of 100cts., and there is a particularly beautiful example of 136cts. in the Geological Institute in London. Peridot was popular in Victorian jewellery and it is possible to find necklaces of quite large stones set with diamonds.

The major source has traditionally been the Island of St. John in the south-east end of the Red Sea. Peridots have also been found in the Mogok region of Upper Burma, Hawaii, Australia, Norway, Brazil and Mexico. Peridot is normally trap-cut, although mixed cutting is not unusual.

Technicalities: Chemical composition: magnesium iron silicate $(MgFe)_2SiO_4$. Crystal structure: orthorhombic, frequently found as water-worn pebbles. Hardness: 6½. S.G.: 3.34. R.I.: 1.65–1.68, with strong bi-refringence. The characteristic oily colour of peridot has been simulated in the laboratory by synthetic sapphire, and also by pastes.

QUARTZ

Quartz is the most common semi-precious stone used in jewellery. It has a wide colour range, and forms in large clear crystals. Each colour has a different name: crystal or rockcrystal – colourless; citrine – yellow; smoky quartz – brown (in Scotland this is known as 'cairngorm'); amethyst – purple; rose quartz – pink; green quartz – green; and aventurine quartz – green, spangled with mica flakes.

Crystal has been used in jewellery from ancient times and together with white sapphires has imitated diamonds. Paste jewellery is regularly confused with crystal jewellery, as the two can look alike, although faceted and foiled crystals do have more life than paste. Clear crystals have been foiled with different colours to simulate various stones. Crystals may occasionally have inclusions of the mineral rutile which looks like short pieces of hair and when red or golden-coloured is known as 'Venus hair-stone'. Citrine is misnamed topaz, or quartz-topaz, and should not be confused with precious or Brazilian topaz. Citrines and smoky quartz were both popular in the 19th century. Amethysts have long been associated with the Church, as purple robes are strongly connected with Christianity. They have been used consistently in bishops' rings and crosses, and were also popular in Georgian, early Victorian and art nouveau jewellery. The finest amethysts are a rich purple showing red flashes of colour when turned in the light. Rose quartz is less common than other varieties and is seldom completely clear, usually having a milky look about it. Green quartz is not much used in jewellery. Another form of quartz, known as cat's eyes, are a greyish opaque colour with a whitish band of light. They are generally coarser than the fine chrysoberyl cat's eyes, but it is possible to confuse the two if the quartz cat's eye is of excellent quality. Crocidolite is asbestos which has been metamorphosed into quartz. It may be brown, blue or black. A whitish band of light across the base colour gives it the appearance of watered silk. Brown crocidolite is known as tiger's eye; blue and black as hawk's eye.

Quartz is found all over the world in large quantities and when it occurs in clear crystals it is worth cutting for use in jewellery. However, very large crystals, full of inclusions, also occur in all the colour ranges and have been cut and carved for ornamental purposes, for instance Chinese snuffbottles, bowls, crystal balls and German Renaissance crystal carvings. Citrines come from Brazil and smoky quartz from Scotland and Manchuria. The finest amethysts are found in Siberia and Madagascar. Rose quartz is largely found in Brazil, aventurine quartz in India, crocidolite in Africa and quartz cat's eyes in Sri Lanka.

Quartz is cut in most of the different styles, and the quartz cat's eyes are naturally cut *en cabochon* to show the chatoyancy. Crocidolite may be plaque cut or *en cabochon*. Quartz beads are common, and may be faceted or rounded.

Technicalities: Chemical composition: silicon dioxide (SiO_2). Crystal structure: trigonal, forming prisms with pyramids. Hardness: 7. S.G.: 2.65. R.I.: 1.54. Amethyst may be treated with heat to turn quartz yellow. Clear quartz is often used in doublets and triplets to imitate emerald, or as the top layer of an opal triplet.

SPINEL

Spinel is normally found as a red stone, although it does occur in light and dark blue, green and black.

Red spinel is known as 'Balas ruby' and is infamous in that it is often mistaken for and passed off as ruby, since it is found in the same areas in south-east Asia. Its colour range is similar to ruby, although it can never be compared to the 'pigeon's blood' Burma rubies, and is found in much larger sizes. One of the best-known spinels must be the Black Prince's ruby in the Imperial State Crown. Pale blue spinel, which is not a particularly expensive stone, is used to imitate aquamarine, but can be identified as it is a considerably denser stone. Spinels are not much used in western jewellery today, but occur frequently in Asiatic jewellery in conjunction with coloured sapphires.

The principal sources are Sri Lanka and south-east Asia. They are usually trap-, step- or mixed-cut when meant to simulate other stones.

Technicalities: Chemical composition: magnesium aluminate ($MgAl_2O_4$). Crystal structure: cubic. Hardness: 8. S.G.: 3.58–3.90. R.I.: 1.71–1.74. Spinels are synthesised in the laboratory, particularly colourless ones used to imitate diamonds.

TOPAZ

Topaz is a gem species in its own right. Two different colours of topaz are used in jewellery: yellow-brown, which is known as 'Brazilian' or 'precious', and pink. Yellow citrine (quartz) is sometimes wrongly called topaz, or quartz-topaz, but it is a completely different stone.

The beautiful sherry-coloured topaz is hard and polishes well, giving it a bright appearance. It is transparent and usually of even colour, but is easily fractured, so it must be treated with care. Precious topaz was popular with the Georgians and Victorians, probably because it was found in Brazil in the 18th century, and is frequently set in foiled settings with pearls. Pink topaz is rare as a natural stone and the colour is more often induced by heating the sherry-brown stones until they change to pink. However, it is used in Georgian jewellery, usually mounted in a closed setting and backed with pink foil to heighten the colour.

Because topaz is formed in long crystals, it is often cut as a long thin stone, sometimes trap-cut, but more usually mixed-cut, as this shows off its brightness to advantage.

Technicalities: Chemical composition: a fluosilicate of aluminium ($Al_2(F,OH_2)2SiO_4$). Crystal structure: orthorhombic. Hardness: 8. S.G.: 3.53. R.I.: 1.63–1.64.

TOURMALINES

Tourmaline is a stone with a wide variety of colours. Apart from its interest to jewellers, it is used widely in the scientific field, since it will conduct electricity. In jewellery it is best known for its fine pinkish-red stones, sometimes called rubellite, which can command quite high prices and occur in large sizes. Dark green tourmalines are becoming more popular. Blue tourmalines are occasionally found in jewellery, although they are not common. Some modern jewellery makes use of the whole natural tourmaline crystal, which in one crystal is found divided between the pink and green colours, and forms an unusual colour combination.

Tourmaline was probably introduced to Europe from Sri Lanka in the early 18th century. It is found all over the world but the better stones come from Russia, Burma (Mogok area produces fine rubellites), Sri Lanka, Brazil, Madagascar and California. South-west Africa produces a bright green tourmaline called 'chrome' tourmaline because it is coloured by chromium.

The mixed-cut is normal, although step-cutting is used for the better stones. Tourmaline may also be carved, with geometric or floral designs on pieces of lesser quality which are not clear enough to facet or cut as beads.

Technicalities: Chemical composition: a complex borosilicate of aluminium and alkalis with iron, magnesium, calcium, manganese, lithium, potassium, fluorine and water. Crystal structure: trigonal. Hardness: 7¼. S.G.: 3.01–3.06. R.I.: 1.62–1.64. Because tourmaline can create an electrical charge, when it is heated, as in a shop window, it will attract dust and look dirty.

ZIRCONS

Zircons are semi-precious stones which in natural form are usually a dull green or brown colour. When heated, they become white, golden-yellow or blue stones.

They have a high refraction which gives them a brilliant appearance, and for centuries the white stones have been used to imitate diamonds in Asiatic and Middle Eastern jewellery. White sapphires are used in the same way and both are referred to as 'jargoons'. The most common zircon in western jewellery is the blue stone, the colour having been induced artificially by heat treatment. These stones, when set with diamonds, were popular in jewellery of the 1930s and 1940s. When red, orange and brown zircons occur naturally, they are known as 'jacinths'. Zircons are not a particularly popular stone in the West today, but are still used a great deal in cheap Eastern jewellery.

The principal sources are Burma, Thailand and Sri Lanka. In eastern jewellery jargoons are flat- or rose-cut, backed with foil and usually set in gold. In the West they are nearly always brilliant-cut to show their 'fire' at its maximum.

Technicalities: Chemical composition: zirconium silicate ($ZrSiO_4$). Crystal structure: tetragonal. Hardness: 7–7½. S.G.: 4–4.70. R.I.: 1.92–1.98, with strong bi-refringence in some cases.

SCOTTISH PEBBLE JEWELLERY

Queen Victoria inadvertently attracted tourism to Scotland when she set up household at Balmoral in the 1840s. Her move, coupled with the development of the railways, made the Scottish 'season' popular and triggered off all the normal money-making projects we associate with the tourist industry today. Not least was the manufacture of local jewellery.

Agate and granite is found in many parts of Scotland and when small pieces are cut, faceted and polished, the resultant range of colour can be put together in pretty shapes and forms – from traditional plaid pins to thistles, buckles and necklaces.

The mounts for the pebbles were usually hand-made in silver, although expensive suites were also produced in 18ct. gold. This form of 'souvenir' jewellery rapidly became fashionable and soon, to meet demand, the silver mounts were produced in Birmingham by diecasting and therefore bore the Birmingham hallmarks. Naturally the standard of workmanship suffered accordingly. The fashion became so popular in the latter part of the century that pebble jewellery was even exported to France and Germany. This further demand in the industry resulted in complete pieces being made in Birmingham, often in ignorance of the range of stones involved. Hence some examples have apparently inexplicable pieces of malachite and Connemara marble included in the designs, neither of which occur north of the border. Scottish tourist jewellery extended into printed tartan papier mâché and tin strung on elastic to make cheap bracelets to cater for even the humblest purchaser.

The only semi-precious stones found in Scotland are of the quartz family. Yellow, brown and reddish quartz are called cairngorms but are really citrines in gemmological terms. These stones were cut and polished in the same way as any other stones and set in conjunction with the plaque for faceted 'pebbles'. Poor quality amethyst (pale purple quartz) was also used.

The original firms to make top quality pebble jewellery were Makay & Cunningham of Edinburgh, and Muirhead of Glasgow, whilst Rettie of Aberdeen produced larger, coarser pieces, usually set with granites.

The examples shown here are dated c.1850+.

Plate 19.

1. Engraved silver strap bracelet set with agates and cornelian. £350 – £500.

2. Crowned 'Mary Queen of Scots' heart in silver, set with bloodstone and cornelian. £200 – £250.

3. Shield-shaped brooch in silver, set with agates and jasper. £350 – £450.

4. Celtic style brooch in silver, set with agates, bloodstone and jasper. £200 – £250.

5. Silver-gilt bracelet with padlock fastening, set with agates. £350 – £500.

6. Circular open-work brooch in silver, the centre a cairngorm (dark citrine), the border of various granites with foiled citrines, amethysts and garnets. £350 – £400.

7. Eight-lobed brooch set with agates and cornelian, on a black slate base, in silver. £200 – £250.

8. Rectangular silver, agate and jasper brooch, the centre silver panel engraved with an ivy motif, probably made in Birmingham. £200 – £250.

9. Ring brooch of agates, bloodstones, citrine, foiled citrines and amethyst in silver. £500 – £550.

10. Eight-lobed brooch set with bloodstone and agates, mounted on black slate and set in silver. £200 – £250.

11. Brooch set with jasper and bloodstone, the engraved corners set with foiled cabochon amethysts. £350.

12. Dirk in Scottish style marked 'SILVER', probably made in Birmingham, set with cornelian, bloodstone and citrines. £250.

13. Scottish dirk brooch set with cornelian, jasper, agates, bloodstone and foiled citrines in silver. £350.

Antiquarius, Thesaurus

PASTE

Paste is glass, and has been used in jewellery since archaic times to simulate precious stones. Although ancient glass cameos and intaglios have survived, little medieval jewellery in paste appears on the market as, being of nominal value and easily broken, it was discarded.

The combination of two separate events in Europe gave rise to the importance of paste as a type of jewellery. In the second half of the 17th century, the English glass manufacturer, Ravenscroft, discovered lead or flint glass, which, when cut and polished, showed remarkable brilliance and clarity. This was followed closely by the development of the brilliant-cut. In the 1720s a jeweller named Strass combined these two processes and started to produce really good paste jewellery in Paris. In time this was copied by other European jewellers who created many beautiful designs, making pastes in different colours and using tinted foils to simulate the range of colour found in natural gemstones. Fine quality paste rarely appears on the market today, as it has been broken up for the use of the original silver and gold settings. Furthermore, it was made only for a comparatively short time between the 1730s and the 1870s. After that date, mass-production techniques meant that the market was flooded with lesser quality articles. However, some French open-backed paste jewellery from the 1920s is noteworthy for its design, and occasionally for the fine hand-made silver mounts.

The quality of setting during the earlier period was extremely high and paste from the 18th and early 19th centuries should not be looked upon purely as costume jewellery, but as jewellery that has a design and an ornamental quality in its own right. The cutting of paste was carried out in the same way as precious stones and the setting and mounting done by the same craftsmen with the same precision and delicacy. Pastes were nearly always brilliant cut, 90 per cent of them being foiled and set in silver. The foiled pieces are essentially closed back. Earlier pastes, in order to simulate the black dot appearance of the culet of a brilliant-cut diamond, when viewed through the table, had a minute spot of black ink or paint put under the base of the paste or on the surface of the foil. Coloured pastes are not necessarily pieces of coloured glass, but can be colourless, with their back facets painted with the appropriate colour. Foiled paste jewellery, like all foiled jewellery, should never be allowed to get wet, or be cleaned in a liquid, since water will get between the stone and the foil and the brilliant surface of the foil will discolour. This is why so much old paste jewellery appears to be grey and lifeless. Modern paste, after the 1870s, is much coarser, flashier, and not so well made. Many of the mounts were stamped out and drilled by machine instead of being individually hand-made. A vast amount has been produced in England and America from the turn of this century onwards and is called 'diamanté', or 'rhinestone'. Paste is often set in conjunction with semi-precious stones and clear crystals.

Technicalities: Flint or lead glass is composed of potash, soda and flint or lead oxide. Lead increases its brilliance and gives it a characteristic greyish tinge. S.G.: 2.5–3.3. Hardness around 6, although lead glass is sometimes lower. R.I.: 1.5–1.7. The later paste was more often made of crown or bottle glass which was cheaper to produce.

Plate 20.

1. Late 18th century foiled pink topaz and white paste necklace set in silver and backed with gold. *£1,500.*

2. French paste open-work button brooch set in silver, closed back, marked with French control mark for 1798–1809. *£450.*

3. Pair of Stuart pink foiled crystal earrings, the crystal drops suspended from rose-cut white pastes, set in silver, English, late 18th century. Note the style of setting of the circular white pastes, similar to cut-card work styles of late 17th century English silver. *£400 – £600.*

4. Mid-19th century crystal and white paste crowned harp, the four large rectangular crystals open set in silver, the pastes set in silver and backed with gold. Probably made in Dublin by West or Waterhouse about the time of the Great Exhibition of 1851. *£500 – £600.*

Michael Poynder

43

Plate 21.

1. Late 19th century harlequin paste necklace, silver-backed, English, c.1880. *£1,200.*

2. Early Victorian blue enamel and paste button set and backed with silver, one of a set of four. *£400 – £500 set.*

3. Georgian flat-cut garnet and paste clasp, the centre set with an ink on ivory monogram, the whole set and backed with gold, c.1800. *£700 – £1,000.*

4. Georgian purple glass and paste button set and backed with silver, c.1810, one of a set of three. *£375 – £475 set.*

5. Georgian green and white paste pavé set flower brooch set and backed with silver, c.1830. *£550.*

6. Georgian blue enamel and white paste oval brooch with a monogram in the centre, backed with silver, c.1800. *£750.*

7. Georgian foiled amethyst surrounded by white pastes as a brooch set in gold, c.1820. *£650 – £700.*

8. Georgian green and yellow paste locket frame set in gold, c.1820. *£300 – £350.*

9. Georgian oval jardinière clasp, the blue glass overlaid with seed pearls, mother-of-pearl and white paste, surrounded by white pastes, set and backed with gold, c.1785. *£600 – £800.*

10. Georgian green paste cluster brooch with a foiled crystal centre, set and backed with gold, c.1780. *£200 – £250.*

11. Early Victorian amethyst paste collet necklace set in gold, c.1840. *£800 – £1,000.*

Harvey & Gore, N. Bloom

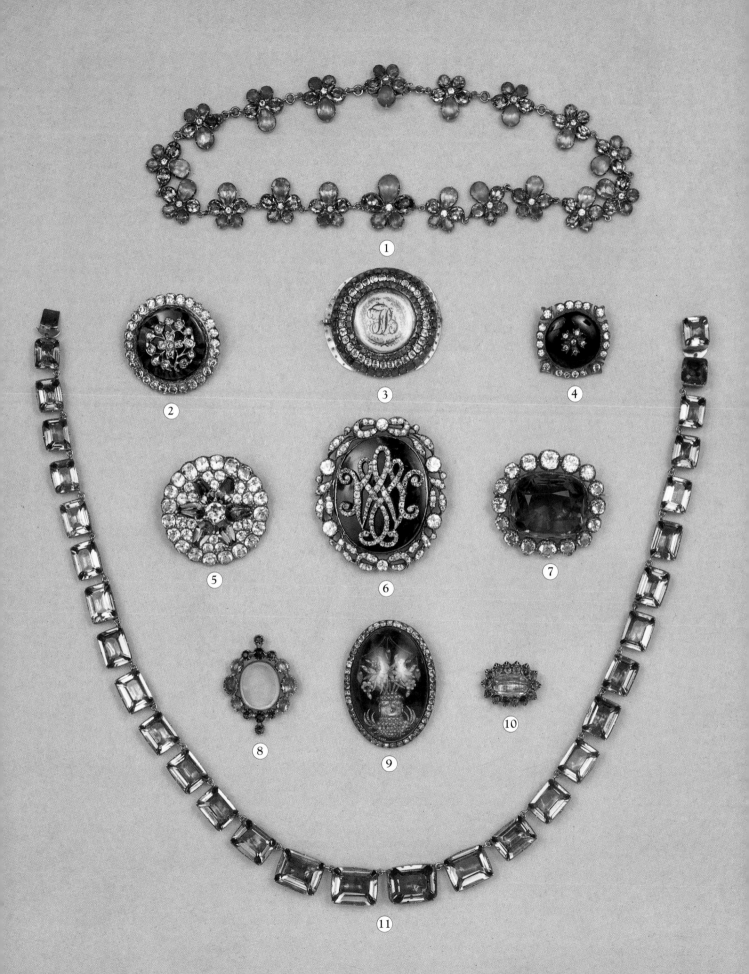

Plate 22.

Late 18th century white paste flower brooch, pavé set in silver, foiled and closed back. Actual size 1¾in. in diameter (4.5 cm), a section enlarged five times. The culet of the paste is accentuated by painting in a black ink dot at the time of setting. *£2,000 – £2,500 pair.*

Michael Poynder

Plate 23.

1. Silver basket of flowers brooch set with cornelians and pastes, c.1940.

2. French multi-coloured paste and silver necklace, c.1925.

3. Silver and paste bar brooch of two monkeys, c.1940.

Varying in price £75 – £250.

Antiquarius, Bellamy

CAMEOS AND INTAGLIOS

A cameo is a relief carving where the top layers of a stone or shell are cut away to reveal a darker contrasting background. An intaglio is the oposite – a design is engraved or incised into a stone. Since ancient times these carved images have reflected man's beliefs and were thought to hold mystical powers. Prior to the 19th century, cameos and intaglios were mainly cut from agates or hardstones such as chalcedony, jasper, cornelian, onyx and bloodstone. Agates were treated with honey, sugar and acid to enhance their colours. Cameos and intaglios went out of fashion after the Renaissance, but came back when a Neo-classical revival in the late 18th century made them desirable again. To meet the rising demand for such items, the Sicilians revived the 15th/16th century art of shell carving around 1800. Shell was an easier material to work with than stone. Different types of mollusc shell were used to create cameos with pink, orange or brown backgrounds. As cameos became increasingly popular during the 19th century, a wide variety of other materials was also used, such as lava stone from Vesuvius, coral from the Naples region, tortoiseshell from the West Indies, Whitby jet, ivory, Wedgwood and even glass.

Before the Victorian era the subject matter of intaglios and cameos was strictly classical and mythological. Gods, heroes and famous statesmen were depicted in a formal manner. From about 1830 styles changed, and while mythological subjects were still popular, they were now presented in a pretty and more decorative manner reflecting the Romantic mood of the age. Settings too changed and simple mounts were replaced by ornate and elaborate frames, often decorated with enamel, pearls and other gems. Enormous popularity led to mass production and inevitably a decline in quality. By the beginning of the 20th century the heyday of the carved gem had passed.

Plate 24 (overleaf).

1. Fine 18th century translucent hardstone cameo in low relief, set as a pendant in a mid-19th century Holbeinesque jewelled and enamelled frame. £10,000.

2. Mid-Victorian profile portrait cameo set in a gold frame of entwined leaves with pearls and diamonds. Note the good use of the colour-banding in the headdress. £4,000 – £5,000.

3. Late 19th century French pendant/brooch set with a cameo signed 'Girometti', in a frame of pearls, rubies, diamonds and lapis lazuli. £8,000 – £10,000.

4. Large early 19th century hardstone cameo of a mythological scene, set as a pendant in an Edwardian platinum and enamel frame with a platinum and pearl chain. £8,000 – £10,000.

5. Mid-Victorian hardstone cameo suite of brooch and earrings set in hollow gold mounts with applied gold surface decoration, c.1860. £5,000.

6. Classical hardstone cameo of an Emperor, set in a late 19th century, ruby, pearl and gold mount. £3,000.   *B. Barnett Ltd.*

Plate 25.

1. Unusual heavy gold-link chain, classical in design, mid-Victorian, c.1860. £2,500 – £3,200.

2. Fine cameo suite of necklace, brooch and earrings, the hardstone cameos depicting mythological scenes and figures, surrounded by green enamel and set in ornate, scrolled gold mounts, the cameos c.1780, the mount Victorian, c.1845. £7,000+.

Harvey & Gore

49

Plate 26.

1. 19th century black Wedgwood intaglio ring in a gold mount. £550 – £750.

2. Black and white glass cameo ring set in gold, c.1790. £550 – £650.

3. Roman nephrite intaglio in an 18th century gold mount. £700 – £900.

4. 18th century cornelian cameo of Medusa's head. £1,000 – £1,500.

5. Agate intaglio of Minerva, 4th century A.D., in a reproduction 18th century gold mount. £700 – £900.

6. Renaissance cameo head in an 18th century mount, set with amethysts and citrines in gold. £1,400 – £1,600.

7. 18th century agate cameo of a child's face. £750 – £900.

8. Victorian chrysoberyl cat's eye and diamond cluster ring set in gold. £1,500 – £2,000.

9. Large oval 19th century agate intaglio of Hercules slaying Antaeus. £1,600 – £1,800.

10. Roman intaglio, cornelian, set in a gold mount. £750 – £950.

11. 18th century eastern European silver wedding ring. £200 – £300.

12. Fine cornelian intaglio of a coat-of-arms. £1,000 – £1,200.

Richard Digby

50

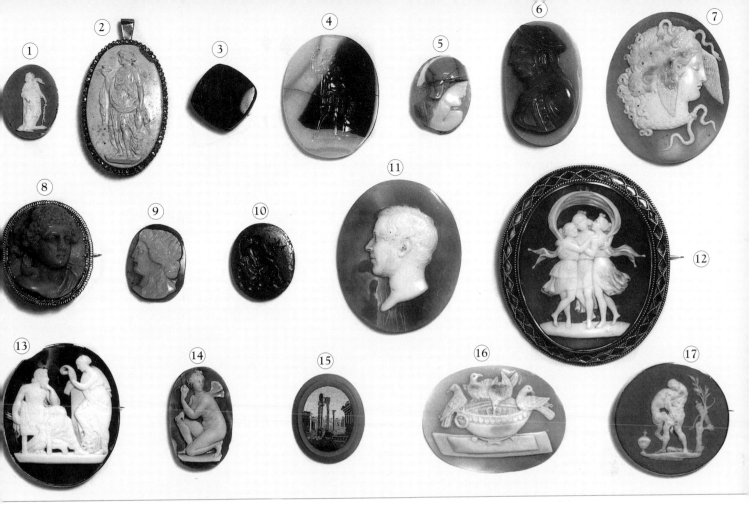

Plate 27.

1. 18th century blue and white Wedgwood cameo of a standing figure. £100 – £150.

2. Early 19th century composite turquoise cameo of a classical figure, set in a rose diamond frame with a fine engraved gold back, French, c.1820. £1,800 – £2,000.

3. 19th century bloodstone intaglio. £100 – £150.

4. 18th century agate intaglio, showing colour-banding (cracked horizontally). £150 – £200, *damaged*.

5. 16th century agate cameo of a warrior's head. £850 – £1,000.

6. 18th century agate cameo, the bust of a man. £500 – £700.

7. Large 19th century oval shell cameo of Medusa's head, with finely carved detail. £600 – £800.

8. 19th century coral cameo brooch of a woman, set in gold. £600 – £800.

9. Small 18th century profile portrait cameo in agate. £500 – £700.

10. 19th century glass intaglio, by Tassie. £150.

11. 19th century portrait shell cameo, with fine clear detail. £350 – £450.

12. Large 19th century shell cameo of the Three Graces, mounted as a brooch in gold, c.1860. £1,000 – £1,200.

13. 19th century Neo-classical shell cameo in a plain gold mount. £600 – £800.

14. Fine early 19th century agate cameo of a kneeling figure. £850 – £1,000.

15. Early 19th century glass mosaic of Rome, in a turquoise-coloured glass frame. £350 – £450.

16. 19th century shell cameo of a group of birds. £350.

17. Early 19th century blue and white Wedgwood cameo of Hercules and the Lion. £300 – £400.

Richard Digby

ENAMELS

The Egyptians discovered and developed the art of enamelling as a natural progression from the process of making glass. Enamel is a form of transparent or opaque glass fused on to or within a metal frame. The metal can be gold, silver, copper or brass and five main techniques are used in jewellery:

Champlevé: Cups or troughs are cut out of a metal base plate in the required form or motif and molten enamel is poured in. When the enamel has cooled and set it is then rubbed down to a flat, even, surface showing the required design, and then polished to reveal the tops of the 'cups' as fine lines of metal. This method is used extensively in Asiatic jewellery.

Cloisonné: Differs from champlevé in that the design or motif is constructed with thin wires soldered on to a back plate. The molten enamel is then poured into the wire-walled chambers in the same way as before, and the cooled surface is rubbed down and polished. This shows the separating wires in the final design. The Chinese are the greatest craftsmen of cloisonné and many incredibly intricate pieces, including some very large 'objets', appear on the market.

Grisaille: A term referring originally to a fashion of painting in black, grey and white tones which was extended to making enamels in Limoges. It was from this area that the finest medieval painted enamels were produced.

Basse Taille and *Tour-à-Guillocher:* Two similar forms of engraving rays and two-dimensional designs into the back plate and building up the enamel in translucent layers to produce a shimmering effect. Used particularly in the late 18th and 19th centuries on lockets and miniature frames, snuffboxes, etc.

Plique-à-Jour: This is the most difficult and delicate type of enamelling. It was developed in the late 19th century, chiefly in France, and was used extensively in art nouveau jewellery. This type of work has no back plate, so the enamel design is clear and translucent, the enamel being held in place by a metal frame. This work is very fragile.

Plate 28.

Butterfly pendant in silver, set with a ruby and decorated in blue enamel, by Child & Child, c.1900. *No quote.* *Wartski, London*

Plate 29.

1. Spanish crowned gold pendant set with diamonds, rubies and emeralds with a centre enamel plaque, 1680–1720. *£4,000.*

2. Spanish gold open-work pendant set with diamonds with an infant Jesus centre, c.1690. *£3,000 – £3,500.*

3. Sentimental brooch mounted with rose-cut diamonds in a silver setting, depicting a Cupid firing an arrow at a heart, c.1740. *£3,500.*

4. Ruby, diamond and centre garnet star pendant in gold and silver, c.1700. *£3,500.*

5. Filigree gold drop pendant with black and white enamel set with small drilled pearls, probably French, c.1680. *£300 – £400 damaged.* *Christie's*

Plate 30.

1. Pair of mid-19th century Swiss enamel earrings, the drops reversible (as shown), set in gold, c.1850. *£1,500 – £1,800.*

2. Fine 19th century Swiss enamel landscape set in an ornate gold frame attached to a flexible gold bracelet, c.1850. *£2,500.* *Cameo Corner*

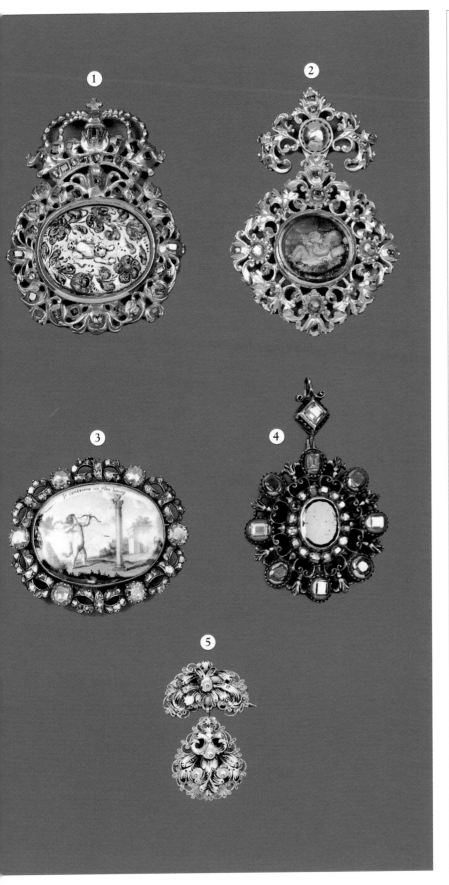

Plate 31.

1. Late 17th century French enamel riband brooch, c.1670, the enamels finely painted. 2½in. (6 cm) diameter. *£12,000 – £15,000*.

2. Mid-17th century Hungarian gold and enamel knot of ribbon brooch. *£8,000 – £10,000*.

3. Mid-17th century gold, enamelled and jewelled foliage spray brooch, probably English. *£6,000 – £8,000*.

4. 16th century Spanish gold, enamelled and gem set pendant, 3¼in. (8.5 cm) high. *£5,000*.

All exceptionally rare.

Christie's

Plate 32.

1. Rose diamond, enamel and gold ring in the form of two doves on a branch, French. £1,500 – £2,000.

2. Diamond, enamel and gold ring watch set with rose diamonds, French. £5,000 – £6,000.

3. Paste, gem-set and gilt pendant watch, English. £800 – £1,000.

4. Circular ring watch set with rose diamonds in gold, French. £3,000.

5. Gold, ruby and enamel ring, the enamel designed to simulate a watch face, but no movement, the shank engraved 'J'aime à tout heure', French. £2,500 – £3,500.

Prices 2–4 depend on working order.   *Christie's*

Plate 33.

1. Mid-Victorian pietra dura and goldstone butterfly brooch set in an ornate gold frame, c.1860. £900 – £1,000.

2. Victorian rectangular pietra dura brooch set in silver. £300 – £400.

3. Mid-19th century pietra dura brooch and earrings *en suite*, set in gold, c.1850. £1,500 – £1,700.

4. Early Victorian floral mosaic brooch and earrings in black glass, contained within a decorative gold mount, c.1840. £1,500 – £1,700.

5. Mid-Victorian architectural mosaic set in a flexible gold bracelet, c.1850. £2,000.   *Cameo Corner*

MOSAIC AND INLAY JEWELLERY

Mosaic jewellery was fashionable throughout the 19th century due to the Classical revival and the influence of original Greek and Roman examples. The method of making a mosaic is to use small sections of fine rods of coloured glass which are glued into patterns or pictures within a frame of hardstone or coloured glass. The whole piece is then set in an outer gold frame which gives added protection to the fragile centre. Classical architecture, landscapes, and even pet dogs, horses, exotic birds and insects were all popular subjects.

Hardstone inlay jewellery is often known as Florentine work or pietra dura. The art of the 18th century snuffbox makers and ébénistes was taken a step further in the development of jewellery. Small pieces of differently coloured agates, lapis lazuli, malachite, turquoise, ivory and coral were cut into shapes to make up the required motif, which was set in carved or flat black marble and mounted in gold or silver, and sometimes in jet.

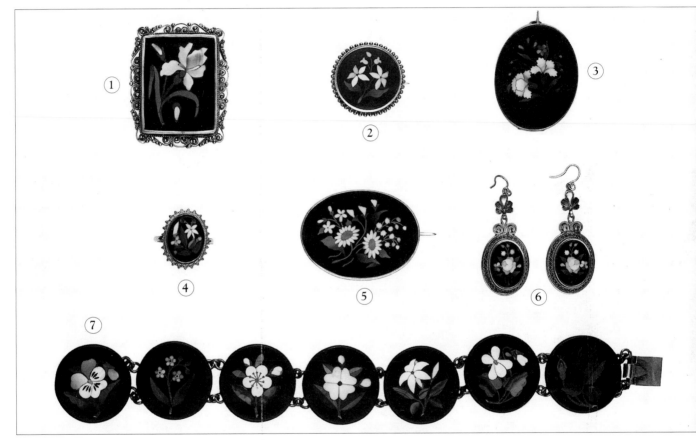

Plate 34.

Examples of Florentine pietra dura work.

1. 19th century brooch set with various hardstones in a rectangular silver mount. *£300 – £400.*

2. Circular floral brooch in a granulated silver-gilt mount. *£200 – £250.*

3. Oval floral brooch in a silver mount. *£100 damaged.*

4. Oval ring in a 9ct. gold mount. *£200 – £300.*

5. Elongated oval floral spray brooch mounted in a plain silver collet. *£300 – £350.*

6. Pair of earrings in 15ct. gold. *£750 – £850.*

7. Bracelet of seven plaques, mounted in silver. *£200 – £250 damaged.*

Antiquarius, Thesaurus, Tony & Sara

CUT STEEL

Cut steel was popular as a form of jewellery from the middle of the 18th century in England and was made in Birmingham where it was an important part of the jewellery industry. A base metal mount, usually brass, was pierced with small holes very close together in the pattern required. Round steel heads, but some crescent or star shaped, were rose-cut and polished and then pavé set in the pierced holes. Each piece of steel was held in place by steel rivets which fitted into the holes in the base plate. This was a long and skilful process which was superseded during the Industrial Revolution in the 19th century by die-stamped cut steel.

Since cut steel will rust if it gets damp or wet, and is difficult to repolish or clean, it was often discarded.

Plate 35.

Fine 18th century cut steel necklace, pavé set, c.1780. £1,000 – £1,300, *very rare*.

E. Ashley Cooper

Plate 36.

1. Scroll and arrow brooch.   2. Twelve petalled flower brooch.

3. Long drop pendant (probably made from an earring).   4. Butterfly brooch.

5. Target brooch.   6. Anchor and star brooch.   7. Horseshoe ribbon slide or buckle.

8. Shoe buckle in openwork design.   9. Bird in flight.   *1–9 varying in price £300 – £350.*

10. Necklace formed of interlinking rosettes with three pendants. *£1,000 – £1,300.*

MARCASITE

Marcasite jewellery dates from the middle of the 18th century and was a fashion which spread from France, where it was very popular at Court. In this country most of it was made in Birmingham. The stones were rose-cut from the mineral iron pyrites and pavé set in silver, and sometimes in pewter. Marcasite jewellery was in vogue after the First and Second World Wars when it was hand set in die-cast silver mounts. A cheaper type was set with jeweller's glue in cast rhodium-plated base metal. Semi-precious stones, pastes and enamels are found in pieces made from the late 19th century onwards.

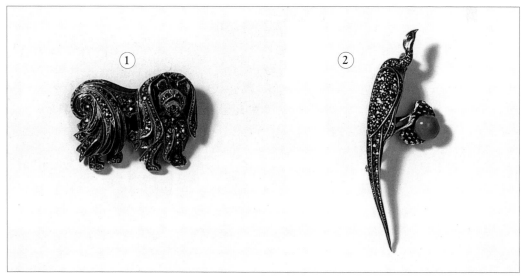

Plate 37.

1. Silver and marcasite brooch of a dog, c.1940.

2. Silver, marcasite and coral pheasant brooch, c.1920.

Varying in price £75 – £150.   *Antiquarius, Bellamy*

BERLIN IRONWORK

Berlin ironwork was produced in Silesia towards the end of the 18th century, at the Royal Foundry and at Count Stolberg's Foundry. It was made by carving and moulding the shapes in wax, pressing these models into a special fine sand, and then filling the impressions with molten iron. These were left to cool, and then finished by hand. Some pieces incorporated niello work, having fine silver wire set into engraved lines in the iron.

The following passage is quoted from *Metal-Work*, edited by G.W. Yapp. 'The asserted origin of these curious castings is interesting. When the final struggle commenced between Prussia and Napoleon I, the Prussians were terribly impoverished, and a grand exhibition of patriotism occurred. The men volunteered their services, and the women sent their jewels and trinkets to the Royal Treasury; those who did so received rings or other ornaments with the motto, 'Ich gab geld um Eisen' (I gave gold for iron), and these trinkets are still kept as heirlooms in the families of the donors.'

Plate 38.

19th century Berlin ironwork bracelet, signed 'Deveranne', Berlin, c.1850. This and the necklace in Plate 191 are similar to the later ironwork illustrated in the Great Exhibition of 1851; the quality is nothing like that of the bracelets shown below. £1,250, *extremely rare*.

Christie's South Kensington

Plate 39.

Fine pair of early 19th century Berlin ironwork bracelets, c.1820. Note the quality and detail in the figures and scrolled floral frames. £3,000 *pair, extremely rare.*   *Private Collection*

CORAL

Gem coral varies in colour from pale pink to rich deep red, and is the product of a small sea creature called a coral polyp. It is formed in sub-tropical waters and thrives in a narrow temperature range between 13° and 16°C.

Coral is graded from white to pale pink – the latter known as 'angel skin' – through rose to red; the darkest of all is known as 'ox blood'. It was popular with the Victorians and regained favour in modern jewellery design, used in conjunction with such materials as onyx, malachite, lapis lazuli and ivory. In many parts of the world it has long been thought to have magical properties and pieces have been eagerly sought and traded far from its original sources.

The best orange-red colour comes from the Mediterranean around Algeria and Tunisia. It is also found in the sea near Naples, off the coast of the Italian islands and in Japan. It is usually collected by dredging machines, although divers have also been used.

Coral is usually fashioned into beads, or cut as cabochons, and it was very fashionable in the 19th century as a material for the reproduction of classical cameos. Pieces are found in their natural state, rather like small twigs, and are carved into figures, flowers, and fantastic animals, following the natural formation of the piece.

Technicalities: Chemical composition: calcium carbonate, $CaCO_3$. Hardness: 3½. S.G.: 2.6–2.7. R.I.: 1.49–1.65. Imitations are made by staining ivory and various plastics have also been used.

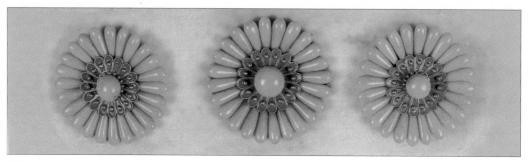

Plate 40.

Pair of coral hair ornaments and a brooch *en suite* by Giuliano, the gold centres of pale green enamel set with coral beads, c.1895. *No quote*.   *Wartski, London*

Plate 41.

1. Coral bead necklace. *£800 – £1,000*.

2. Mid-Victorian carved coral ram's head brooch set in a scrolled gold mount with acorn drops, c.1855. *£1,500 – £1,800*.

3. Mid-Victorian gold and coral circular brooch. *£550 – £700*.

4. Coral clasp set with nine beads. *£300*.

5. Late Georgian gold filigree brooch with coral centre, c.1835. *£250 – £300*.

6. Victorian coral cameo clasp. *£300*.

7. Pair of Victorian faceted coral drop earrings, c.1850. *£550 – £600*.

8. Victorian carved coral, rose spray brooch. It is possible to see the slight colour variation in the coral where successive layers have built up. *£450 – £550*.

9. Fine Victorian carved ivory hand with a rose, c.1875. *£350 – £400*.

10. Coral cameo in a mid-Victorian engraved gold mount, c.1860. *£350 – £450*.

11. Gold hand, holding a coral rose, as a brooch. *£350*.

12. Pair of Victorian coral hat pins. *£300*.   *Cameo Corner*

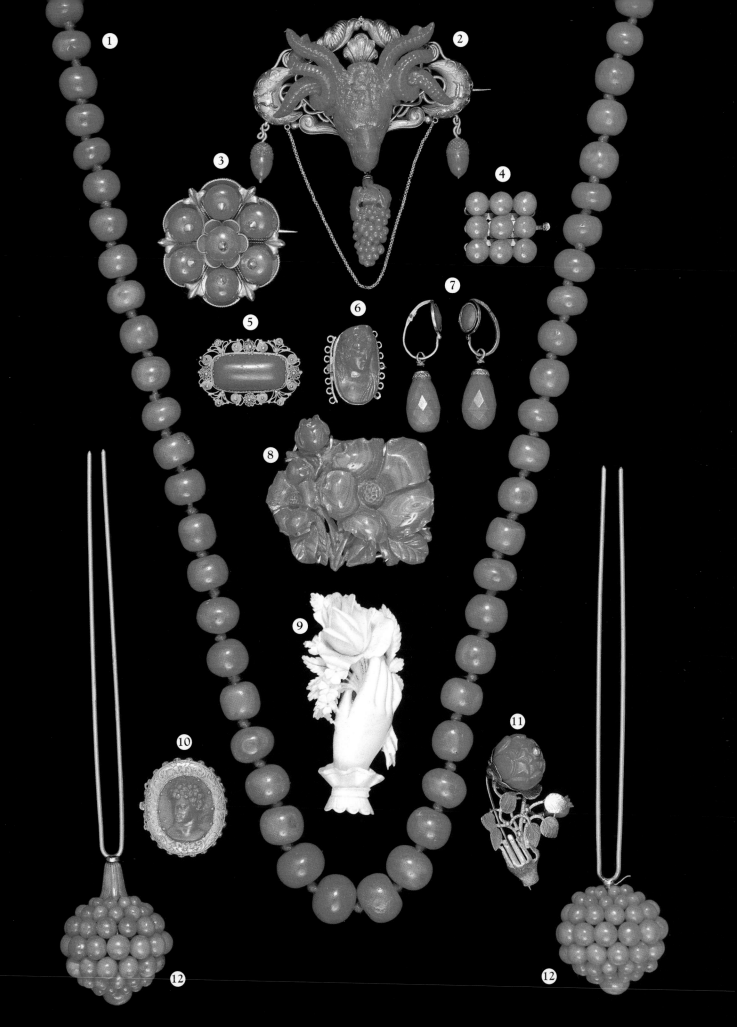

Plate 42.

Early Victorian coral necklace, earrings and a pair of bracelets *en suite*, formed of tiny beads. Jewellery of this type is more commonly made with seed pearls. It is very delicate and therefore can be difficult to repair. £1,200 – £1,500.   *Antiquarius, Thesaurus*

Plate 43 (approx. ½ size).

1. Coral necklace with ivory beads. *£450 – £550.*
2. Late Georgian carved coral drop earrings mounted in filigree gold. *£650 – £750.*
3. Late Georgian coral cameo in filigree gold mount. *£350 – £450.*
4. Three-stranded coral bracelet with coral cameo clasp set in gold. *£350 – £450.*
5. Carved angel skin coral brooch in 9ct. white gold mount. *£350 – £450.*
6. Georgian coral brooch set with nine corals. *£250.*
7. Coral bead necklace with a centre of natural branch coral. *£750 – £950.*
8. Late Victorian coral drop pendant (perhaps once an earring). *£150– £200.*

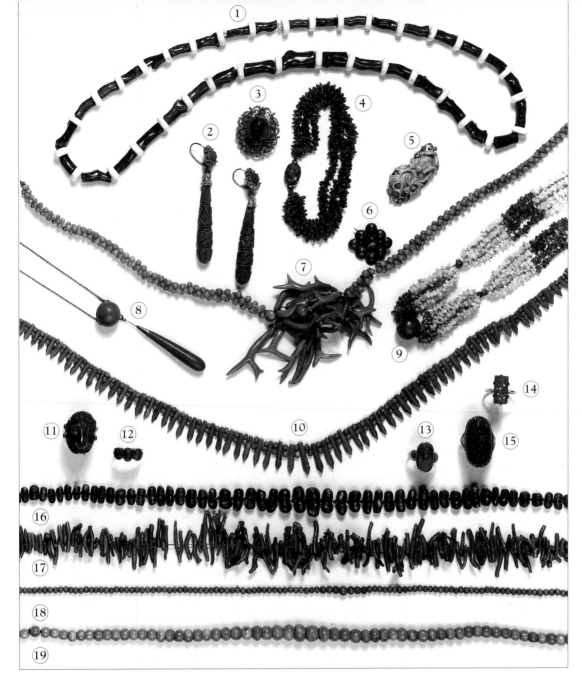

9. Georgian red and white four-stranded coral necklace, 36in. (86.4cm) long. £750.

10. Early 19th century coral fringe necklace. £300 – £350.

11. Coral ring carved as a lion's face, set in 9ct. gold. £400 – £500.

12. Georgian three stone ring set with a coral cameo and two lava cameos. £350 – £400.

13. Coral cameo ring in 9ct. gold mount. £400 – £500.

14. Large coral cameo ring set in gold. £500 – £550.

15. Art deco coral ring carved with a floral motif, in rectangular form. £125 – £150.

16. String of carved coral beads. £450.

17. Necklace of coral in its natural branch form. £150 – £200.

18. String of graduated coral beads. £150.

19. Coral bead necklace with a gold clasp. £250 – £300.

Antiquarius, Thesaurus, The Purple Shop, Anne Tan, Tony & Sara

PEARLS

Pearls are formed by very thin layers of a natural secretion from within the body of a mollusc. This secretion, when hard, is known as nacre, and it builds up as a shield around a diseased part or irritation within the shell.

Natural Pearls: The product of various shells which live either in salt or fresh water. They are normally white, or subtle shades of white; but occasional rarities occur, usually due to disease, and then a pearl can be a steely brown or grey.

The shape, size and colour of the pearl depends on the type of mollusc in which it is formed. Most natural pearls come from the oyster family and are referred to as 'Oriental'; in addition, both freshwater mussels and conch shells produce natural pearls, which are referred to accordingly. Freshwater pearls have a different lustre and sheen from the Oriental pearl. Characteristically they are a soft milky white which the experienced eye will distinguish from the richer sheen of the Oriental pearl; both were highly prized in medieval and Elizabethan times. During these periods Oriental pearls were considered more precious and more costly than diamonds, and were brought to Europe from the Persian Gulf by caravan traders. The weight of pearls is measured in grains, one grain being a quarter of a carat, and it is seldom that Oriental pearls are found in excess of 12 grains. The size of circular pearls is measured in millimetres which makes them easier to grade. The most sought-after pearl is referred to as rosée; this is a pearl of high quality with a delicate pink tinge. Obviously the more regular the shape of a pearl, be it round or pear-shaped, the more valuable it is. Pearls formed on the internal surface of the shell, and which do not become fully round, are known as blister pearls. They are usually semi-circular and are mounted in jewellery as button earrings, or as the centre of a brooch.

Pearls are soft and crack if they are treated badly. They are easily discoloured by acid, a certain amount of which is contained in all brands of perfume. The natural oils and acidity of human skin can be beneficial or detrimental, depending on the wearer of the pearls. Seed pearls have been widely used in jewellery, usually in cluster form, and this fashion reached its height in the late Georgian period, when suites of jewellery were produced (Plate 48). Seed pearls were sewn in large quantities to finely-cut mother-of-pearl backs with white cat gut. When these backs break, it is very difficult to find repairers to mend such delicate pieces.

Pearls are probably the oldest known gems as they were easily available to ancient man, and did not require cutting or polishing in any way to enhance their natural beauty. Freshwater pearls are found in large mussels which breed in many rivers in Europe. The pearls from the Scottish rivers were highly prized by the Romans, and even today pearls are still found in the Tay, Dee and Tweed. However, the great traditional source of pearls is from oysters in the Persian Gulf, and from the Gulf of Manaar in Sri Lanka: hence the name 'Oriental', a term handed down from medieval times. These pearls are usually small, although occasionally large misshapen ones known as 'Baroque' are found and were used as the centre part of magnificent medieval jewels (see Plates 81 and 82).

A very large oyster, as much as one foot across and approximately five times the size of the Persian Gulf oyster, occurs in the South Pacific and off the coast of Australia, and produces large pearls. The conch shell produces a fine pink pearl and is found in the waters of the Gulf of Mexico. However, conch pearls are not often seen in jewellery and have been simulated by light pink coral, stained ivory or porcelain.

Cultured Pearls: These are produced by molluscs in exactly the same way as natural or Oriental pearls, except that the process has been aided by man. The idea of inserting a piece of grit, and more latterly a bead made of glass, plastic or wax, into the shell had been thought of in principle long before Mr. Mikimoto first patented his cultured pearls in Japan around 1915. His discovery of how to open the two halves of the natural shell, without damaging the hinge, enabled him

Plate 44.

Pair of enamelled gold earrings by Carlo Giuliano, in the form of Roman oil lamps, each set with a pearl. *No quote.* *Wartski, London*

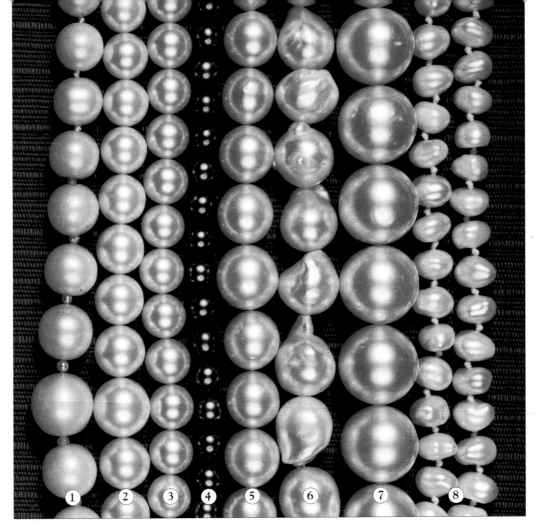

Plate 45.

Necklaces averaging 16in. (40cm) in length.

1. Natural freshwater pearls. *No quote.*

2. Rosée-coloured cultured South Sea pearls of graduated size but regular shape. *£6,000 – £8,000.*

3. Cream-coloured cultured pearls, uniform shape and size. *£2,000 – £3,000.*

4. Cultured black pearls. *£750 – £1,200.*

5. Large South Sea cultured pearls. *£6,000 – £8,000.*

6. Baroque pearls, a variety of irregular formations. *£3,000.*

7. Exceptionally large South Sea pearls. *£30,000+.*

8. Double string of non-nucleated cultured pearls from Lake Biwa in Japan. The squashed 'bun' shape and high lustre is typical of these pearls. *£200 – £500.*

Michael Poynder, Cultured Pearl Company

to insert different-shaped beads, which would then become covered by nacre and form pearls indistinguishable from Oriental pearls – except by laboratory tests. The method used to produce these pearls has meant that millions of women have been able to enjoy wearing pearls that to all intents and purposes are as good as Oriental pearls, but at a fraction of their cost.

However, it is interesting to note that the pearl producers in Japan are so worried about the effects of pollution in the sea and air that the future of the cultured pearl industry is considered to be at risk. Taking this into account, together with escalating production costs, the price of cultured pearls has taken off. Obviously, this applies mainly to the large sizes of excellent quality. Cultured blister pearls can attain large sizes and are known in the trade as 'mabé' pearls (mabé

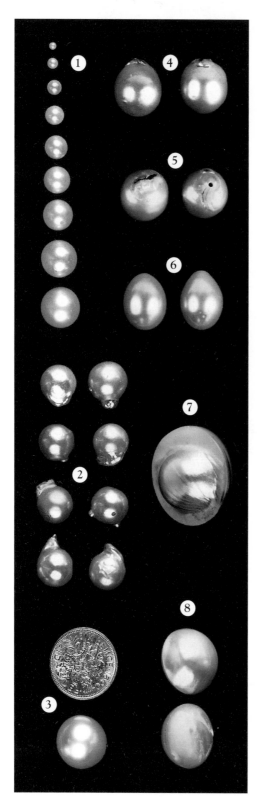

Plate 46.

Cultured pearls.

1. 2mm–10mm. £5 – £1,500. Japanese pearls seldom exceed 18mm.

2. Eight Baroque shaped cultured pearls showing irregularities in their formation. *£50 – £100 each.*

3. 14.5mm cultured pearl from the South Seas, photographed with a sixpenny piece. *£2,500 – £3,000.*

4. Pair of South Sea pearls showing a growth formation which can be disguised in mounting.

5. Side view of 4.

6. Pair of South Sea cultured pearls, drop-shaped, 15.5mm x 12mm, of good quality. *£3,000 – £4,000.*

7. Mabé pearl cut from the shell of the oyster, before trimming.

8. Pair of mabé pearls, top as seen normally, below showing the base which was attached to the inside of the oyster shell, now smoothed off and covered with mother-of-pearl to finish it. *£450 pair.* *Cultured Pearl Company*

Plate 47 (approx. ½ size).

19th century Oriental black pearl necklace, with a black pearl and diamond cluster clasp, formerly in the possession of King Ferdinand of Spain. *No quote.*

19th century, black pearl and diamond brooch with drop. *No quote.* *Christie's*

Plate 48.

Attractive Georgian seed pearl suite of brooch and necklace of oak-leaf design, c.1800. *Very rare, £1,200 – £4,000 depending on condition.*   *Shapland*

meaning half in Japanese).

Freshwater pearls have been produced, particularly from Lake Biwa where they are of a type known as non-nucleated. This means that tissue, which later disappears, has been inserted to cause the irritation within the shell, and subsequently the pearl forms and appears to have no artificial centre bead, unlike the normal cultured pearls. These pearls are round, tending to be Baroque and a flat oval shape, with a stronger lustre than the natural pearl, but whiter in colour.

Apart from the main source, which is Japan, Australia also produces cultured pearls. They come from the very large oysters already mentioned, and pearls in excess of ¾in. (20mm) have been recorded, although at this size they are extremely expensive.

Artificial pearls were far more popular before cultured pearls came within the price range of ordinary women. They were first made in the 17th century, when it was discovered that wax beads could be covered with a product of fish scales which was known as *essence d'orient*. Another early type of artificial pearl was made of glass which was then filled with wax. Plastic or wax-coated beads can readily be identified from Oriental or cultured pearls by gripping them lightly between the teeth and rubbing the surface against the sharp edge of a tooth. The artificial pearl will always feel smooth, whereas nacre grits very finely. Artificial pearls are considered to be costume jewellery and are not illustrated.

Technicalities: Chemical composition: aragonite and conchiolon. Hardness: 3½. S.G.: 2.60–2.78. R.I.: 1.54. Natural and cultured pearls can be difficult to distinguish. The only sure way is to have them laboratory-tested where they will be X-rayed. This will reveal the false centre of a cultured pearl.

TORTOISESHELL

Tortoiseshell is the natural shell of the sea-going turtle, and has nothing whatever to do with tortoises. The shell is dark brown to yellow, usually mottled, and because it is easily worked and takes on a pleasant shine when polished, it was much used in 19th century jewellery. Tortoiseshell jewellery was sometimes inlaid with gold or silver piqué work in geometric patterns and designs. Wet tortoiseshell is very malleable and when pressed into moulds and carefully dried the resulting cameo effects will be permanent. Moulded tortoiseshell was used in mid-Victorian earrings, lockets, chains and small boxes. The colour of tortoiseshell is enhanced by cutting it thinly and backing it with gold or red foil. It was also used for the fashioning of combs and snuffboxes, and as an inlay for furniture.

The turtle which produces tortoiseshell lives in the warm waters of the Pacific Ocean and the West Indies.

Technicalities: Hardness: 2½. S.G.: 1.29. R.I.: 1.55. Tortoiseshell is frequently imitated by bakelite and other plastics.

Plate 49.

19th century Victorian piqué tortoiseshell jewellery, inlaid with gold and silver in intricate designs, as brooches, buttons, earrings, pendants.
Varying in price £250 – £1,200.
                                                                Cameo Corner

IVORY

Ivory is a natural bone formation and is normally white, discolouring with age and body grease to a brownish-yellow. It is a porous material, although reasonably hard, and forms the teeth of mammals. In some cases these teeth have developed into large tusks, as in the case of elephants, walrus and boars. It has a nerve centre and consequently the sharp end of the tusk or tooth will be solid, and the base hollow.

The major source of ivory is obviously the elephant, both African and Indian, but hippopotamus and hog and several other mammals also have ivory teeth, although their use in jewellery is more limited. The walrus, narwhal and cachalot whale are other sources. The use of ivory became popular with the expansion of British colonialism in India and Africa, and with the birth of whaling as a commercial industry. As a result, ivory jewellery and other objects, such as knife handles, became common during the Victorian era.

Ivory is seldom faceted and is usually carved in floral motifs, or used in conjunction with other materials to form crosses, beads, buckles, etc. Chinese carving is the best in the world, but seldom in jewellery form.

Technicalities: Chemical composition: calcium phosphate. Hardness: 2½. S.G.: 1.70–1.85. R.I.: 1.56. Ivory has been widely imitated by plastics, the most common of which is called 'ivorine'. However, none of these copies can be compared with the fine criss-cross graining of true elephant ivory.

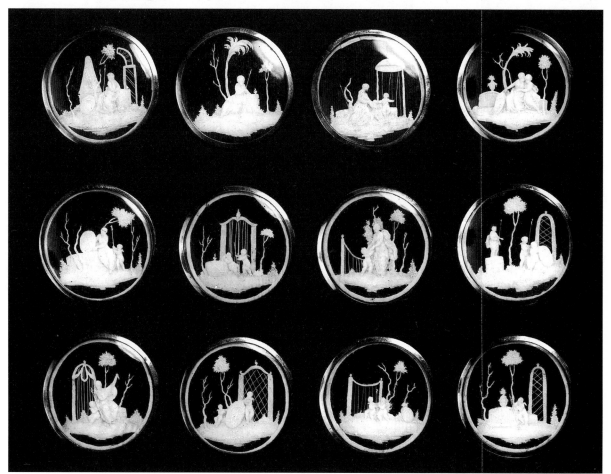

Plate 50.

Fine and unusual set of twelve carved ivory chinoiserie buttons, set on a background of cloth, in gold frames, late 18th century. £5,000.
Richard Digby

Plate 51 (approx. ½ size).

Mid- to late Victorian ivory jewellery.

1. Faceted ivory bead necklace.   2. Victorian ivory buckle inlaid with silver.

3. Ivory cherub stickpin, late 19th century.   4. Ivory plaque brooch with carved ivory birds on a branch.

5. Composition ivory link bracelet with Victorian 9ct. gold hand clasp.

6. Floral carved ivory cross, c.1855. A fine piece of delicate carving, easily damaged.

7. Chinese ink-stained ivory bangle.   8. Ivory horse brooch.

9. Ivory hand pendant, designed as a chatelaine with gold and gold-plated miniature pendants, c.1870.

10. Ivory link bracelet with metal-gilt padlock.   11. Ivory rose pendant.

12. Indian ivory bangle with carved lion motif around outer edge.

13. Ivory cherub pendant, made in 1975, a good example of modern craftsmanship.

14. Ivory rose pendant.   15. Long carved ivory link chain.

16. String of graduated ivory beads. Wear and tear evident in 15 and 16.

Difficult and uncertain market; varying in price £150 –£500.   *Antiquarius, Bellamy, The Purple Shop, Thesaurus*

JET

Jet is an intense opaque black substance, closely allied to coal in that it is a form of fossilised wood, and very light in weight.

It became popular in the Victorian era, particularly after the death of Prince Albert in 1861 when Queen Victoria went into life-long mourning. Victorian sentimentality and an obsession with death prescribed new forms of etiquette which lasted past the turn of the century. Mourning cards and letters of sympathy were written on black-edged paper, in black ink, and widows wore the veil and attendant black jewellery as a mark of respect.

Jet was the obvious mineral to be used for this form of jewellery, as there was an abundant supply found in Yorkshire, near Whitby. Yet demand was such that during the height of its popularity jet was even imported from Spain, and many factories were turning out beads, crosses, earrings, brooches and pendants. Jet carving also became a cottage industry, with many little front-room windows acting as selling space at Whitby. A high degree of carving was obtained because of the comparative ease of cutting.

Technicalities: Composition: fossilised wood. Hardness: 2½. S.G.: 1.30–1.35 (not very dense). R.I.: 1.66. Jet has been imitated by moulded glass which is commonly known as 'French jet' or 'Vauxhall glass' and the beautiful comb in Plate 269 is an example of this. It is reasonably easy to detect the difference between real jet and French jet, as the back of French jet has a texture rather like the skin of an orange, showing the bubbles found in moulded glass. Vauxhall glass was always mounted on japanned black metal plates. Black onyx, a form of agate, is often confused with jet and was used extensively in the 1920s and 1930s. It was at this time that black bakelite was used to simulate jet in the same way that white bakelite simulated ivory. The normal test for jet is to touch it with a heated needle when it will burn with a smell similar to coal. Glass and agate will not respond, and bakelite will give off a smell of burning plastic.

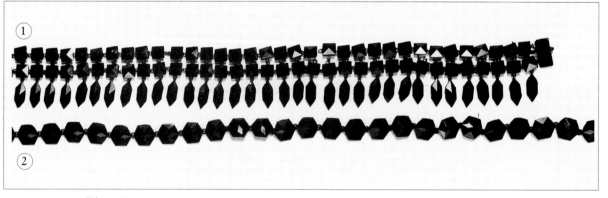

Plate 52.

1. Vauxhall glass fringe necklace.

2. Vauxhall glass hexagonal collet necklace.

Varying in price £50 – £250.   *Antiquarius, Tony & Sara, Thesaurus, The Purple Shop*

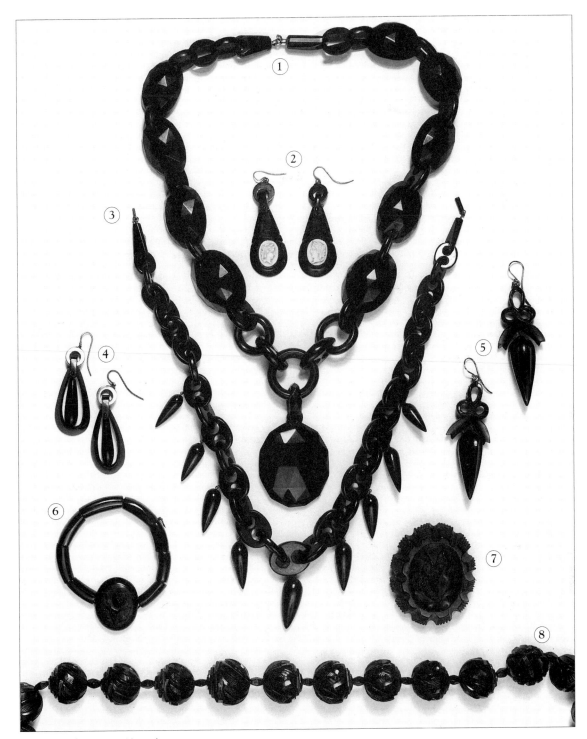

Plate 53 (approx. ½ size).

1. Jet necklace with locket pendant, *damaged*.   **2.** Pair of jet drop earrings with shell cameos inset.

3. Jet necklace with tassel-shaped drops, c.1850.   **4.** Pair of open loop-shaped jet drop earrings.

5. Pair of jet earrings, the metal-backed bows suspending tassel-shaped drops, c.1850.

6. Jet bracelet on elasticated thread with carved oval rose centre.   **7.** Victorian carved jet cameo brooch.

8. String of carved jet beads.

Varying in price £100 – £600.   *Antiquarius, Tony & Sara, Thesaurus*

MISCELLANEOUS MATERIALS

The Victorians' eclectic taste included the desire for jewellery made from unusual materials. Lava, a light, porous substance from the Vesuvius area in Italy was carved into cameos, earrings, etc., and sold as souvenir jewellery. The three bracelets illustrated in Plate 54 indicate the variety of shades of lava, from pale yellows and greys to pale pinks, darker greys and browns. The colours are always muted and the surface matt, taking little polish. As lava is relatively soft and easily damaged, pieces should be carefully examined, especially to ensure that noses on cameos have remained intact.

Hair, used in jewellery throughout the 17th and 18th centuries, increased in popularity during the 19th century, especially after the death of Prince Albert in 1861. Jewellery made from the hair of a deceased loved one was a token of fond remembrance. Hair was used in a variety of ways – it could be set under glass as part of a scene in a brooch, pendant or ring, often with seed pearls; or it was woven and plaited and then mounted in gold or metal as chains, necklaces, bracelets or earrings. Amateurs made their own hair jewellery, using kits and manuals available at the time. Cat gut – the twisted intestines of sheep or horses – was sometimes used instead of hair.

Bog oak, preserved wood from Irish peat marshes, provided an alternative to jet (as later on did black bakelite). Bog oak is dark brown with a matt finish and was carved into various forms. Occasionally other types of wood, such as ebony, feature in jewellery.

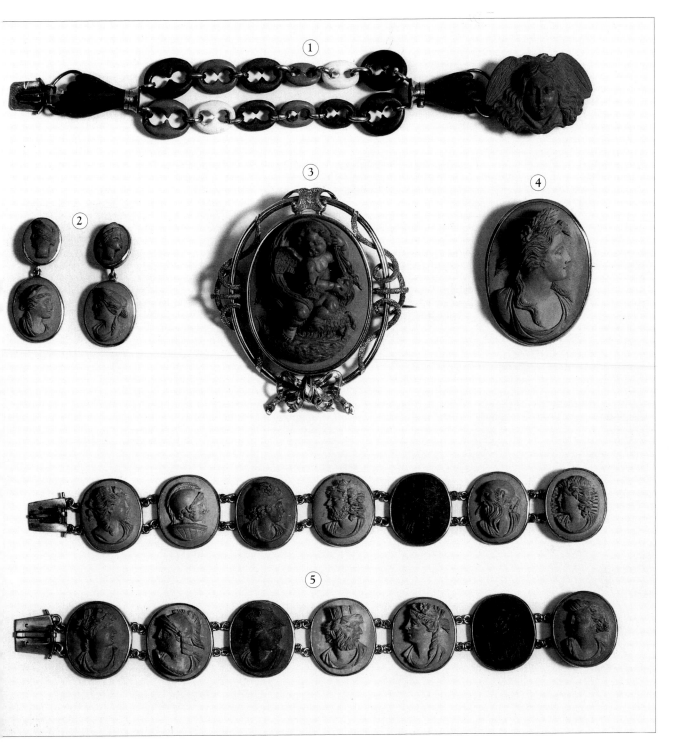

Plate 54.

1. Lava bracelet of carved links, the clasp formed by two hands and an angel's head, c.1850. £800 – £1,200.

2. Pair of lava cameo drop earrings, c.1850. £350– £450.

3. Large, Victorian lava cameo brooch of a cherub with a basket, in a scrolling open-work gold frame, c.1845. £800 – £1,200.

4. Lava cameo brooch of a woman, in a plain oval mount. £350 – £400.

5. Lava cameo plaque bracelets, c.1845. £600 – £1,000 pair, depending on gold or pinchbeck set.   Cameo Corner

Plate 55.

Collection of Georgian and early Victorian hair jewellery made from woven hair with gold or metal fastenings and decorations as necessary. Hair is much stronger than might be expected when plaited and woven in this fashion. *Varying in price £100 – £350.*

Cameo Corner

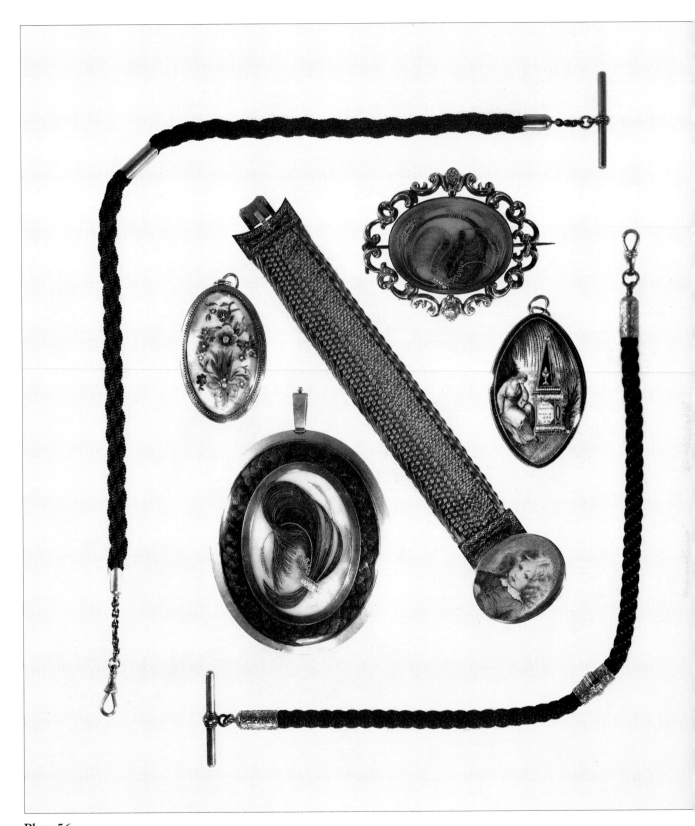

Plate 56.
Early 19th century gold mounted hair set jewellery in the form of pendants, brooches, a bracelet and two Alberts. *Varying in price £250 – £750.*

Tessiers

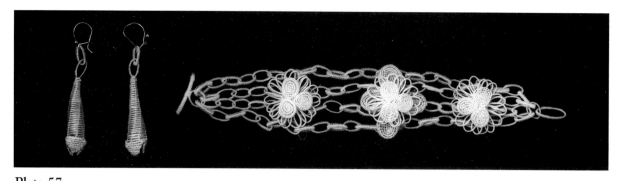

Plate 57.

19th century bracelet and earrings made of drawn cat gut, in imitation of the hair jewellery of the early 19th century. £150. *Antiquarius, Tony & Sara*

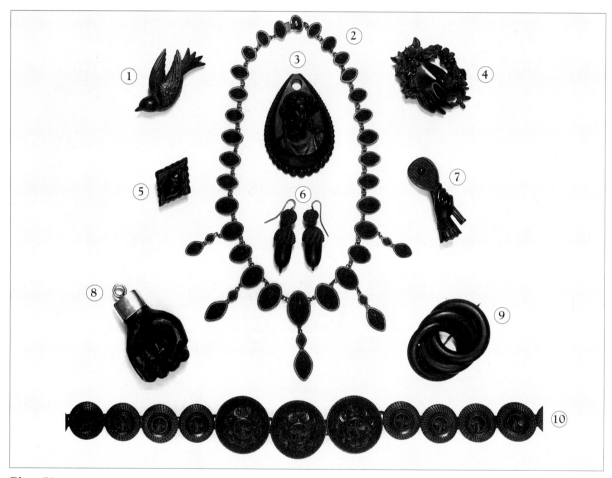

Plate 58.

1. Bog oak bird brooch. **2.** Necklace of bog oak in gilt metal with pendent drops.

3. Bakelite cameo pendant. **4.** Bog oak hand and floral wreath brooch.

5. Bakelite diamond-shaped beetle brooch.

6. Pair of mid-19th century bog oak earrings in the form of acorns.

7. Bakelite hand with racket brooch. **8.** Stained wood and silver hand pendant.

9. Bakelite triple circle brooch. **10.** Bog oak necklace.

Varying in price £50 – £250. *Antiquarius, Tony & Sara, Thesaurus, The Purple Shop*

80

JEWELLERY STYLES

fashions from the earliest to modern times

2500B.C. — A.D.1600

A considerable amount of jewellery from the Ancient World has survived. Because virtually all ancient peoples had a materialistic concept of the next world, the rich provided their dead with status symbols to impress those they would meet in the next world. Due to the fact that gold is nearly immutable, and may be recovered in a pristine condition, while objects buried at the same time have decayed, most surviving ancient jewellery is gold. Much ancient jewellery is of such a flimsy construction that we must assume that most of it was supplied by the undertaker rather than the jeweller although this is not always the case, particularly with such personal objects as rings.

Egyptian gold is very rare and for the most part impure, usually being alloyed with silver. Gold was relatively rare in Europe until the end of the 4th century B.C. when Alexander the Great captured the Persian King Darius's Treasury, which provided the main source of gold in the West for the next few centuries.

Gold was mined in the Wicklow Hills in Ireland in prehistoric times, and in the Iberian Peninsula in the second millennium B.C.

The Greeks preferred silver or electrum, a natural alloy of gold and silver, as they said it resembled the light of the moon rather than the heat of the sun, and it is only with the development of the Hellenistic Empire, after the death of Alexander the Great (323B.C.), that gold became relatively common. During the Ptolemaic period (late 4th century B.C.), gold became increasingly popular and most jewellery was made in Alexandria and Carthage until the end of the Roman Empire.

The Etruscans furnished the tombs of their illustrious dead more sumptuously than most races. However, this was mainly with bronzes and furnishings. Etruscan jewellery, particularly gold, is very rare indeed although it is now extensively faked. This work is usually obvious but there are some deceptive pieces.

Most Roman jewellery came from the Eastern Empire (modern Turkey) and, continuing the Ptolemaic tradition, from North Africa.

The advent of Christianity as the official religion of the Romans under the Emperor Constantine at the beginning of the 4th century A.D., did not interrupt the manufacture of jewellery, which continued until the Dark Ages. Then gold more or less disappeared from the European scene with the exception of the loot of the Vikings towards the end of the period. Europe remained largely devoid of gold until the mid-14th century, and the supply increased about one hundred and fifty years later with the discovery of the riches of the New World.

Much ancient jewellery is set with stones which were culled from all over the then known world. Hardstones came from as far away as the Red Sea, and gem stones were acquired from mysterious central Asia along the silk route, which extended to China. The most common stones were the many varieties of agate, followed by garnets, mostly from the East. Diamonds make their appearance in a very few instances during the Roman period. These stones presumably came from North India, along with sapphires and the occasional ruby. Glass beads were extensively used, and there are accounts of Roman forgers of engraved gems using paste (glass).

The legal requirements of ownership gave rise to the use of seals from about 3000B.C. and they were carved from various hardstones. Some archaic Greek seals of the 6th century B.C. are of scarab form and their backs are carved in relief. This eventually developed into the craft of cameo cutting which reached its zenith in the 1st century B.C. and it was not until the Renaissance that this exceptional level of craftsmanship was repeated.

Beads are the simplest form of jewellery and are virtually impossible to date, as the stones involved do not decay. Consequently, beads which might have been of immemorial age, even in the Roman period, have been used again and again over the centuries. Certain shapes are distinctive of a period, but it is prudent to regard beads as timeless and their origins obscure because of their portability. Sometimes beads and stones that have lain buried in the ground for a long time show surface etching that, to a practised eye, gives an indication of age. However, style and experience with ancient jewellery, particularly engraved gems, are the best guides to authenticity.

The designs are classical and occasional pieces of prehistoric jewellery have come down to us in the form of primitive and folk jewellery from the remoter parts of Europe and Asia. The designs of many pieces have hardly altered to this day. They are not imitations but evidence of a continuing tradition.

Parthian

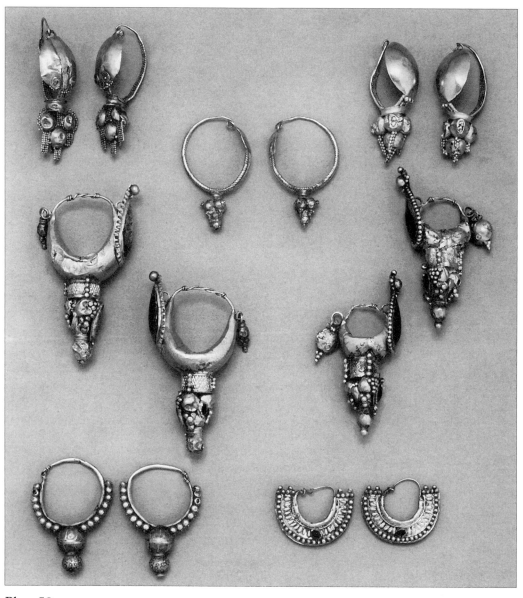

Plate 59.

Selection of gold earrings, mostly of complicated traditional form, from Parthia (modern Persia), set with pastes, c.1500A.D. £1,000 – £3,000, *very variable*.   *Christie's*

Plate 60.

Three bead necklaces, typical of what is available in Persia today. These necklaces are made up of assorted beads of any period back to about 3000B.C. There is no way of telling the age of beads as they are more or less indestructible and are frequently re-used, even if they have lain in a tomb for a millennium or more. *The prices are for archaic pieces.*

1. Emerald and aventurine quartz beads, typical traditional Islamic manufacture; short of definite evidence could be of any period. *£1,500 – £2,500.*

2. Garnet and crystal beads in gold with pendant. *£1,000 – £1,200.*

3. Hollow gold and emerald beads. *£300 – £800.*   *Christie's*

Plate 61.

Egyptian gold necklace from the New Kingdom period (1567–1085 B.C.). Note the resemblance of design the work of the 19th century jeweller Giuliano bears to this example of ancient jewellery (Plates 136 and 137). *£12,000 – £15,000.* *Simone de Montbrison*

Plate 62.

Necklace made up of Egyptian gold amulets and hardstone beads. Amulets usually sell for between £150 and £200 individually, and would originally have been bound in the mummy wrappings. £8,000.   *Sotheby's*

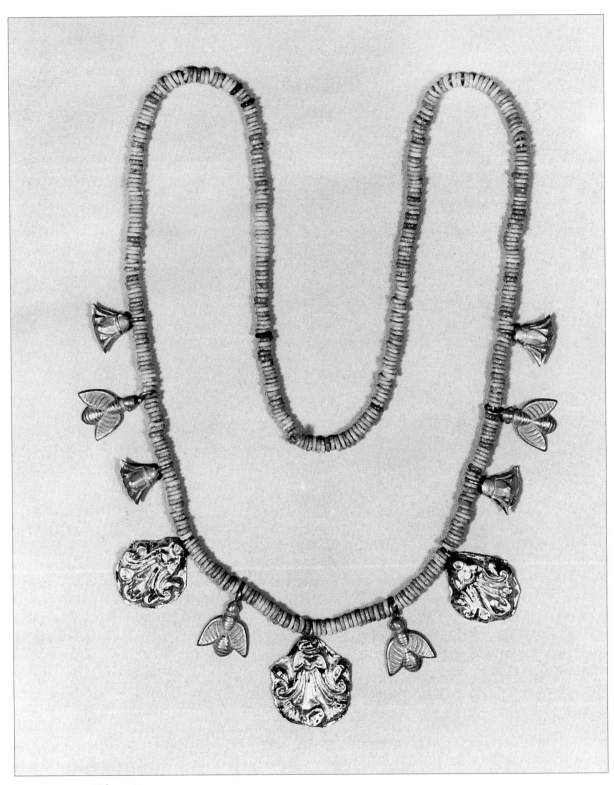

Plate 63.

Egyptian necklace of faïence beads with gold palmette, fly and lotus pendants. Faïence disc beads of this type are particularly common from Egyptian tombs of virtually all dynasties, mainly from the 18th Dynasty (c.1560–1320B.C.) onwards, and are still reasonably obtainable from about £100 upwards, but are obviously considerably more expensive when there are gold additions. £6,000 – £8,000.   *Christie's*

86

Plate 64.

Irish gold 'ribbon' torque (necklace), c.1200–600B.C. £10,000 – £14,000.
Richard Falkiner

Plate 65.

Irish gold armlet dating between 1800 and 1000B.C. Dug up in Cheshire. A section taken across the spiralling shows that this is cruciform rather than the single spiral of the 'ribbon' torque. £30,000 – £60,000. *Christie's*

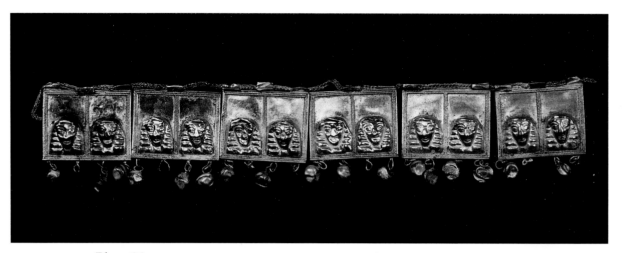

Plate 66.
Greek pectoral (chest ornament) of gold repoussé work, Rhodes, 7th century B.C.
£8,000 – £10,000.   *Christie's*

Plate 67.

Northern Greek silver snake bracelet, 6th century B.C., These bracelets are also found in gold
and would cost in the region of £8,000 – £12,500.   *Christie's*

Plate 68.

Greek or Etruscan gold funerary wreath, made of fine gold leaf, 5th–3rd century B.C. Funerary wreaths were usually made in laurel, ivy or oak leaf designs. *£10,000 – £20,000.* *Christie's*

Plate 69.

1. Hellenistic gold medallion of Apollo, on a flexible plaited gold chain, 4th–3rd century B.C.

2. Pair of Greek Erotes earrings in gold, 4th–3rd century B.C.

3. Hellenistic gold fringe necklace on a flat plaited mesh chain, 3rd–2nd century B.C.

All three pieces have been questioned and are probably reproduction; no quote.   *Christie's*

Plate 70.

1. Pair of Greek gold earrings designed as bulls' heads, threaded with glass beads, 3rd century B.C. £1,100 – £1,500.

2. Pair of Greek gold earrings designed as dolphins' heads, threaded with glass beads, 3rd century B.C. Dolphins' heads are much rarer than earrings with bulls' or lions' heads. £1,100 – £1,500.

3. Hellenistic style embossed gold medallion. £2,000 – £3,000.

4. Necklace of genuine Egyptian faïence scarabs on a modern Cairo work necklace, suggesting the ancient style. £1,000 – £2,000.

5. Pair of traditional Islamic gold earrings. £400 – £600.   *Christie's*

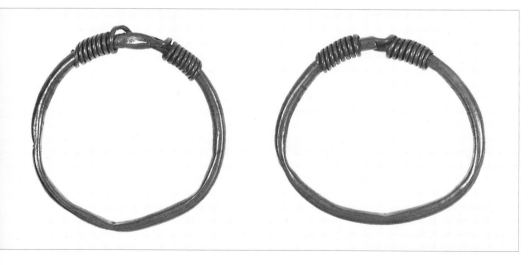

Plate 71.

Roman gold chain necklace with a high relief embossed medallion of the head of Medusa, 2nd century A.D. £4,000 – £6,000.

Christie's

Plate 72.

Two fine Roman gold bracelets, 2nd century A.D. The construction of the spiral is such that they can be expanded slightly. Today distorting them for wear is unwise as the metal, particularly if silver, tends to have crystallised with the passage of time and this can result in their fracture. £4,000 – £6,000 each.

Mrs. D. Papadimitriou

Plate 73.

Two Roman gold bracelets, 2nd–3rd century A.D. £2,000 – £3,000 each.

Sotheby's

Plate 74.

Selection of Roman earrings, 1st–3rd century A.D., all in gold, and some set with garnets or red pastes, faïence, amethysts or cornelians. Numbers 4 and 5 are typical of early granulated patterns (No. 5 is probably Eastern Empire) and No. 9 incorporates stylised dolphins of the later Roman period of the 3rd century A.D. £1,000 – £4,000 pair. *Christie's*

Plate 75.

Byzantine gold pierced and engraved pendant and chain. The work on the pendant is typical
Byzantine work of the 4th–6th century A.D. £35,000 – £45,000. *Christie's*

Plate 76.

Byzantine solid gold cross on gold chain. A typical piece of Byzantine jewellery, more often found in bronze than in gold, 6th–7th century A.D. £4,000 – £6,000.

J. Ogden

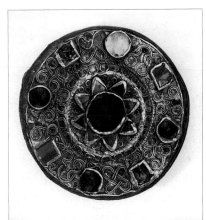

Plate 77.

Early 7th century Frankish circular gold brooch on bronze back, set with blue and red glass, malachite and shell. £10,000 – £12,000.

J.R. Ogden Ltd.

Plate 78.

Garnet and gilt bronze 'fibula' or safety pin, North European 500–800A.D. £10,000.

Spanish bronze belt buckle in the Byzantine style, Mediterranean, c.500A.D. £1,000 – £1,200.

Casper Fleming Collection

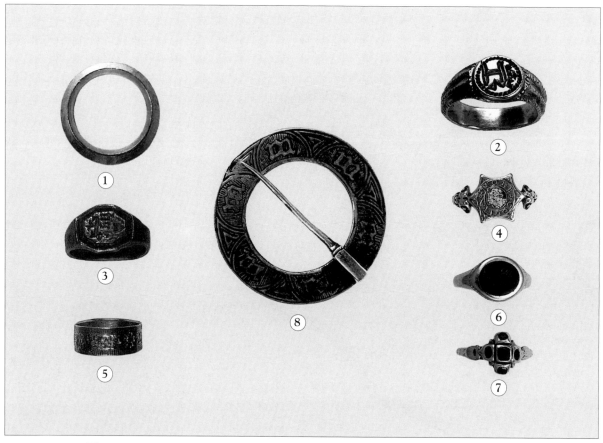

Plate 79.

1. Heavy rare Anglo-Saxon plain gold ring, 6th–7th century A.D. £5,000 – £6,000.

2. Silver signet ring with crowned 'R', perhaps relating to Richard III, late 15th century. £1,200 – £1,500.

3. Bronze signet or merchant's ring, 16th century (usually gilt). £400 – £500.

4. Elizabethan gold memorial ring, 16th century, with white enamel skull with motto reading 'COGITA MORI'. £3,000 – £4,000.

5. Gold Sergeant's at Law ring, English, 16th century, with motto reading 'VIVAT REX ET LEX', probably relating to Henry VIII. £3,000 – £6,000.

6. Gold signet ring set with an intaglio cut stone, English, 16th century. £2,500 – £3,500.

7. Early 17th century gold ring set with rubies and emeralds, £2,000 – £3,000.

8. Medieval silver ring brooch of Scottish type. £800 – £1,000.   *James R. Ogden Ltd.*

CONTINENTAL
16TH, 17TH AND 18TH CENTURY JEWELLERY

Continental jewellery during this period followed the three dominant artistic styles – Renaissance, Baroque and Rococo. Jewellery was made for the rich and powerful, the aristocracy and wealthy merchants, and was worn by both men and women. During the 16th century, Europe continued to follow the Italian taste for sumptuous jewels in the classical Renaissance style. Stones were polished and cut according to their natural shapes and set in elaborate gold and enamelled mounts, which were lavishly decorated front and back. Cameos were skilfully executed in stone by Italian cameo carvers, and pearls were widely used. Subjects tended to be mainly biblical or mythological.

As the century progressed the lively Baroque style became increasingly popular, especially in the form of the pendant jewel. Subjects were modelled three dimensionally, often with a large Baroque pearl forming the body of the piece (Plates 81 and 82), then gold and enamelled sections, chains and pearl drops were added.

Jewellery designs evolved during the 17th century largely due to advances in diamond cutting techniques, as well as new diamond discoveries. Craftsmen began to use diamonds more than gold and enamel as the main element in jewellery design. Diamonds were silver set and gold mounted in closed back and often foiled settings. Floral pieces became very fashionable as a botanical craze swept Europe.

From the French Rococo period, circa 1730 onwards, diamonds were pre-eminent in jewellery. Elegant, lighter, asymmetrical pieces featuring flowers and foliage, ribbons and feathers, were fashionable across Europe. This love of diamonds in naturalistic forms continued for many decades.

Plate 80.

1. Gold and enamel pendant of Amphrite, set with jewels and pearls, possibly Italian. 4½in. (11.5 cm) high.

2. Gold, enamelled and jewelled 'Pelican in her Piety'. 4½in. (11.5 cm) high.

3. Gold, enamelled and jewelled pendant with the bust of a classical warrior. The frame is German, c.1600, the centre of a later date. 4⅜in. (11cm) high.

4. Gold, enamelled and jewelled ship pendant. 4in. (9.6 cm) high.

Varying in price £15,000 – £25,000, all exceptionally rare museum pieces.   *Christie's*

Plate 81.

Late 16th century Italian eagle pendant, formed by a large Baroque pearl set as the body, surrounded by gold and enamel, with a carbuncle between the feet. 3in. (7.2 cm) high. £20,000, *exceptionally rare.*

Christie's

Plate 82.

Fine late 16th century south German pendant composed of a large and unusually shaped Baroque pearl mounted with diamonds, pearls and enamel to form a merman with an arrow. A beautiful example of the imaginative use of an odd shaped Baroque pearl. 4in. (9.6 cm) high. £30,000+, *exceptionally rare.*

Christie's

Plate 83.

Important 16th century enamelled gold pendant jewel, set with precious stones, made in Augsburg c.1570, close to the manner of Erasmus Hornick. 3⅛in. (7.5 cm) high. *Exceptionally rare, no quote.*

Christie's

Plate 84.

Late 16th century gold, enamelled and jewelled chain, probably German. 17¾in. (45 cm) long. £25,000.

16th century Italian pendant, the enamelled and jewelled frame set with a fine cameo. *Exceptionally rare, no quote.* *Christie's*

Plate 85.

1. Gold and enamel crucifix in red, blue and white enamel with three pendent pearls, the Corpus Christi in white enamel. £4,000 – £6,000.

2. Gold and enamel jewel composed of a crowned eagle in black and white enamel on a ruby rosette, the mount of blue, red, green and white enamels. £4,000 – £6,000.

3. Gold and enamelled parrot pendant in red, blue, green and white enamel with pendent pearls. £4,500 – £6,000.

4. Gold and enamelled stag pendant with red, blue and mauve enamel, set with emeralds. £4,000 – £5,000.

All exceptionally rare.   *Christie's*

Plate 86.

Late 16th century south German necklace and pendant of Diana and a hound, the necklace enamelled in various colours, set with table-cut diamonds, rubies and emeralds, the pendant similar, with the addition of three pearls. *Exceptionally rare, no quote.* *Christie's*

Plate 87.

1. 16th century crystal talisman mounted in silver strapwork bands. 1¾in. (4.5 cm) high. The wearing of large pieces of rock crystal was supposed to ward off evil and disease. £5,000.

2. Late 16th century Italian gold and enamel pendant, the sardonyx cameo of a woman in the Roman style, the reverse (right) a sacrificing priestess, the frame enamelled and set with white pastes. 2¾in. (7.2 cm) high. £5,000.

3. 17th century Spanish emerald and green beryl earrings in girandole form, set in gold. £1,500.

4. Late 16th century Spanish, rock crystal and enamel, oval pendant jewel, depicting Adam and Eve and the Tree of Knowledge. 3in. (7.5 cm) high. £3,500 – £4,500.

All exceptionally rare.   *Christie's*

103

Plate 88.

1. 17th century Italian gold and enamel earrings, the enamel in pale blue, black and white with pearls, surmounted by a gold nymph. £3,500.

2. 17th century Spanish gold and enamel rosary, the beads wooden, a double-spiral green enamel cross supporting the gold Corpus Christi. £2,500.

3. 17th century Italian pendant jewel, the agate cameo set in a frame of rubies, emeralds and pearls. £3,750 – £5,750.

4. Late 17th century French oval gold and enamel pendant, the stylised flowers set with rubies, emeralds, diamonds and pearls. This pendant opens to show St. George and the Dragon in coloured enamels, c.1670. *No quote*.

All exceptionally rare.   *Christie's*

Plate 89.

17th century Spanish emerald and enamelled necklace, the emeralds collet-set and foiled behind, surrounded by enamelled mounts set with pearls and table-cut diamonds, each cluster linked by sections of enamelled chain set with rubies and pearls. (Note the interesting repair in the bottom cluster where a missing table-cut diamond has been replaced by a teardrop shaped diamond set in a collet, probably from a piece of Indian jewellery.) *Exceptionally rare, no quote.*   *Armytage Clarke*

Plate 90.

Gold, enamelled and jewelled eagle pendant with pearls pendent from the wing tips. The style of workmanship is coarser than many of the enamelled pieces of the 16th century. £8,000.

Gold enamelled and jewelled necklace. £10,000 – £12,000.

Both exceptionally rare.

Christie's

Plate 91.

1. Italian *verre eglomisé* and rock crystal oval pendant with silver gilt mount. £3,800 – £4,200.

2. German enamelled double bird brooch, the centre birds of white enamel with black markings, surrounded by six birds on a green enamel frame. £2,500.

3. German *verre eglomisé* pendant scent flask in silver-gilt and painted enamels showing the Annunciation and the Agony in the Garden. £2,500 – £3,000.

4. Italian oval pendant of the Annunciation, enamelled in red, green, blue and white with a black enamel frame. £1,500.

All exceptionally rare.   *Christie's*

Plate 92.

1. Enamel cross with Corpus Christi and skull, mounted with gold, possibly German. *£1,000 – £1,200.*

2. Spanish gold and enamel oval religious pendant with stylised bow top. *£1,000 – £1,200.*

3. German garnet and gold cross, the garnets inlaid with enamelled symbols depicting scenes from the Betrayal and Crucifixion of Christ. The loops from each arm and the base of the cross were probably to suspend pearls. *£1,200 – £1,400.*

4. North European stone cameo set in an enamelled frame with rubies and diamonds, c.1650. (*Now in the Victoria & Albert Museum jewellery display.*)

5. Spanish pendant, the miniature set in a frame of filigree gold with a stylised floral crown. *£750 – £950.*

6. English enamelled gold cross set with rubies, suspended from a bow. *£3,000 – £4,000.*

7. English stylised cross enamelled and set with foiled rubies. *£1,000 – £1,500.*   *S.J. Phillips*

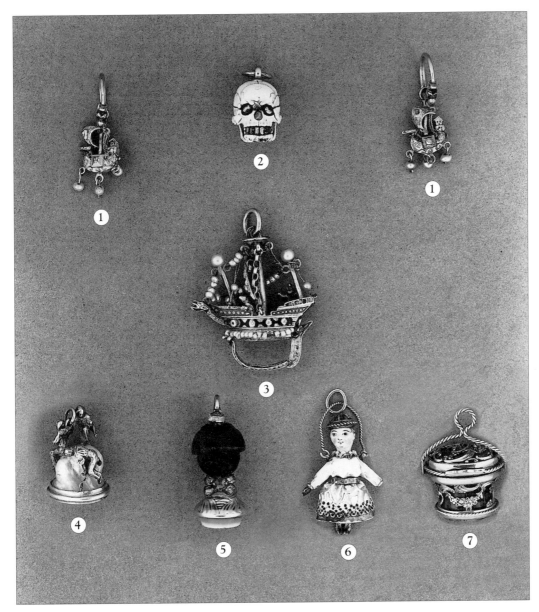

Plate 93.

1. Pair of 16th century Italian earrings in the form of ships, gold with white enamel and pendent pearls.

2. 17th century French 'memento mori' in the form of a white enamelled skull which opens to show an altar with a crucifix and a skeleton below.

3. 16th century Venetian ship pendant, blue, green and white enamel with seed pearls in gold.

4. 18th century south German seal formed of a Baroque pearl with parcel-gilt figures.

5. Louis XV blackamoor seal in sardonyx and gold, c.1730. (There was a considerable interest in negroes as slaves and servants at this period, although to find them in jewellery form is not common.)

6. 19th century Spanish gold and enamel doll pendant, c.1830.

7. George III vinaigrette in the form of a basket in agate and gold, late 18th century.

Varying in price £2,000 – £5,000, all exceptionally rare　　　　　　　　　　　　　*Christie's*

Plate 94.

1. 16th century Spanish gold pendant of a centaur, enamelled in blue and white, his body set with an emerald. 2¾in. (7 cm) high.

2. Late 17th century Flemish gold and enamel fob seal, two putti at the altar of love, their wings of gold, their bodies of blue and white enamel, the cornelian intaglio on the base of a seated Roman. 1¼in. (3.2 cm) high.

3. Rare mid-16th century pendant, the gold roundel of David with the head of Goliath. Italian or French. 3¾in. (9.5 cm) high.

4. Late 16th century Spanish pendant jewel of the crucifixion. 2¼in. (5.8 cm) high.

5. Large Baroque pearl mounted as the torso of a merman, gold and enamelled. 3¾in. (9.5 cm) high.

6. 18th century German table seal, set with Baroque pearls, diamonds, coloured enamels, the intaglio of the base sardonyx matrix engraved with Hercules strangling a viper. 2½in. (6.5 cm) high.

Varying in price £3,000 – £5,000, all exceptionally rare.   *Christie's*

Plate 95.

1. Pair of 17th century Spanish earrings, the brown-foiled topazes set in silver.
   £1,500 – £1,800.

2. 18th century brown-foiled topaz girandole brooch set in silver. *£1,500.*

3. 18th century oval brooch pavé set with chrysoberyls in gold. This type of jewellery of the
   17th and 18th centuries is often referred to as 'chrysolite jewellery', and was particularly
   popular in Spain and Portugal since chrysoberyls were mined in Brazil. *£1,500 – £2,000.*

4. 17th century Spanish enamel brooch in a gold and emerald frame. *£2,500 – £3,000.*

5. 17th century Stuart oval memorial ribbon slide, formed of hair surmounted with two putti
   supporting a skull, under a section of faceted crystal, mounted in gold, dated 4 June 1696.
   £1,500.

6. Early 18th century octagonal memorial ribbon slide, the hair-work decorated with gold
   thread under crystal. *£1,200 – £1,500.*

7. 18th century oval memorial ribbon slide of crystal and gold, dated 1714. On either side it
   is just possible to see the shallow gold loops where the slide was threaded on a ribbon and
   worn round the neck, or possibly the wrist. *£1,000.*

8. 17th century black and white enamel, garnet and emerald pendant of open-work design,
   the back enamelled. *£1,500.*

Cameo Corner

111

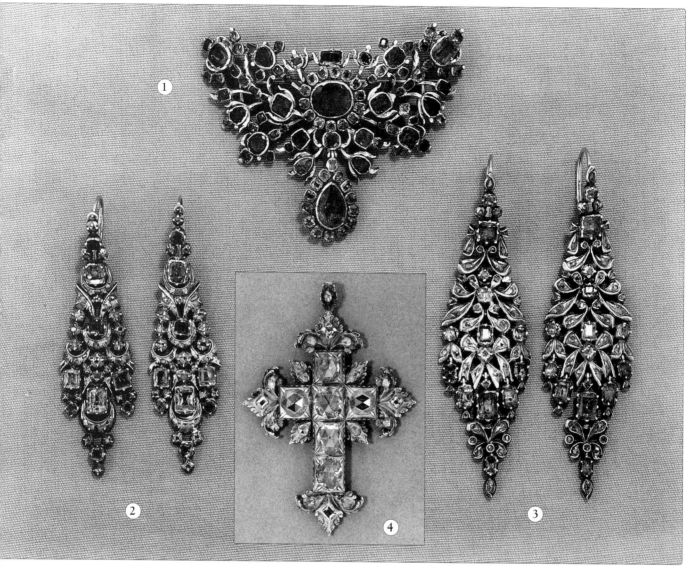

Plate 96.

1. 17th century Spanish emerald and green beryl brooch, the stones foiled and set in gold. *£2,500 – £3,000.*

2. 18th century Spanish emerald and green beryl earrings with small rose-cut diamonds. *£2,500.*

3. 18th century Spanish emerald, green beryl and rose diamond earrings. These long drop earrings are typical of 17th and 18th century Spanish and Portuguese designs. *£2,500 – £2,700.*

4. Late 17th century French diamond and enamel cross, set with large rose diamonds in silver, the reverse painted in enamels with peonies on a white ground, the centre compartment hinged. *£15,000 – £20,000.*

Christie's

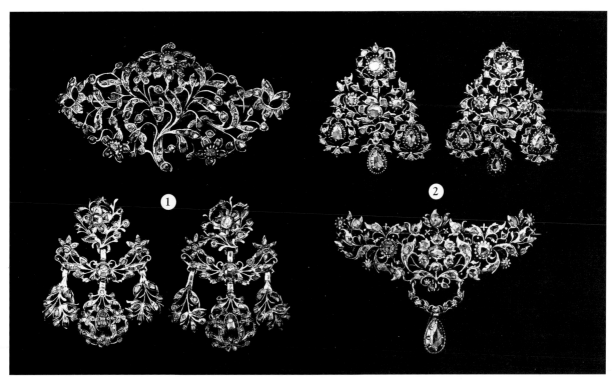

Plate 97.

1. 18th century rose diamond set stomacher brooch and earrings *en suite*, probably Spanish. Note the flat stylised design of the brooch which was pinned centrally on the bodice, hence the term 'stomacher'. £3,000 – £4,000.

2. Late 17th century Spanish rose diamond brooch and earrings *en suite*, of open floral design with pendent drops. The design of the brooch suggests that pendent drops are missing from either side of the central motif. £3,000 – £4,000   *Christie's*

Plate 98.

Mid-18th century suite of brooch and earrings in a floral pattern, rose diamonds set in silver, probably French, c.1730. The delicate floral setting shows the minimum use of silver in the setting of the small rose diamonds. The suite is complete with original fittings. £5,000 – £6,000.
                                                                                          Michael Poynder

Plate 99.

Mid-18th century Spanish gold and rose diamond open-work necklace. This piece would probably have been sewn on to a ribbon and tied at the back of the neck. £5,000 – £6,000.

Cameo Corner

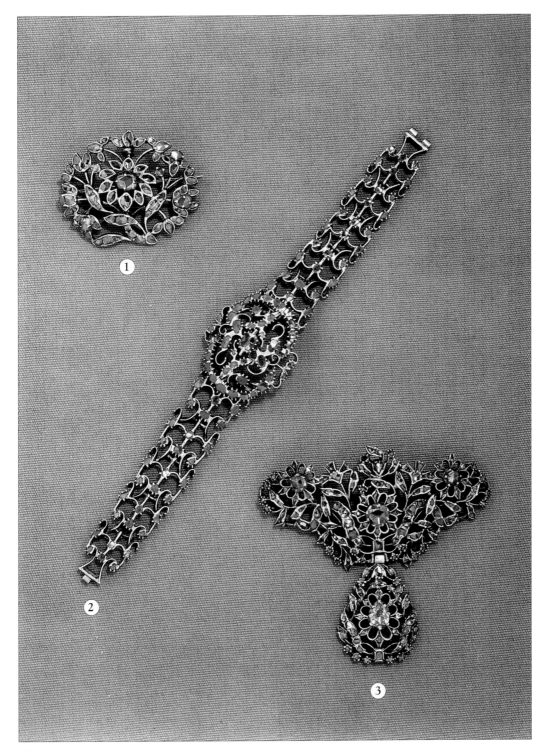

Plate 100.

1. 18th century Spanish rose diamond flower cluster brooch set in silver. *£1,500.*

2. 18th century Portuguese rose diamond bracelet, the open-link scroll design in silver. *£2,500 – £3,000, depending on foiling.*

3. 18th century Spanish or Portuguese rose diamond floral pendant with a floral cluster drop, set in silver. The side drops are missing, the bars to take them being clearly visible. *£2,000 – £3,000.* *Christie's*

Plate 101.

18th century French diamond bow brooch set in silver. £8,000 – £10,000.

Pair of 18th century Spanish emerald and green beryl earrings set in gold, the emeralds pale in colour and foiled. The tops of the original earring fittings are visible. £2,500 – £3,500.

Christie's

Plate 102.

Suite of corsage ornament and cross pendant with earrings. Metal gilt and glass, probably south European, c.1750. £650 – £750.

Pair very large jacinth (hessonite garnet) and gold drop earrings, Spanish or Portuguese, c.1750. £2,000.

Cameo Corner

117

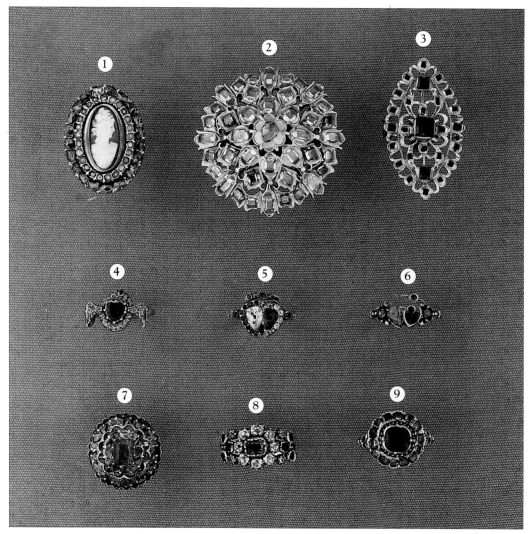

Plate 103.

1. 18th century Spanish ring, the pearl and rose diamond mount set with a classical style cameo. £1,500 – £1,800.

2. 17th century Spanish diamond cluster ring set in gold with diamonds, typically Spanish and Portuguese. French and English work of the same date will normally be mounted either in silver throughout, or the stones set in silver and backed with gold for strength. This ring was originally a brooch. £2,000 – £2,500.

3. 17th century Spanish marquise-shaped ring, of gold open-work design set with emeralds. £2,000.

4. 18th century ruby and diamond heart-shaped ring. £1,200 – £1,300.

5. 18th century ruby and diamond crowned double heart ring. £2,000 – £2,500.

6. 18th century French ruby and diamond, crowned double heart ring. £1,500 – £1,800.

7. 18th century Spanish emerald and rose diamond circular cluster ring, all the stones foiled and set in gold. £1,500 – £1,800.

8. 18th century French emerald and diamond cluster ring with gem-set shoulders. £2,500 – £3,000.

9. 18th century English ruby and diamond ring, the centre ruby surrounded by table-cut diamonds. £1,200 – £1,500, *the ruby is weak in colour which affects the price.*   *Christie's*

GEORGIAN AND VICTORIAN JEWELLERY

During the 18th and 19th centuries, jewellery was designed and made in a fascinatingly diverse range of styles and materials. Depending on the wealth of the purchaser and the fashion of the day, a lady in vogue could be seen wearing jewellery made from diamonds or tortoiseshell, paste or woven hair. European influences, especially French, helped to determine what was fashionable. Developments in industry and its effects on society, together with an abundance of raw materials, meant that jewellery was available to more people than ever before. The wealth of a burgeoning middle class created a market for symbols of affluence. Jewellery worn at Court was copied at all levels and one craze rapidly followed another. The following plates illustrate some of the diversity found in the design and conception of Georgian and Victorian jewellery.

Diamond jewellery, silver set and gold mounted in closed back and sometimes foiled settings, predominated throughout the 18th century. Designs based on flowers and foliage, birds and butterflies, ribbons and feathers, were popular. About 1820, the development of open-backed settings gave diamonds a lighter and brighter appearance. Botanical motifs in diamond jewellery continued well into the 19th century, but designs became more refined, organic and realistic, especially with the perfection of the *tremblant* style by Massin (see Plates 107 and 108).

Quality goldwork, using cannetille decoration, gilding and granulation, was also a feature of 19th century jewellery. English goldsmiths produced elegant pieces in classical styles, frequently set with coloured stones such as garnets, amethysts and turquoise. Great archaeological discoveries of the 18th and 19th centuries together with foreign travel created the desire for Classical Revival jewellery based on designs from ancient times. The mosaic pieces in Plate 123 are based on Greco-Roman and Egyptian symbols, while the silver brooches in Plate 124 hark back to a Celtic past. Sentimental jewellery, in the form of both memorial pieces and love tokens, was worn throught the period (see also pp.141–153).

Fasionable jewellery did not always have to be of great intrinsic value, as the paste examples in Plate 122 show. Paste was worn as a fashion statement in its own right by ladies who probably possessed similar items made from diamonds.

Plate 104.

1. Late 18th century topaz set bow with pendant drop, the topazes foiled and set in silver, c.1770. £1,000 – £1,400.

2. Mid-18th century open-work floral drop brooch, with table-cut amethysts and rose-cut diamonds set and backed with silver, probably French. £2,500 – £3,000.

3. Mid-18th century flat-cut garnet double cluster brooch, pavé set in silver, c.1760. £750 – £900.

4. Late 18th century marquise-shaped blue enamel and diamond brooch, set with a large 18th century cushion-cut diamond in silver, the whole brooch backed with gold, c.1790. £4,000 – £5,000.

5. Early 18th century cross pendent from a bow, set with table-cut and rose-cut diamonds in gold, Spanish or Portuguese. £3,000 – £4,000.

6. Georgian emerald and diamond, circular cluster brooch, the emerald open-set, the diamonds in a close setting in silver, c.1780. £20,000+.

7. 18th century floral open-work Catherine wheel brooch, the centre of black enamel set with rubies and diamonds, the frame of rubies, emeralds and diamonds in silver and backed with gold, c.1770. £2,200 – £3,000.

8. Early 18th century ruby and rose diamond cross, set and backed with silver and gold. £2,000 – £2,500.

9. 18th century rose diamond cluster necklace, set and backed with silver, c. 1770. £15,000+.

S.J. Phillips

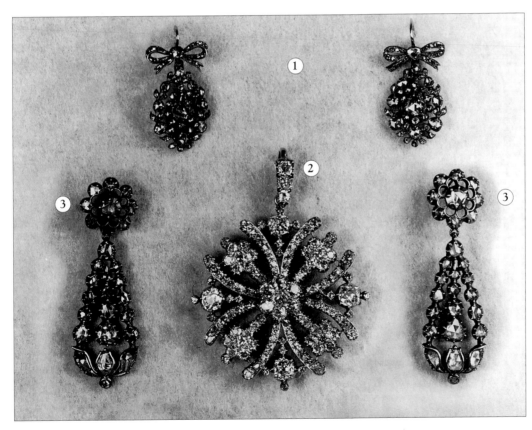

Plate 105.

1. Mid-18th century rose diamond drop earrings of open-work design with ribbon bow tops, set in silver, English, c.1760. £2,000 – £2,500.

2. Late 18th century stylised Maltese cross set with old brilliant-cut diamonds, English, c.1790. £8,000+.

3. Pair of late 18th century rose diamond drop earrings set in silver, c.1790. £2,000 – £2,500.

Christie's

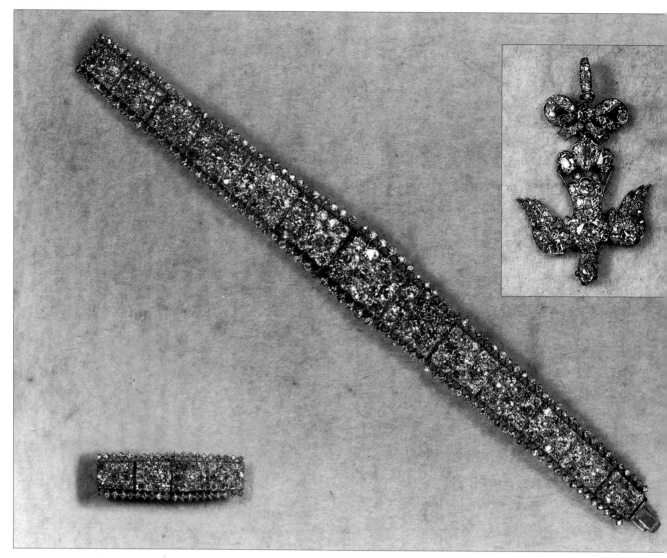

Plate 106.

18th century pavé set diamond St. Esprit, c.1780. St. Esprits, symbolising the Dove of Peace bearing an olive branch, were usually made in Flanders and were popular throughout the late 18th and first half of the 19th century. They are frequently seen with large sprays of foliage. £8,000+.

Late 18th century diamond choker formed of graduated linked sections (four extra sections also shown), c.1800. A beautiful and rare piece of jewellery. £12,000 – £15,000.   *Christie's*

Plate 107.

1. Pavé set diamond butterfly, English, c.1770. £6,000 – £8,000.

2. Diamond ostrich plume brooch with diamond set bow, c.1867, by O. Massin. £8,000 – £12,000.

3. Diamond set Maltese cross, English, c.1780. £5,000 – £6,000.   *Christie's*

Plate 108.

Fine pair of diamond ostrich feather brooches with articulated sections giving *en tremblant* effect. They were probably worn in a high towered hair style, c.1780. £15,000+ pair.

Christie's
Plates 107 and 108 include examples of the best designs and workmanship of the late 18th century.

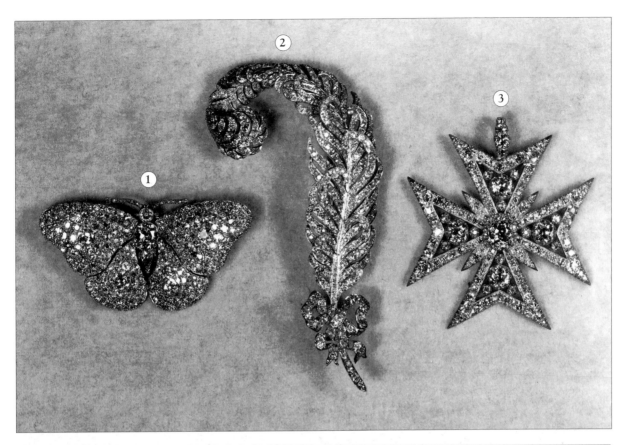

Plate 109.

Late 18th century necklace of rose diamonds surrounded by small cushion-cut diamonds forming graduated circular and lozenge-shaped clusters, set in silver. The double snaps of the necklace can be fitted to a central brooch or pendant (not shown), in which case the necklace would be worn with the brooch or pendant at the front. £30,000+.

Early 19th century Maltese cross with fleur-de-lys at the intersections, cushion-cut diamonds set in silver and backed with gold. £15,000+.   *Christie's*

Plate 110.

18th century diamond necklace in the form of a chain set in silver. The necklace will divide
to form two bracelets. £30,000+.

Christie's

Plate 111.

1. Six-petalled flower brooch set with rose-cut diamonds, each petal linked by a diamond collet. £4,000.

2. Marquise-shaped rose diamond cluster ring, the stones pavé set. £1,800 – £2,500.

3. Pair of diamond drop earrings, cushion-cut diamonds set in a cut-down collet setting, with rare pendeloque-cut diamond drops. £14,000 – £18,000.

4. Rose diamond set wheatsheaf brooch, backed with gold, c.1770. £2,000 – £2,500.

5. Stylised four-lobed target brooch, the open-work design set with cushion-cut and rose-cut diamonds, c.1780. £2,000 – £2,500.

6. Six-petalled diamond flower brooch, the cushion-cut diamonds set in silver, the mount curved to give the brooch shape. £7,000 – £9,000.

7. Round diamond cluster ring, set with cushion-cut diamonds. £3,000 – £4,000.

8. Pair of large diamond drop earrings, the centre diamond sections unusually backed with glass. £25,000.

9. Pavé set diamond St. Esprit, set with rose diamonds in silver, c.1780. £1,500 – £2,000.

10. Pair of diamond leaf spray brooches, set with cushion-cut diamonds, c.1760. £1,700 – £2,200.   *S.J. Phillips*

Plate 112.

1. Late Georgian shell cameo mounted as the clasp of a chain bracelet, c.1830. £800 – £1,200.

   Cameo Corner

2. Late Georgian cameo set as a bracelet clasp in a gold filigree and chain link bracelet, c.1830.
   £1,200 – £1,800. *N. Bloom*

3. Victorian pinchbeck bracelet of hinged plaques with floral and scrolled motifs, c.1840. £400 – £600.

4. Victorian amethyst paste and pinchbeck bracelet with foliage design, c.1850. £400 – £600.

5. Early Victorian mother-of-pearl, pink paste and pinchbeck link bracelet, c.1845. £400 – £600.

6. Georgian pinchbeck mesh bracelet with a Regard clasp in coloured pastes, c.1830. £600–£800.

   3–6 Cameo Corner

127

Plate 113.

1. Set of six Georgian diamond buttons, set and backed with silver. c.1800. £8,000+.

2. Early Victorian diamond-set brooch in the form of a wild rose, in silver and gold – a delicate setting with a minimum of metal, and showing the naturalism of design that developed at this period, c.1840. £6,000 – £7,000.

3. Victorian diamond collet necklace set in silver and gold, c.1850. £12,000.

4. Victorian diamond Maltese cross pendant with brooch fitting, set in silver and gold, c.1845. £6,000 – £8,000.

5. Georgian diamond five-petalled flower brooch set in silver and gold, c.1800. Compare the stiffness of design in this brooch to the wild rose brooch . £6,000 – £8,000.

6. Mid-Victorian diamond flower spray brooch set in silver and gold. £7,000 – £9,000.

Michael Poynder, Christie's

Plate 114.

Victorian diamond set wild rose spray brooch with rose-bud leaves, c.1840. Note the mount for a detachable brooch fitting showing through the centre. *£12,000 – £14,000.*

Late 18th century diamond fern brooch, set with cushion-cut diamonds in silver and gold, c.1780. *£8,000 – £10,000.*   *Christie's*

Plate 115.

Pair of large early 19th century diamond oak sprays, set with cushion-cut diamonds in silver and gold, English, c.1810. A lovely pair of spray brooches, unusual in jewellery, a design illustrating English patriotism during the Napoleonic Wars and the Regency period. *No quote*.
Christie's

Plate 116.

Mid-Victorian suite of brooch and earrings set with cushion-cut diamonds in silver and gold, c.1850. Although this was sold as a suite, the earrings and brooch pendant do not match, as close examination of the mounting and style will show. *Earrings £15,000. Brooch £10,000.*

Christie's

Plate 117.
Set of five Victorian diamond butterflies set in silver and gold, worn individually or on a frame as a tiara, c.1875. £20,000 – £30,000.   *Christie's*

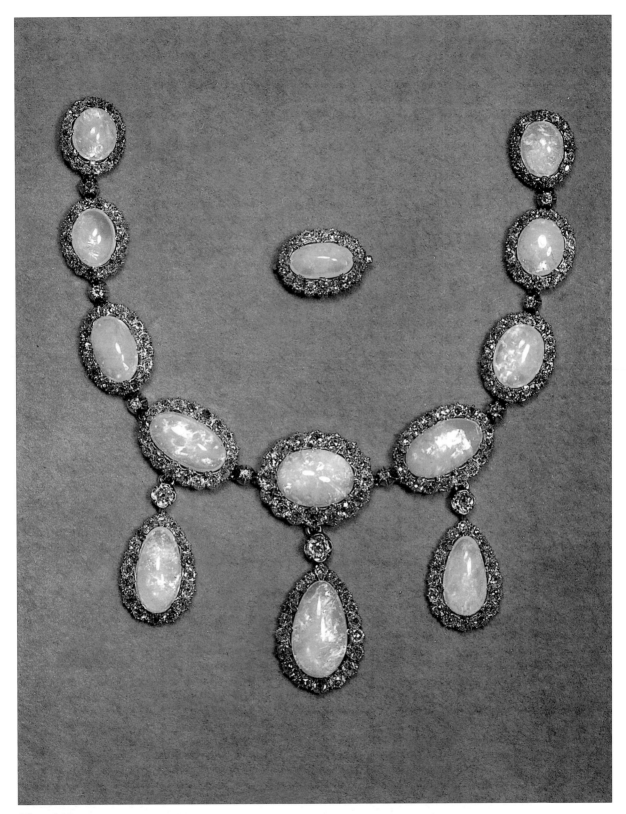

Plate 118.

19th century opal and diamond drop necklace with a brooch to match, English, c.1850. The oval clusters of the necklace should continue to graduate around the neck but have been removed, probably to make rings or earrings. £20,000 – £25,000.   *Christie's*

Plate 119 (approx.¹/₂ size).

Mid-Victorian emerald, diamond and gold snake necklace cum bracelet, the head having a second clasp opening in order to reduce the length as required, c.1860. A superb example of the goldsmith's work, the feel and sheen of the articulated body is extremely lifelike. *£25,000, very rare.*

Christie's

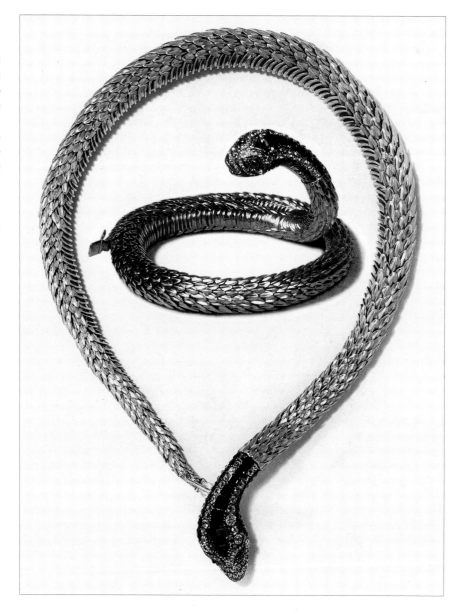

Plate 120.

1. 19th century gold target brooch, c.1860. *£450 – £500.*

2. Gold pendant/brooch set with garnets in a scrolled and engraved mount, c.1870. *£850 – £950.*

3. Tudor rose brooch in 18ct. gold, by Carlo Doria, c.1865. *£1,400 – £1,600.*

4. Oval gold locket with applied anchor, c.1850. The anchor is a symbol for hope. *£650 – £850.*

5. Early Victorian pink topaz and gold brooch of fretwork design, showing classical influence, c.1840. *£1,500.*

6. Oval gold locket set with a pearl and corals, c.1860. *£750 – £950.*

7. Gold pendant designed as a ship's wheel, with a centre design of turquoise glass, gold-stone and enamel, c.1860. *£1,000 – £1,200.*

8. Victorian gold brooch, the centre designed as a fly, set with a ruby and pearls, c.1870. *£800 – £900.*

9. Oval agate and gold brooch by Waddesden & Brogden, c.1870. *£1,200 – £1,400.*

10. Mid-Victorian gold hinged bracelet of classical design with a centre circular section set with turquoises and applied gold thread decoration, c.1850. *£1,400 – £1,600.* *Richard Digby*

Plate 121 (approx.$^{1}/_{2}$ size).

1. Pair of silver and piqué earrings.
2. Silver and gold piqué Maltese cross brooch.
3. Hexagonal silver and gold piqué brooch.
4. Tortoiseshell link bracelet with tortoiseshell and silver padlock fastening, c.1875.
5. Carved tortoiseshell link chain with pendant locket, the front carved with a beetle.
6. Pair of tortoiseshell gold and rose diamond set combs.
7. Pair of carved tortoiseshell urn earrings, c.1860.
8. Carved tortoiseshell locket pendant with mirror in centre.
9. Tortoiseshell and silver decorated bangle.
10. Blond tortoiseshell chain.

Varying in price £200 – £950. *Antiquarius, The Purple Shop, Anne Tan, Thesaurus*

Plate 122 (approx. ¹/₂ size).

1. Paste and enamel Masonic badge, dated 'May 3 1780'. £800 – £1,000.

2. Oval white paste open-work floral brooch, c.1825. £350 – £450.

3. White paste sunburst target brooch, c.1800. £500 – £600.

4. Victorian paste star brooch, c.1870. £350.

5. Mid-Victorian paste floral brooch with three drops, c.1850, in the French style of Lemonier. £500.

6. Late Victorian shell-shaped paste brooch, gold-backed, c.1880. £300 – £400.

7. 18th century paste girandole pendant. £200, *dull foiling accounts for the low price*.

8. Pavé set paste six-petalled flower brooch, c.1780. £1,250.

9. Pavé set paste button brooch, c.1800. £375.

10. Perfect late 18th century crystal collet necklace set in silver and gold-backed, with pendant ring in centre. c. 1800. £1,500.

11. Paste bracelet clasp pavé set in silver. £250 – £350.

12. Mid-Victorian paste sunburst brooch, c.1790. £1,250+.

Harvey & Gore

137

Plate 123.

1. Pair of gold earclips with fine mosaic flies, c.1860. £650 – £750.

2. Mosaic pendant with three pendent drops, set in a gold frame. The fine quality of the mosaic in this and the two pieces above is enhanced by iridescent pieces of glass incorporated in the design which simulate the natural iridescence of insects' wings. £1,000 – £1,200.

3. Real scarab necklace, the scarabs of a greenish iridescent colour, set with amethysts on a 9ct. gold and pearl necklet, c.1880. £750 – £850.

Private Collection, Antiquarius, The Purple Shop

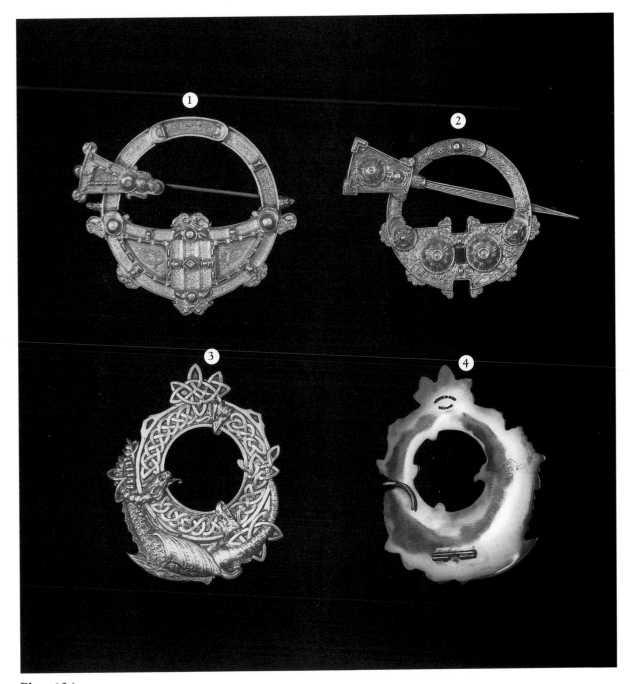

Plate 124.

1. Mid-Victorian Celtic revival brooch in silver-gilt by Waterhouse of Dublin, c.1850. £550 – £650.

2. Celtic Tara brooch, silver-gilt, unmarked, c.1850. £250 – £350.

3. Celtic style dragon brooch, silver-gilt, by West of Dublin, dated 1871 by its British Registry Mark. £300 – 450.

4. Reverse of 3, showing engraved maker's name at the top, and on the right the British Registry Mark (see Plate 305).

A number of these brooches were made in the mid-19th century following archaeological finds in Ireland shortly before. The revival brooches were made in gold, silver, silver-gilt and parcel gilt.

Michael Poynder

Plate 125.

1. Victorian silver-gilt, mesh link chain, 60in. (144cm) long. £200 – £250.
2. Three-colour gold watch chain, with powder flask. £550 – £750.
3. Mid-Victorian silver watch chain. £250.
4. 9ct. gold snake link chain, 24in. (57.6cm) long. £150.
5. 9ct. gold disc link chain, 26in. (62.4cm) long. £150 – £200.
6. Victorian 9ct. gold curb chain, 60in. (144cm) long. £500 – £600.
7. Mid-Victorian silver watch chain. £250.
8. 9ct. gold watch chain. £500 – £600.
9. Silver-gilt flat mesh link chain, 30in. (72cm) long. £200 –£250.
10. Silver and goldwash watch chain with medallion. £250 – £350.   *Thesaurus at Antiquarius*

MOURNING JEWELLERY

Mourning or memorial jewellery became popular in the 15th and 16th centuries in England, and the earliest examples prior to the Commonwealth period, 1649–1660, were usually in the form of a head or skull, enamelled in black and white. After the Civil War it was considered a status symbol to wear mourning rings. Retrospective rings were not unusual and at this time many were produced to commemorate the execution of Charles I.

In the early 18th century, fine scrolled rings were made, with white enamel when mourning a single person, and black enamel for a married person. The name, age and dates of birth and death were recorded round the shank of the ring which was set with a diamond, crystal or paste, depending on the pocket of the purchaser. A loved one's hair, plaited and set under thin pieces of crystal or glass, was also used in conjunction with the dates of birth and death inscribed on the inside of the shank, or on the back of a brooch or ribbon slide.

The Classical Revival at the end of the 18th century extended into mourning jewellery, and rings and brooches were produced depicting, or even shaped like, funereal urns. Plaited hair would surround an ivory plaque, frequently bearing a portrait of the deceased; and this in turn would be enclosed in a fine frame of blue, black or white enamel set with diamonds, garnets, pastes, pearls, etc.

During and after the Regency period, whole suites of jewellery – chains, bracelets, lockets, rings, pendants and brooches – were all made of finely plaited hair from the head of the loved one. It is strange to note that most of the hair used seems to have been a nondescript brown: fine blonde or jet black hair is not often seen, so one wonders if the hair did in fact come from an individual's head?

The sentimental attachment to mourning jewellery during the Victorian era, particularly after the death of Prince Albert in 1861, is seen in terms of jet jewellery, and in the brooches, pendants and rings enamelled in black and bearing the words 'In Memoriam' or 'In Loving Memory'. During Queen Victoria's reign coral and pearls were allowed at court as half mourning jewellery, and these became popular throughout the country. Fortunately, the fashion for all mourning jewellery came to an end after Victoria's death.

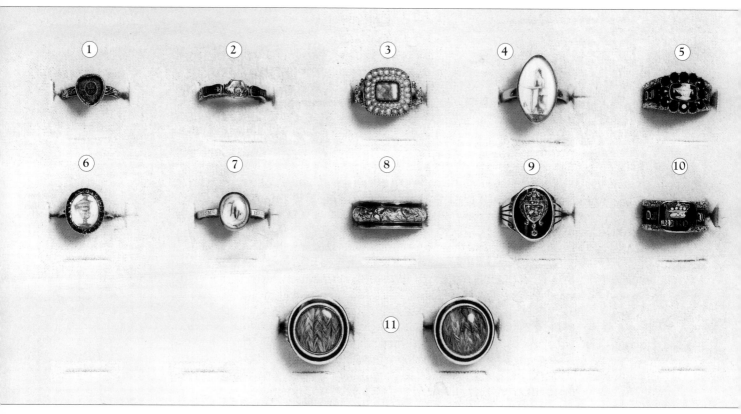

Plate 126.

1. Charles II memorial ring in gold with a carved shank showing traces of original enamelling, the heart-shaped head with gold thread monogram on blue cloth under crystal, in commemoration of Charles I. £2,000 – £2,500.

2. Early 18th century black enamel memorial ring set with a crystal, dated 1736. The scrolled black enamel on gold is typical of mourning rings of this period. £800 – £1,000.

3. Late Georgian seed pearl memorial ring with hair centre, on a carved split shank, dated 1827. Seed pearls denote tears in mourning jewellery. £600 – £800.

4. Late 18th century marquise-shaped miniature ring depicting a woman and an anchor, drawn with ink on ivory, set in gold. In the late 18th and early 19th centuries many memorial rings are associated with death at sea during the Napoleonic Wars. £650 – £700.

5. Georgian black and white enamel ring in gold, the shank engraved 'In Memory Of', the head set with jet and a white enamel urn, the reverse inscribed with the remainder of the memorial, and with a hair inset, English, dated 1819, in perfect condition. £700 – £800.

6. Late 18th century oval memorial ring, the urn detailed in ink on ivory, surrounded with amethysts, c.1785. £650 – £800.

7. George III ivory monogrammed ring with a white enamel and gold shank, dated 1774. £650 – £750.

8. Early 19th century wide-carved gold band with black enamel, dated 1800. £500 – £550.

9. Georgian diamond memorial ring, a brilliant-cut diamond set as the centre of an urn, surrounded with rose diamonds in black enamel, with a wide gold shank, dated 1802. £2,200 – £2,500.

10. Late Georgian black enamel ring with red and white enamel crown, the wide shank with a carved gold border, black enamel and gold inscription in mourning for Byron, dated 1824. £1,500 – £2,000.

11. Fine and rare pair of late 18th century black and white enamel oval rings with centres of pale plaited hair, dated 1793. £1,500 – £2,000 pair.

Private Collection, Richard Digby

142

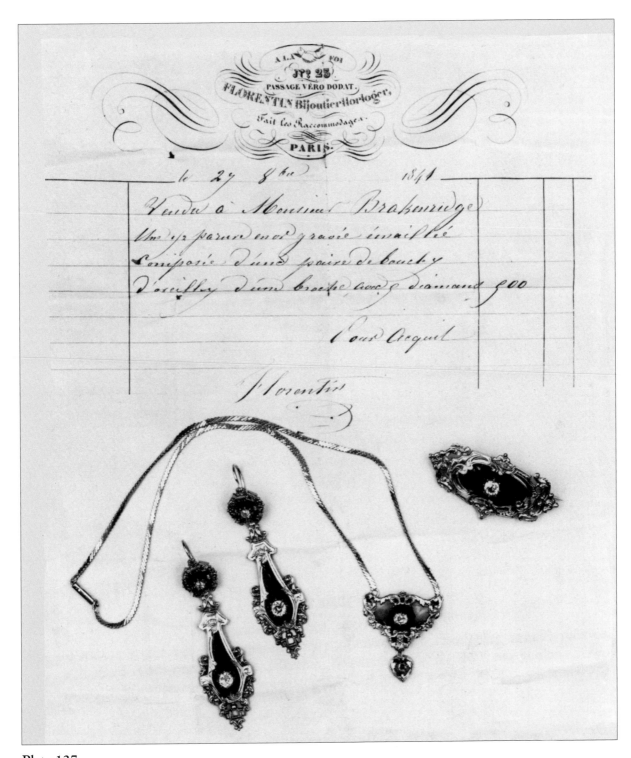

Plate 127.

Mid-19th century French suite of memorial jewellery, the brooch, earrings and pendant in black enamel, set with cushion-cut diamonds in an ornate gold frame of Neo-classical inspiration, accompanied by the original bill of sale, dated 1841. £3,000 – £4,000.

S.J. Phillips

Plate 128.

1. Victorian black enamel and gold memorial ring, dated 1881. *£250.*

2. Mid-Victorian black enamel and gold memorial ring. *£250.*

3. Georgian half-pearl and hair cluster brooch, c.1820. *£200 – £250.*

4. Georgian circular coral and hair cluster brooch, c.1820. *£150 – £200.*

5. Dark blue and white enamel and hair centre brooch, c.1825. *£250 – £300.*

6. Georgian blue enamel, pearl and ruby snake choker, the body of the snake formed of plaited human hair, c.1825. *£850 – £950.*

7. Early Victorian black enamel, gold and rose diamond memorial brooch, dated 1843. *£500 – £600.*

8. Mid-Victorian black enamel brooch inlaid with gold in an ivy pattern, set with a sardonyx, dated 1874. Ivy is the symbol for eternity. *£500 – £600.*

9. Georgian oval scrolled gold memorial ring with hair centre, dated 1818. *£250 – £300.*

10. Georgian blue and white enamel marquise-shaped ring with seed pearl flower centre, formerly a brooch, c.1790. *£550 – £600.*

11. Georgian half-pearl cluster memorial ring with two-coloured interwoven hair centre, c.1820. *£350.*

12. Georgian black enamel memorial ring with a gold heart in the centre, dated 1810. *£250 – £300.*

13. Georgian gold memorial ring in the form of a belt with a buckle, the belt formed of plaited hair on a gold shank, c.1830. *£250 – £300.*

14. Georgian marquise-shaped gold and hair ring, c.1815. *£350 – £400.*

15. Victorian gold memorial ring of black enamel with a half-pearl cross. *£250 – £300.*

16. Georgian flat-cut garnet and gold locket pendant, c.1780. *£400.*

17. Georgian gold witch's heart brooch with small memorial hair heart, c.1750. *£500.*

18. Late 18th century marquise-shaped painted ivory memorial brooch, c.1785. *£500 – £600.*

Antiquarius, The Purple Shop, Bellamy, Thesaurus, Tony & Sara

144

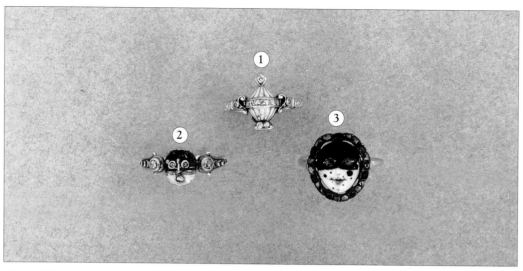

Plate 129.

1. Diamond, enamel and gold urn ring, the gold shank engraved: 'L'amitié la donne'. £2,200 – £2,500.

2. Diamond, enamel and gold masked harlequin ring, with gold 'chain link' shank. £2,200 – £2,500.

3. Enamel masked head ring set with rubies and rose diamonds, French. £2,200 – £2,500.

Christie's

Plate 130.

1. Jet bangle, each section threaded on elasticated silk.

2. Jet cameo brooch.

3. Mid-Victorian funereal jet earrings, c.1850.

4. Jet drop earrings set with shell cameos, c.1855.

5. Jet necklace with oriental influenced floral engraved pendant, c.1885.

6. Carved jet cross with silver pendant attachment.

7. Jet cross.

Varying in price £100 – £600.

Cameo Corner

Plate 131.

1. Early Victorian floral locket in the form of a gold heart with a matt gold finish, set with various stones, one flower spelling Regard, and the other Dear, c.1840. The initials of various stones were used to spell out these words, e.g. Dear is Diamond, Emerald, Amethyst and Ruby. *£2,000.*

2. Georgian circular locket set with graduated pearls in gold, the crystal centre empty, c.1820. *£400 – £600.*

3. Georgian Regard brooch in a rectangular, gold mount, c.1835. (Illustrated in colour in Plate 132.) *£1,900.*

4. Early Victorian floral gold and turquoise locket with empty glass centre, c.1845. *£500 – £600.*

5. Victorian gold and pearl locket with fine gold work, c.1855. *£450 – £550.*

6. Early Victorian pavé set turquoise heart locket in silver-gilt, c.1845. *£300.*

Michael Poynder

148

LOVE JEWELLERY

The most usual form of 'love jewellery' is obviously the ring given on marriage and often suitably engraved inside. Gem set rings were expensive luxuries until comparatively recent times, as it was not until the 18th century and the opening up of trade with the Middle East and Asia that the flow of gemstones appeared on the European market. Lovers' knots (the 'Staffordshire knot') and hearts were usual forms of brooches either in silver, gold or stones.

French was the smart, aristocratic language of Regency England and many jewels were given bearing such delightful designs, often in precious stones, as 'Souvenir d'amitié', 'Souvenir d'amour', 'Regard' and 'Dearest'. These can be spelt out in coloured stones as was done with rings and pins until about 1850, and often included a lock of hair or a painted miniature of the giver. However, the severity and piousness of Victoria's reign soon stopped this sentimentality and memorial love jewellery superseded romantic love jewellery. Various plants (which were considered lucky) started to be used in design forms – acorns, holly, ivy, four-leaf clover, mistletoe and heather all appeared in silver and gold jewellery form, often set with precious or semi-precious stones.

A very popular trait between parting lovers, particularly soldiers going off to fight in campaigns in far off parts of the Empire, was the giving of 'Mizpah' rings. This name is taken from a quotation in Genesis which reads: 'The Lord watcheth between me and thee when we are parted one from the other.'

Key and heart lockets were obvious mementoes between lovers – the key to unlock the heart and suitably engraved. Women gave their men gold or silver lockets containing hair or portraits in the shape of small pocket watches, probably because Victorian men didn't like to show their sentimentality. The coyness of Victorian women towards birth is manifest in naïve little brooches, in silver and gold, showing chickens emerging from eggs and love birds on branches.

Plate 132.

1. Georgian crowned paste witch's heart, set in silver, c.1810. £450.

2. Late 18th century almandine garnet and gold witch's heart, set in gold. £475.

3. Late 18th century rose diamond set witch's heart. £1,400.

4. Victorian Staffordshire lover's knot in blue paste, pearls and gold, c.1840. £350.

5. Early 19th century rose diamond heart pendant with moonstone centre. £1,400 – £1,500.

6. Victorian red enamel and seed pearl link brooch, with pearl pendant heart, c.1850. £900.

7. Early 19th century rose diamond set swallow brooch with ruby collar and eye. £2,700.

8. Late 18th century diamond witch's heart set in silver and gold. £2,350.

9. Late Georgian Regard brooch, with a rectangular gold setting, c.1835. £1,900 – £2,000.

10. Late Georgian granulated gold, turquoise and ruby heart pendant, c.1825. £650.

11. Late Georgian memorial Regard brooch in gold with plaited hair centre, c.1830. £1,500.

12. Mid-Victorian double pearl and diamond heart, in a green and white enamel single heart, surrounded by pearls. c.1860. £2,200.

13. Mid-Victorian pavé set turquoise and pearl heart on a gold chain with a turquoise and pearl cluster, c.1865. £950 – £1,000.

14. Victorian double heart brooch set with an amethyst and a citrine surrounded by diamonds and crowned with a bow, c.1870. £2,500.

15. Victorian ruby and diamond heart-shaped cluster ring set in gold. £1,300.

16. 18th century Fede ring, gold hands holding a garnet. £700.

17. Edwardian blue enamel heart-shaped ring set with a freshwater pearl. £700 – £750.

18. Reproduction Regard ring in 9ct. yellow gold. £500.

19. Early Victorian Regard ring in gold, c.1840. £1,200.

20. Early Victorian pavé set diamond heart brooch set in silver and gold, c.1880. £4,000.

21. Late Victorian double opal heart in a knot of diamond ribbons set in silver and gold, c.1880. £3,000.

22. Victorian turquoise and diamond miniature heart brooch. £1,200.

23. Late 19th century gold bar pin with interlocking crowned hearts. £1,000 – £1,100.

24. Georgian pavé set rose diamond pendant heart. £2,200.

25. Late Georgian filigree gold Regard brooch with turquoise-set flower. £1,900 – £2,000.

26. Textured gold pendant heart. £350.

27. Mid-19th century pavé set diamond pendant heart. £3,200.

28. Late 18th century crystal heart pendant with garnet crown. £900.

29. Victorian double heart pendant of opals surrounded with diamonds, with a ribbon bow and opal and diamond drop. £2,400.

30. Mid-19th century dark blue opal and seed pearl pendant, a heart padlock, with gold key attached. £2,200.

Photograph © Vogue Magazine, Michael Poynder, Richard Ogden

Plate 133 (front and reverse).

1. Georgian filigree gold heart, the border set with aquamarines, the centre stones of the flowers spelling out DEAR, i.e. Diamond, Emerald, Amethyst and Ruby. English, dated 1778, with a plaited hair memorial inset in the reverse. £1,200 – £1,500.

2. Late 18th century two-colour woven hair heart set in gold, the reverse embroidered with a monogram using hair for thread, c.1780. £650 – £750.

3. Early 18th century ribbon slide in gold with hair centre, embroidered with a gold monogram and engraved with the same initials on the reverse. £650 – £750.

4. Early 19th century paste and silver buckle with hair centre and seed pearls, c.1820. This buckle has been converted to a brooch and on the reverse a silver loop has been 'pewtered' on, or soft-soldered; if a hard solder at high temperature had been used, the foil behind the pastes would have been discoloured. £500 – £600.

5. Late 18th century gold filigree brooch with hair centre which is backed with gold, c.1800. £200 – £250.

6. Georgian gold heart with hearts stitched on a cloth centre, the reverse monogrammed and dated 1765. £500 – £600.

7. Late George II memorial heart pendant with hair scrolled and curled in the centre with gold thread, the reverse engraved, dated 1759. £500 – £600.

8. Late 18th century hair pendant set in a graduated paste frame; the centre is hinged to open on the reverse. £450. *Richard Digby, Private Collection*

CASTELLANI AND GIULIANO

Castellani (1793–1865) was an Italian goldsmith and jeweller, working in London, who specialised in the reproduction of Roman and Etruscan gold-work, which he discovered was still being produced by the original methods in the small village of St. Angelo, Vado, in Italy. His two sons, Alessandro and Augusto, continued and expanded his business and many of their pieces have been exhibited in museums throughout the world. Because of the excellent quality, their work is much sought after when it appears in the salerooms.

Carlo Giuliano was another Italian goldsmith, and much influenced by the work of Castellani. In the 1860s he set up shop at Frith Street, London, moving to 115 Piccadilly in 1875. His work concentrated more on the reproduction of Italian Renaissance jewellery rather than Roman and Etruscan designs, and he fashioned his pieces to the taste of the Victorians of the time. After his death his two sons, Carlo and Arthur, continued the business until it finally closed in 1914. As with Castellani, their work is collected and the prices rise steadily.

Plate 134.

Suite by Carlo Giuliano comprising a necklace, bracelet, comb and brooch. The openwork gold is decorated with black and white enamel and is set with opals, green zircons and diamonds. *No quote.* *Wartski, London*

154

Plate 135.

Jewellery by Giuliano.

1. Turquoise and ruby heart brooch of open design, set in gold, c.1875. £3,000 – £3,500.

2. Enamel portrait set in a frame of green, blue, white and black enamel, and pearls, c.1890. £2,750.

3. Sapphire, diamond and pearl spray flower brooch, c.1880, retailed by Giuliano though not made by the firm. £1,650.

4. Rose diamond, enamel and pearl three-row necklace, Carlo and Arthur Giuliano, c.1890. £15,000 – £20,000.

5. Green tourmaline, cinnamon diamond, enamel and pearl pendant. £8,000 – £10,000.

6. Black and white enamel pendant in the form of a stylised cross, set with rubies and pearls. £8,000 – £9,000.

Wartski, London

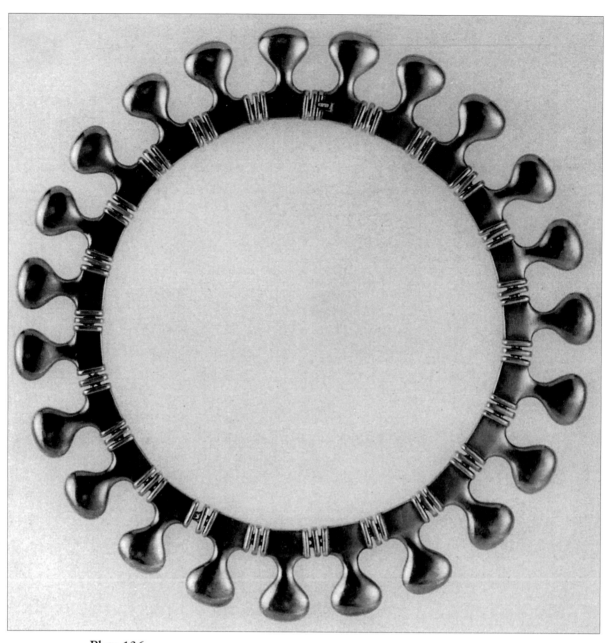

Plate 136.
Articulated silver necklace by Carlo Giuliano, signed with his initials. *No quote.*
Wartski, London

Plate 137.

Late 19th century gold fringe necklace in the Hellenistic style, by Giuliano, c.1885. The S-link clasp is typical of his work. The maker's mark is clearly visible on this clasp; it could be argued that the necklace might therefore be faked. However, the quality of the goldwork is such that it could not be reproduced economically today. £8,000 – £10,000.   *Sotheby's*

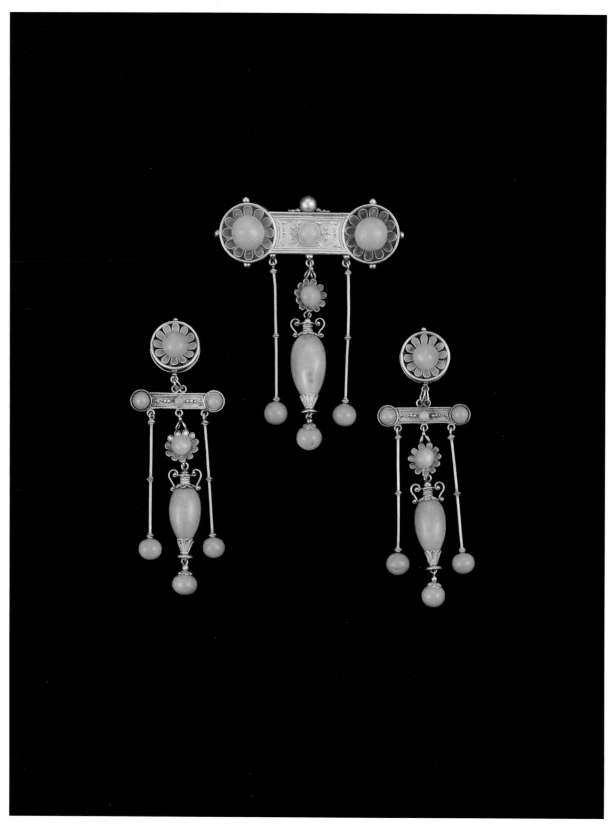

Plate 138.
Gold-mounted coral demi-parure in the archaeological taste. English, c.1870. *No quote.*
Wartski, London

Plate 139.

Necklace and earrings of agate and gold beads, and necklace in silver gilt and green hardstone beads, both by Carlo Giuliano. *No quote.*   *Wartski, London*

Plate 140.

1. Finely enamelled butterfly brooch by Giuliano, c.1890. £10,000.

2. Blue enamel and gold floral pendant with the gold figure of a child in the centre, by Castellani. £3,000.

3. Square mosaic brooch with gold rope border, in the Greek style, with Greek mosaic lettering, by Castellani. £1,500.

4. Circular hollow gold ram's head brooch, by Castellani. £2,500 – £3,000.

5. Gold target brooch with a ram's head, by Giuliano (more influenced by Castellani's work than many of his pieces). £3,000 – £4,000.

6. Pair of enamel and rose diamond earrings in the form of a pelican entwined with a snake, by Giuliano. £6,000.

7. Pair of classical scarabs mounted by Castellani in a gold setting as a brooch. £3,000.

8. Turquoise, ruby, diamond and enamel fan brooch, by Giuliano. £1,100 – £1,450.

9. Layered agate, blue and white enamel pendant with locket opening on reverse, by Giuliano. £4,000.

10. Classical Greek coin set in gold as a brooch, by Castellani. £2,000.

11. Carved cabochon amethyst brooch set in gold, by Castellani. £1,500.

12. Lapis lazuli and gold bead necklace, by Giuliano. £10,000.

13. Black and white enamel pendant set with five moonstones, by Giuliano. £2,500.

S.J. Phillips

THE HOUSE OF FABERGÉ

The Fabergé family owned a manufacturing and retail jewellery business started in St. Petersburg in 1842 by Gustav Fabergé (1841–1881) and inherited by his son Peter Carl Fabergé (1846–1920). The Fabergés were goldsmiths to the Tsars and the Russian nobility, who with their immense wealth gave them full rein to produce magnificent and extravagant examples of the goldsmith's and enameller's art, probably unrivalled since the days of Cellini. Fabergé and his craftsmen are renowned for their 'objets d'art' and 'objets de vertu', which include Easter eggs, dinner services and, in particular, hardstone animals and flowers. They also produced many of the flamboyant, jewelled Orders of the time. Surprisingly enough they seemed to neglect small pieces of jewellery, and examples are rare. However, when found, they are always of the extremely fine quality that one would expect.

ФАБЕРЖЕ

Plate 141.

Early 20th century, gold and enamel fur clasp, set with agates and diamonds, by Fabergé.
£15,000 – £18,000.

Fine Edwardian diamond, pearl and platinum choker, a fine example of the trellis-work and
milled setting typical of the early 1900s. £38,000+. *Christie's*

Plate 142.

1. Russian art nouveau star sapphire and diamond-carved moonstone, ruby and enamel flower spray brooch. £8,500.

2. Enamel, pearl and diamond orchid pendant, c.1900. £6,000.

3. Fine aquamarine and diamond square cut-corner brooch, the aquamarine set in a diamond lattice-work mount, by Fabergé, c.1900. *No quote.*

4. Enamel, gold and diamond rose bud brooch, hallmarked in Moscow. *£11,000.*

5. Cabochon sapphire, diamond and gold circular open-work brooch by Fabergé. *£4,500.*

6. Russian apple green enamel and gold brooch, set with small diamonds. £6,500.

7. Cabochon sapphire, diamond, gold and enamel elongated diamond-shaped brooch, by Fabergé. £5,000. *Wartski, London, Private Collection*

AMERICAN INDIAN JEWELLERY

In the middle of the 19th century Mexicans and the Navajo Indians of New Mexico and Arizona started trading silver trinkets for horses. By 1890 most Indian settlements (pueblos) were producing these trinkets in their own styles, made out of American or Mexican dollars. They decorated necklaces, rings and buckles with roughly polished pieces of locally mined turquoise.

In 1890 the American Government banned this defamation of its currency and by 1930, when the Mexicans followed suit, white traders had already started to increase considerably the import of silver to meet the demand for native jewellery. Little of the jewellery made at the end of the 19th century was produced commercially, but other crafts, such as potting, carving and weaving, have given way to the more lucrative silver-work. Most jewellery craftsmen have normal jobs as well, using their skills as silversmiths and stone cutters to supplement their incomes, as they find a ready market for their output in North America and in Europe.

The Santo Domingans make many of the shell and turquoise bead necklaces and supply other tribes, as well as taking their wares to sell in other parts of America. The Navajo, Hopi and Zuni tribes produce the most distinctive silverwork. The Navajo has the largest population of a total of thirty-nine tribes. The design of their jewellery is simple and massive, although the early work was light and hammered out very thinly, due to the shortage of silver. The Navajo was the first tribe to use sand-casting, in 1895. The best known Navajo silver design is the squash blossom necklace (Plate 143), with a crescent-shaped Naja hanging from its centre.

The Hopi tribe is known for overlay designs. In 1938 the museum of Northern Arizona started to encourage this tribe to translate its pottery designs into jewellery using the overlay technique. A fretted piece of silver is sweated to a solid base plate. A pitted decoration is emphasised by blackening it with liver of sulphur, deepening the three-dimensional effect. Very little use is made of stones in this work.

The Zuni tribe relies mainly on the manufacture of jewellery for its income. By 1890 they had developed a distinctive style, making use of clusters and rows of small turquoises, delicately set in finely worked silver. In 1935 they started using channel setting. A piece was prepared rather as in *cloisonné* enamel, but instead of enamelling, the spaces between the silver walls were filled with cut pieces of jet, shell and turquoise and firmly glued, nowadays using modern adhesives. The whole surface was then polished and a very colourful mosaic effect achieved.

Plate 143 (approx. ³/₄ size).

American Indian jewellery based on traditional 19th century designs.

1. Hopi Indian silver bangle with turquoise matrix centre, made by Begay whose family is well known for traditional craftsmanship. £500 – £600.

2. Navajo Indian dead pawn silver and turquoise sand-cast bangle, made in the 1940s. £300 – £400.

3. Navajo Indian dead pawn bangle, five pieces of turquoise matrix set in silver. £400 – £450.

4. Santo Domingan silver 'Heishi' (water-cascade necklace), made from small silver cylindrical beads with larger coral ones in between. A traditional piece of contemporary manufacture. £200.

5. Navajo Indian squash blossom necklace, the beads and discs made from American silver dimes, quarters, half dollar and dollar pieces, inlaid with turquoise matrix. The latest date on any coin here is 1938. By tradition, the necklace should have stylised squash blossoms made of silver instead of the turquoise-mounted coins. £4,000. *Antiquarius*

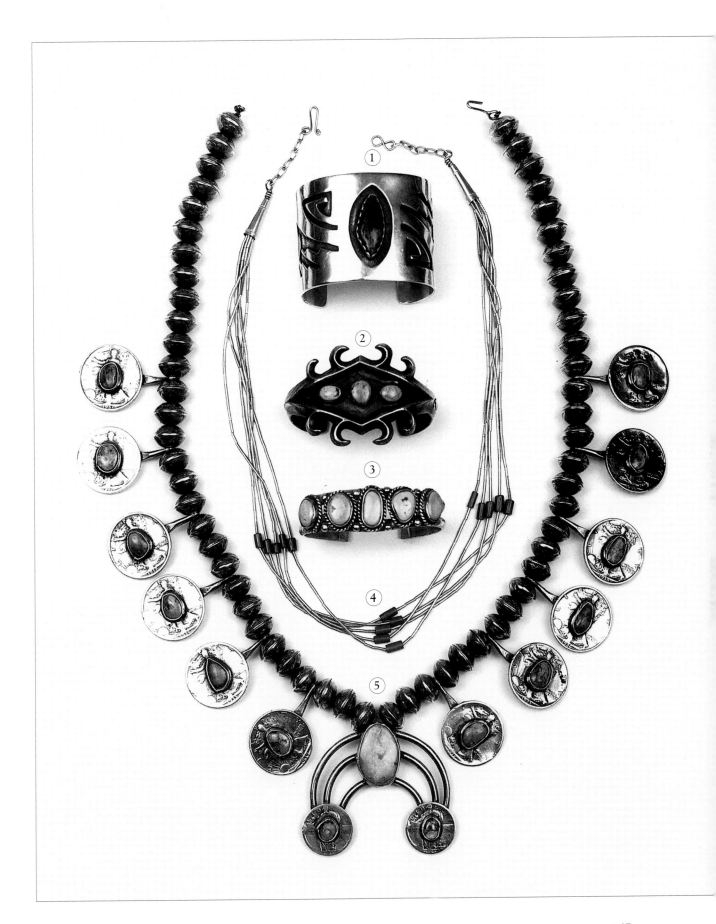

167

INDIAN AND ORIENTAL JEWELLERY

Indian jewellery is usually mounted in gold with a combination of colourful enamels, precious and semi-precious stones, native-cut or in the form of beads. It is interesting to note that sapphires are seldom used because of superstition about their colour. The design of Indian jewellery is traditional, i.e. styles have not varied greatly over the years, and it is difficult to differentiate between modern and antique pieces.

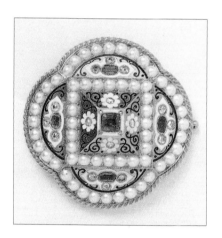

Plate 144.

Gold brooch decorated with white enamel and set with pearls, emeralds and rose diamonds, once the detachable centre of a bracelet given by the Maharajah Duleep Singh to Princess Helena. The shape of the jewel seems to be influenced by Italian medieval themes but the use of enamel and gemstones echoes the exotic origins of the giver. *No quote.*

Wartski, London

Plate 145.

Indian jewellery.

1. Pair of ruby and emerald cloak studs, the reverse (left) enamelled in red, green and white on gold. *£1,000.*

2. Pair of diamond, pearl and enamel earrings in the form of a fish, the reverse enamelled. *£1,250.*

3. Foiled crystal plaque necklace, each crystal in an enamelled frame. *£2,000 – £2,500.*

4. Gold plaque bracelet with hand-painted ivory miniatures of Indian scenes (one of a pair). *£3,000 – £4,000.*

5. Pair of ruby bead, diamond and pearl earrings in gold. *£1,500 – £2,000.*

6. Emerald and pearl necklace with its finely enamelled back shown. *£5,000.* *S.J. Phillips*

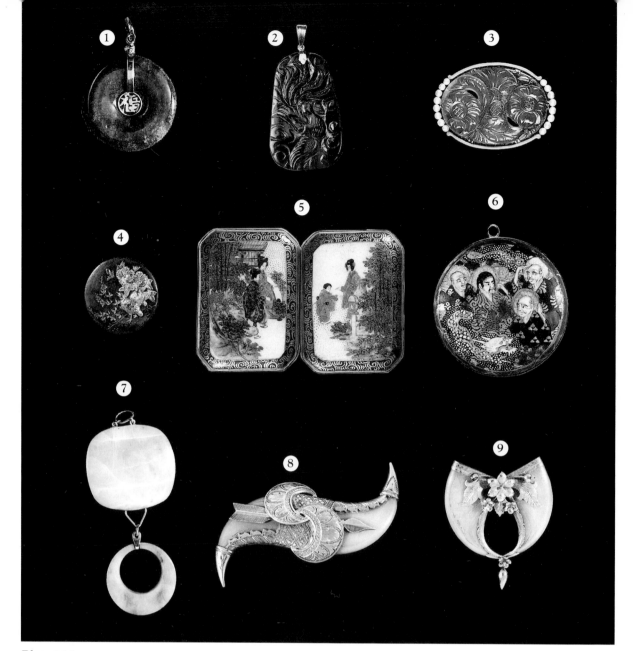

Plate 146.

Oriental jewellery based on traditional designs.

1. 20th century green jade and gold circular pendant in the form of a 'pi', made in China for the export market. £620 – £850.

2. 19th century spinach-green carved jade pendant. £1,500 – £2,000.

3. 20th century carved cornelian, enamel and pearl brooch, c.1920. £650 – £1,000.   *1–3 N. Bloom*

4. Japanese circular bronze brooch, the surface applied with quails and peonies in gold and silver. £150 – £200.

5. Late 19th century Japanese Satsuma buckle, enamelled and gilded pottery. £150 – £200.

6. Late 19th century Japanese Satsuma enamelled circular pendant. £150 – £200.

7. Art deco jade drop pendant. £500.

8. Late Victorian double tiger's claw brooch set in an engraved silver mount. £200.

9. Late Victorian double tiger's claw brooch in a floral gold mount, c.1880. Tiger's claw jewellery was popular soon after Victoria became Empress of India in 1876. £250 – £350.   *4–9 Thesaurus at Antiquarius*

ARTS AND CRAFTS
AND ART NOUVEAU JEWELLERY

In England during the second half of the 19th century traditional jewellery continued to be made as usual. However, a new style was developing in parallel under the influence and sentiments of the Pre-Raphaelite artists, and, later, the designer William Morris. This style was developed to counter stiff, factory-made objects which, although often of excellent quality, were unimaginative and dull. Small groups of designer craftsmen formed themselves into individual guilds around the country and started producing colourful, hand-made articles in inexpensive materials, using naturalistic forms and lines, hoping to influence the public taste. The 'Arts and Crafts Movement', as it was called, was to continue in changing form until the 1930s, encompassing the styles known in turn as 'art nouveau' and, later, 'art deco'. Some of the members were emancipated women, and many jewellers and silversmiths who were associated with the movement are now well-known names as designers of imagination and talent: C.R. Ashbee, J.P Cooper, Alexander Fisher, Arthur Gaskin and his wife Georgina, A.H. Jones, the MacDonald sisters, C.R. Mackintosh, William Morris and Henry Wilson – to mention a few.

In jewellery the use of precious stones set in gold was largely ignored for colourful, cheaper stones in silver, often combined with the use of different enamelling techniques – *cloisonné*, *champlevé* and *plique-à-jour*. Several established retail businesses contracted work from individual jewellers and even mass-produced some of their designs under the firm's name, notably Liberty & Co. in England and Tiffany in the States.

In France, the greatest art nouveau jewellery designer was René Lalique. His highly innovative concepts broke new ground in design, often combining the female form with elements from nature, such as insects, flowers and foliage. Lalique's new shapes were skilfully executed in fusions of precious and non-precious materials, together with *plique-à-jour* enamelling. His jewellery was widely acclaimed following his success at the Paris Exposition of 1900. Henri Vever, one of the foremost exponents of French art nouveau jewellery after Lalique, also created highly original, stylised pieces.

This was a fascinating period of design and craftsmanship and many original and beautiful pieces of jewellery were made.

Plate 147 (overleaf).

1. Blue and green enamel pendant set in silver, c.1900. £500.

2. Blue enamel floral pendant set in silver, c.1905. £200.

3. Oval silver pendant set with mother-of-pearl, surrounded by blue and green enamel, with a pendant heart, c.1900 by S. & Co. £500 – £600.

4. Enamel mermaid pendant set in silver. £250 – £300.

5. Opal and silver brooch. £800 – £1,000.

6. Silver bat brooch set with a wood opal body and opal head. £750.

7. Blue and green enamelled necklace in silver, set with mother-of-pearl, c.1900 by Liberty & Co. £1,000.

8. Amethyst and purple enamel necklace in silver, c.1905 by Liberty & Co. £1,000.

The Purple Shop, Private Collection

Plate 148.

1. Opal, enamel and silver brooch by Liberty & Co. £800 – £1,200.

2. Silver and enamel pendant and necklace, c.1905 by Ramsden & Carr. £2,500 – £3,000.

3. 18ct. gold necklace set with turquoises and freshwater pearls, by Liberty & Co. £2,500 – £3,000.

4. Enamel pendant with mother-of-pearl on silver chain, by Otto Prutscher. £1,000 – £1,200.

5. Scrolled 18ct. gold pendant set with mother-of-pearl and fire opals, by Edouard Colonna. £3,000 – £4,000.

6. *Plique-à-jour* enamel pendant-cum-powder compact set with long freshwater pearls between the enamelled sections. £650 – £750.

The Purple Shop, Private Collection

Plate 149.

1. Silver and opal rectangular brooch, by Arthur and Georgina Gaskin. *£750.*

2. Emerald, opal, tourmaline and enamel pendant on a silver chain, by Arthur and Georgina Gaskin. *£1,500.*

3. Enamel and silver pendant with three drops, on a silver chain, by Omar Ramsden, unmarked. (Omar Ramsden is better known as a silversmith.) *£1,000.*

Antiquarius, The Purple Shop

Plate 150.

Lapis lazuli and silver necklace, the long chain threaded with lapis lazuli beads. £500.

The Purple Shop, Private Collection

Plate 151.

1. Green enamel flower brooch set with two cabochon amethysts in silver-gilt, c.1900. *£250 – £300.*

2. *Plique-à-jour* enamel vine leaf with seed pearl bunch of grapes suspending a green enamelled watch. *£1,000 – £1,200.*

3. Green enamel and mother-of-pearl pendant. *£400 – £500.*

4. Enamel brooch set with cabochon garnets in silver-gilt. *£400 – £500.*

5. Green enamel, lozenge-shaped brooch set with mother-of-pearl and marcasites. *£250 – £300.*

6. Green and yellow enamel pendant set with an opal, marcasites and pendent freshwater pearls. *£700 – £750.*

7. Enamel slide on a silver chain. *£300.*

8. Green and yellow enamel pendant set with marcasites, a paste and a freshwater pearl in silver-gilt. *£800.*

9. Blue enamel wing-shaped pendant set with mother-of-pearl in silver-gilt on a chain with Baroque pearls inset. *£1,500.*

10. Enamel and *plique-à-jour* enamelled butterfly set with a cabochon garnet in silver-gilt. *£500.*

11. Enamel eel brooch in silver with chrysoprase eyes. *£1,500 (as by Fahrner).*

12. Enamel dragonfly brooch set in silver-gilt. *£500.*

13. Pink and blue enamel pendant, set with blue pastes and seed pearls in silver. *£550.*

The Purple Shop, Private Collection

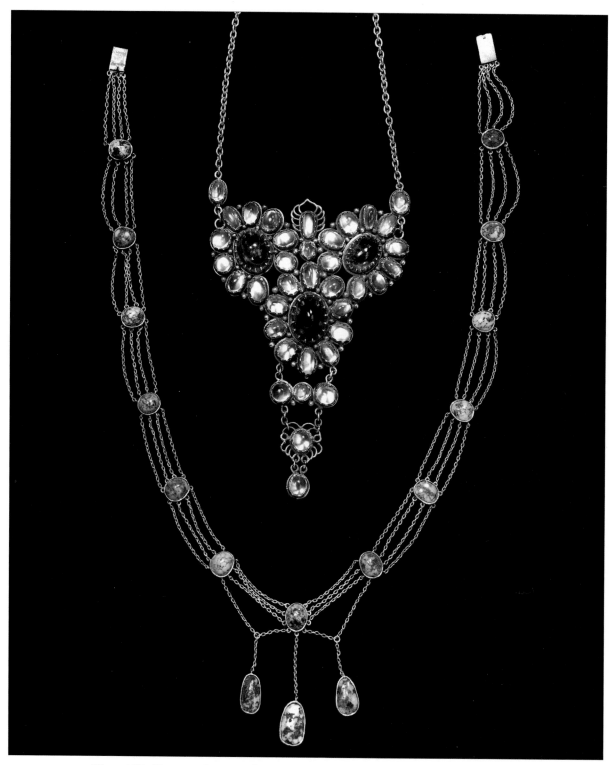

Plate 152 (front and reverse).

Arts and Crafts, amethyst and moonstone pendant of three large clusters, set in silver, possibly by Sybil Dunlop. £800 – £900.

Late Arts and Crafts turquoise matrix and silver chain necklace. £350 – £400.

Antiquarius, Bellamy

The reverse of both pieces shows the methods of setting (see also pp.336–343.)

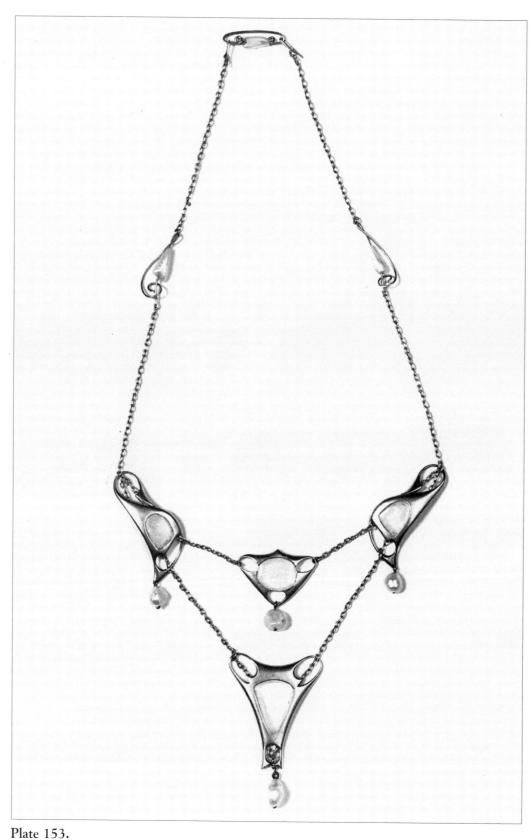

Plate 153.

Art nouveau 18ct. gold, opal and freshwater pearl necklace, c.1900 by Liberty & Co.
£5,000 – £7,000.
The Purple Shop, Private Collection

Plate 154.

1. Sapphire, pearl and enamel pendant in 9ct. gold, c.1900. £300.

2. *Plique-à-jour* enamel, mother-of-pearl and silver brooch, c.1910. £300 – £400.

3. *Plique-à-jour* enamel and pearl lotus flower pendant in silver-gilt, Egyptian influence, c.1925. £200 – £300.

4. Gold, ruby and rose diamond brooch, French c.1900. £500.

5. Art nouveau metal pendant with a female profile, French, c.1905. £250 – £300.

6. *Plique-à-jour* enamel and silver 'Egyptian' brooch set with a cabochon garnet, c.1925. £250 – £300.

7. Freshwater pearl 'bunch of grapes' pendant with silvery-green enamel leaves, set in 14ct. gold, French, c.1900. £400 – £500. *Antiquarius, Bellamy, The Purple Shop*

Plate 155.

Fine art nouveau tropical butterfly brooch in gold and diamonds with delicately coloured *plique-à-jour* enamels varying from carmine pink to bronze, green and violet, giving an effect of iridescence, c.1905. £10,000+. *Sotheby's*

Fine art nouveau dragonfly brooch in *plique-à-jour* enamels, set with a ruby, diamonds and emeralds, by Lalique. £20,000+. *Christie's*

Plate 156.

French enamelled peacock feather buckle, the centre set with green and blue 'peacock eye' paste, signed 'PF', dagger between, c.1900. £500.

French coloured enamel butterfly buckle in gilt metal, signed 'PF', dagger between, c.1900. £500.   *The Purple Shop, Private Collection*

Plate 157.

Art nouveau *pâte de verre* pendants.

1. Insect pendant in shades of yellow, green and brown. £400.

2. Dragonfly pendant in greens, blues and browns. £1,200.

3. Insect pendant, browns, yellows and oranges, signed 'A.V.N.'. £600.

4. Cicada pendant, purples, browns, blues and black. £1,500.

5. Bat pendant, iridescent blues and purples, on a silver chain. £350.

6. Scarab pendant coloured with iridescent blues and purples, with a 9ct. gold setting. £300.

The Purple Shop, Private Collection

Plate 158.

Two pendants of frosted glass, one of a pelican, one of anemones, both French c.1920.
£500 each.   *Antiquarius, Bellamy*

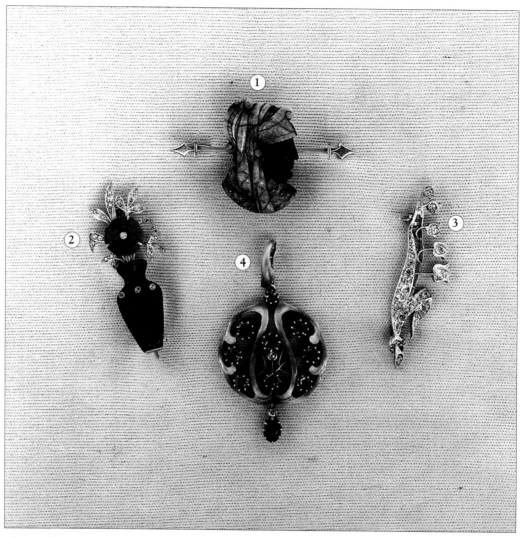

Plate 159.

1. Opal cameo mounted as a brooch on a gold pin, c.1900 by Newman of Melbourne. A good example of carving, the head-dress of black opal carved from the matrix which forms the face. £4,000, *rare*.

2. Art deco lapis lazuli vase brooch containing a cornelian flower with diamond set leaves, c.1930. £2,500 – £2,800.

3. Edwardian diamond lily-of-the-valley spray brooch, set in silver and gold. £700 – £900.

4. Art nouveau pendant of scrolled enamel set with Montana sapphires, c.1905. The delicate, almost iridescent enamel sets off the metallic colour of the sapphires. £1,100.

Michael Poynder

186

Plate 160.

1. Circular silver compact, designed to be worn as a pendant. £300 – £400.

2. Art nouveau pendant, the ivory face surrounded by a silver-gilt frame set with turquoises, garnets, emeralds and corals, on a silver-gilt chain with orange and green *plique-à-jour* enamel sections. £900 – £1,000.

3. Silver pocket-watch, signed 'Huguenin'. £800 – £900.

4. 'Egyptian' head made of ivorine, set in gilt metal with red and white enamelled scarabs and lotus flowers. £250 – 300.

5. French silver and silver-gilt buckle set with opals, rubies, diamonds and sapphires. £750 – £950.

The Purple Shop, Private Collection

Plate 161.

French art nouveau horn birds and insects.

1/2. Dragonfly brooches (approx. ½ size). *£150*. **3.** Dragonfly pendant, by Bonté. *£1,000*.

    4. Reverse of 3, showing signature. **5.** Moth brooch. *£150*.

    6. Flying duck brooch. *£150*.

Bellamy, Antiquarius

Plate 162.

1. Turquoise matrix and hammered silver buckle, marked 'Cymric'.

2. Opal and open-work silver buckle, by Liberty & Co.

3. Silver and enamel buckle, by Liberty & Co.

4. Silver buckle with female bust, French, factory-made.

5. Silver buckle with green, red and blue enamel, by Liberty & Co.

6. Open-work silver buckle with green, brown and blue enamel, by Liberty & Co.

7. Silver buckle formed of the letters 'ER' for Edward VII, unmarked, but probably made to commemorate his coronation in 1901.

8. Silver cloak fastener set with turquoise matrix, c.1905, marked 'Cymric'.

Varying in price from £500 – £1,500. *The Purple Shop, Private Collection*

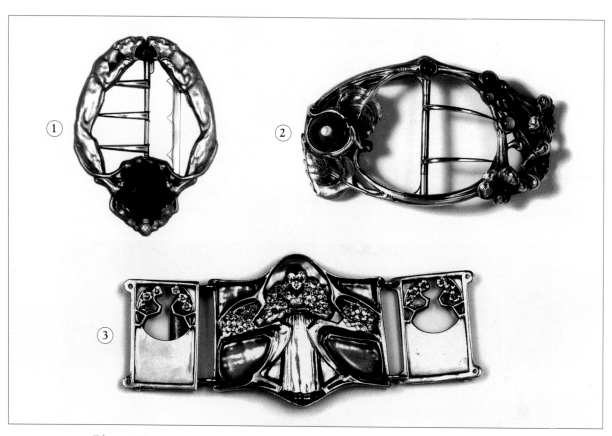

Plate 163.

1. Art nouveau gold buckle in the form of two lionesses fighting over a cornelian heart, the base formed of a moulded, olive green, glass lion's mask, by Boucheron. Exhibited at the firm's exhibition in Paris in 1900. £5,000+.   *Sotheby's*

2. Agate and silver buckle of floral design, by Vever of Paris. £2,000.
                                                            The Purple Shop, Private Collection

3. Silver buckle in three sections, set with mother-of-pearl, made in London in 1902 by William Hutton & Sons. £800 – £1,000.   *The Purple Shop, Private Collection*

Plate 164.

1. Fire opal and silver pendant. £800.

2. Moonstone, opal and silver pendant on a silver chain. £600 – £800.

3. Agate and cornelian necklace set in silver. £1,000.

All by Wilson & Cooper, late 19th century.   *The Purple Shop, Private Collection*

EDWARDIAN, ART DECO,
AND MODERN DRESS JEWELLERY

The Edwardian era was an age of wealth, refinement, elegance and security. Often referred to as La Belle Epoque, it was a brief period of extravagance and sophistication between the sombre late Victorian years and the First World War. Edwardian jewellery was feminine, delicate and characteristically light in all its elements – in the new calibré- and baguette-cut stones, in the millegrain settings using the new metal, platinum, and in its refined, graceful designs. Diamonds were the most popular stones, set into chokers, collars, tiaras, fine bracelets and rings. Pearls were fashionable, especially elegant pearl sautoirs. The necklace in Plate 168 is typically Edwardian – lavish in its use of stones, yet still delicate and feminine.

The art deco style originated in France, its name derived from L'Exposition Internationale des Arts Décoratifs et Industriels Modernes held in Paris in 1925. The movement was a post-war reaction against art nouveau's naturalistic style. Art deco jewellery forms were geometric, angular and elongated, emphasising strong design and strong colours. Diamonds were platinum-set in bold designs and combined with stones such as onyx and jade to create stylish contrasts. Geometric plaque bracelets and brooches, dramatic necklaces and the versatile double clip brooch were popular. Costume jewellery made from chrome, bakelite, marcasite and paste was also very fashionable. Following the discovery of Tutankhamun's tomb in 1925, Egyptianesque jewellery in silver and metal and novelties such as mummy cases were in demand, though not always of good quality.

The shortage of precious stones after the Second World War encouraged jewellery designers to become more versatile. Design, rather than content, became the main element and post-war jewellery was characterised by flamboyant designs, good quality gold work and the use of gold in different colours. Jewellery was showy and colourful, with swirls, twists, cascades and stylised flowers abounding in brooches, double clips, rings and bangles.

Throughout the 20th century, the jewellery from the great French houses, such as Cartier, Boucheron, Van Cleef & Arpels, has stood the test of time as examples of the best each era of design has had to offer. Pieces made and signed by them are always sought after.

Plate 165.

Edwardian diamond lace ribbon bow brooch, bordered with small calibré emeralds, set in platinum, c.1905. The setting is of good quality and the mount is curved, giving the brooch shape. *No quote.* *Sotheby's*

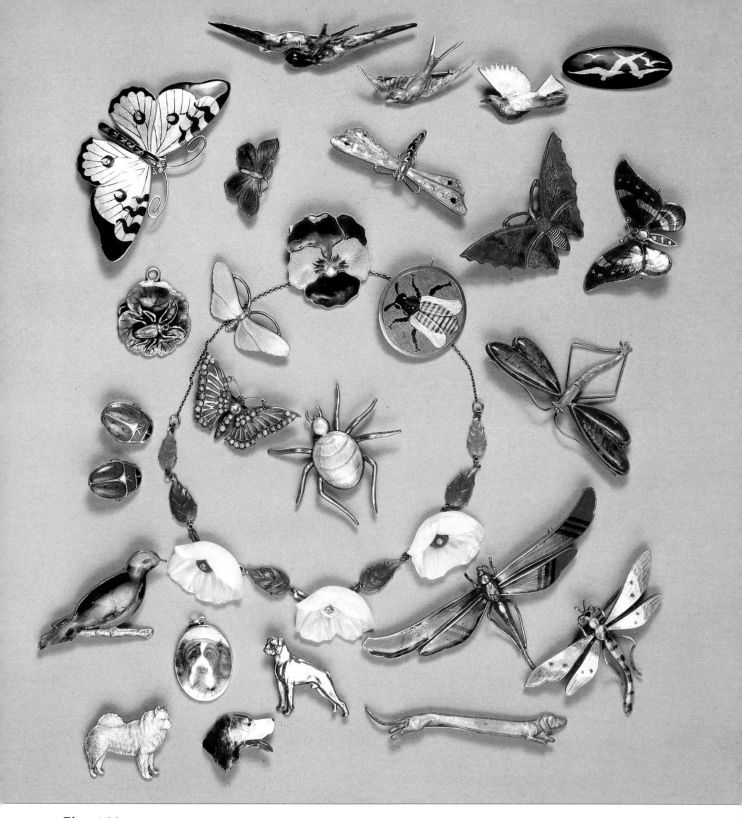

Plate 166.

Group of art nouveau and 20th century enamelled animals, in silver or metal, using a variety of techniques and materials, including turquoises with *plique-à-jour* enamel (butterfly brooch inside necklace), real butterfly wings and glass.

Enamelled brooches £100 – £300.   Necklace £150 – £200.   *Plique-à-jour* butterfly £300.

Antiquarius, Tony & Sara, The Purple Shop, Bellamy, Chimera, Thesaurus

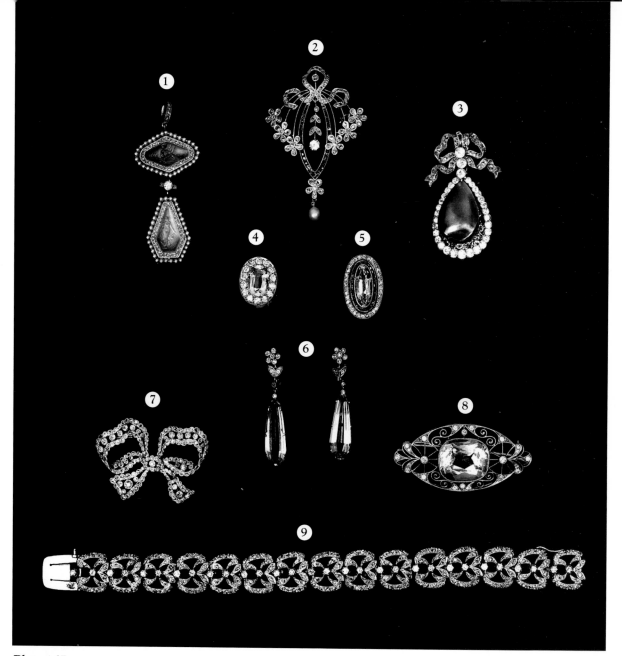

Plate 167.

1. Carved moonstone pendant with drop, set in a frame of diamonds and pearls in platinum, c.1910. £3,500 – £4,000.

2. Floral drop pendant set with diamonds, calibré-cut rubies and a pearl in platinum, c.1905. £4,000 – £4,500.

3. Black pearl and diamond drop pendant with a diamond ribbon top. (The pendant chain is showing behind the pearl.) £2,500 – £2,750.

4. Aquamarine and diamond cluster ring. £1,200 – £1,700.

5. Edwardian 'Suffragette' ring of pink topaz surrounded by green garnets and diamonds, c.1913 (pink, green and white were the Suffragette colours). £3,000 – £3,500.

6. Pair of aquamarine and diamond drop earrings, c.1910. £2,500 – £3,000.

7. Decorated ribbon bow brooch set with brilliant- and rose-cut diamonds in platinum, c.1910. £4,000.

8. Late 19th century aquamarine and diamond brooch of open-work design, by R.S. & E. £1,800 – £2,000.

9. Late Victorian flexible diamond bracelet of ribbon design, set with brilliants and rose diamonds in silver and gold, c.1890. £6,000 – £8,000.
Cameo Corner

Plate 168.

Edwardian, diamond, open-work pendant in the form of a bow with pendent quatrefoil and drops, set with mixed brilliant and rose-cut diamonds in platinum. £7,000 – £10,000.

Diamond and cabochon ruby trellis-work necklace set in platinum. If broken up, this could be made into an attractive brooch and earrings, four ruby and diamond cluster rings and a range of hundreds of small extra diamonds. *No quote.*   *N. Bloom, Christie's*

Plate 169.

1. Brown and yellow enamelled belt buckle set in silver. £150.

2. Red and black enamelled buckle in chrome. £75.

3. Elongated octagonal buckle enamelled in yellow, brown, blue, green and black, set in brass. £75.

4. Blue and red enamelled buckle in chrome. £75.

5. Black onyx open circle brooch set with a bar of rose diamonds in platinum, c.1920 by Cartier. £4,000 – £5,000.

6. Multi-coloured paste necklace of floral design, set in silver, c.1925. £300.

7. Necklace of geometric design set with cornelians and onyx in silver. £350.

8. Multi-coloured enamel necklace set in gilt metal. £150.

9. Yellow, black and blue enamelled figure set in silver. £200 – £300.

10. Blue enamel yacht brooch in chrome, c.1930. £150.

Antiquarius, Bellamy, The Purple Shop, E. Ashley Cooper

Plate 170 (overleaf).

1. Art deco black plastic and paste buckle. £50 – £80.

2. Art deco paste, chrysoprase and marcasite brooch in silver. £200 – £250.

3. Red and white paste stylised bow brooch, c.1940. £150.

4. Green, red and white paste butterfly brooch in silver-gilt. £175.

5. Green, red and white paste lizard in silver. £120 – £150.

6. Painted metal peacock set with pastes. £50.

7. Silver-plated buckle set with a cornelian and pastes, signed 'T.B.'. £75 – £100.

8. Silver and gilt metal dress clip set with pastes, c.1940. £75.

9. Art deco paste and metal chain link necklet. £75.

10. Paste drop earrings set in metal, c.1940. £80 – £120.

11. Blue and white paste brooch set in silver, c.1930. £200 – £250.

12. Green and white paste bracelet and clasp, c.1930. £100.

13. Art deco black glass, paste and metal stylised flower brooch. £100.

14. Blue and white paste on metal flexible bracelet, c.1940. £75 – £100.

Antiquarius, Bellamy, John Taylor, The Purple Shop, Tony & Sara, Lynda Perkin Antiques

Plate 171.

Diamond fringe necklace set with baguette- and brillian-cut diamonds. £40,000+.

Diamond brooch designed as a buckle and scarf, set with pavé set brilliants and a fringe of baguettes. £15,000 – £20,000.   *Christie's*

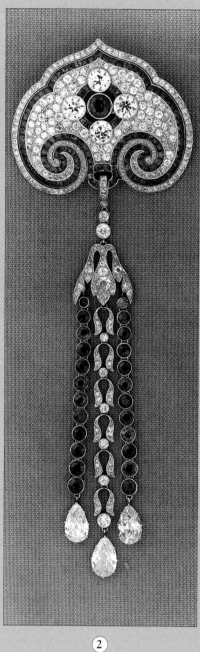

Plate 172.

1. Art deco sapphire and diamond drop brooch/pendant, set with two fine briolette-cut sapphire drops, c.1925. *No quote.*

2. Art deco sapphire and diamond brooch/pendant of good quality, in the Indian style, c.1920. *No quote.*

3. Green garnet and diamond floral spray brooch. Green (demantoid) garnets of this size are unusual. *No quote.*

Christie's

Plate 173.
Art deco aquamarine and diamond necklace of formal scroll design, mounted in platinum.
£25,000+.
Christie's

Plate 174.

Art deco suite of brooch, pendant and earrings in onyx, diamonds and platinum, by Cartier. *No quote. Christie's*

Plate 175.

1. Peridot and diamond brooch with peridot drops set in silver and gold. £4,000 – £8,000.   *N. Bloom*

2. Art deco sapphire and diamond drop earrings, c.1930. £8,000 – £12,000.   *N. Bloom*

3. Diamond and emerald lily spray brooch set in platinum, c.1920. £2,500 – £3,000.   *Michael Poynder*

4. Art deco jade and diamond brooch set in platinum. £1,500 – £2,500.   *N. Bloom*

5. Early 20th century brooch and earrings of frosted crystal, amethysts and diamonds. £2,000 – £2,200.
    Michael Poynder

6. Art deco jardinière brooch set in platinum with diamonds and a variety of coloured stones.
    £3,000 – £4,500.   *N. Bloom*

7. Art deco pavé set diamond hexagonal pendant with centre bar, in platinum. £6,000 – £8,000. *Christie's*

8. Diamond, sapphire and ruby Union Jack, c.1920. £2,000 – £2,500.   *Michael Poynder*

9. Art deco sapphire and diamond rayed oblong plaque brooch. £5,000 – £6,000.   *Christie's*

10. Art deco aquamarine emerald and diamond buckle brooch. £8,000 – £10,000.   *Christie's*

11. Edwardian diamond and demantoid garnet open-work bar brooch set in platinum, c.1905.
    £5,000 – £7,000.   *N. Bloom*

Plate 176.

Items representative of the craze for Egyptian style jewellery which swept Europe after the discovery of Tutankhamun's tomb in 1925.

1. *Plique-à-jour* enamel, paste and silver-gilt Ba-bird brooch. £600 – £700.

2. Carved amethyst scarab, ruby and rose diamond drop pendant in gold. £800 – £1,000.

3. Enamel and silver-plated circular buckle. £75 – £100.

4. Carved cornelian scarab ring with 22ct. gold mount. £450 – £500.

5. Carved green turquoise scarab ring in 14ct. gold. £400 – £500.

6. Faïence scarab ring in 9ct. gold. £250 – £350.

7. Cornelian, chrysoprase and enamel link bracelet in silver plate, the cornelian and chrysoprase carved as scarabs. £250.

8. Enamel and silver-gilt oval plaque bracelet. £200.

9. Enamel and silver-gilt bracelet with Egyptian landscapes. £300.

10. Bloodstone scarab pendant in gold. £200.

11. Bracelet set with lapis lazuli in silver-gilt and enamelled, copied from bracelets worn by the High Priest Pi-nudjem II from Thebes. £1,000.

12. Egyptian, silver 'head' brooch. £75 – £100.

13. Oval open-work gilt metal pendant of an Egyptian figure. £75.

14. Scarab brooch with *plique-à-jour* enamel wings and enamelled body. £250 – £275.

15. Silver and enamel brooch with a pyramid in the centre. £100 – £150.

16. Enamel and silver-gilt mummy case (empty). £50 – £75.

17. Enamel and silver-gilt Moses in a Basket (closed). £50 – £75.

18. Enamel and silver-gilt mummy case. £50 – £75.

19. Silver-gilt Moses in a Basket (open). £50 – £75.

20. Silver-gilt mummy and case. £50 – £75.

21. Blue enamel and metal plaque bracelet in the Egyptian style. £100 – £120.

Antiquarius, The Purple Shop, Bellamy, Thesaurus, Chimeras

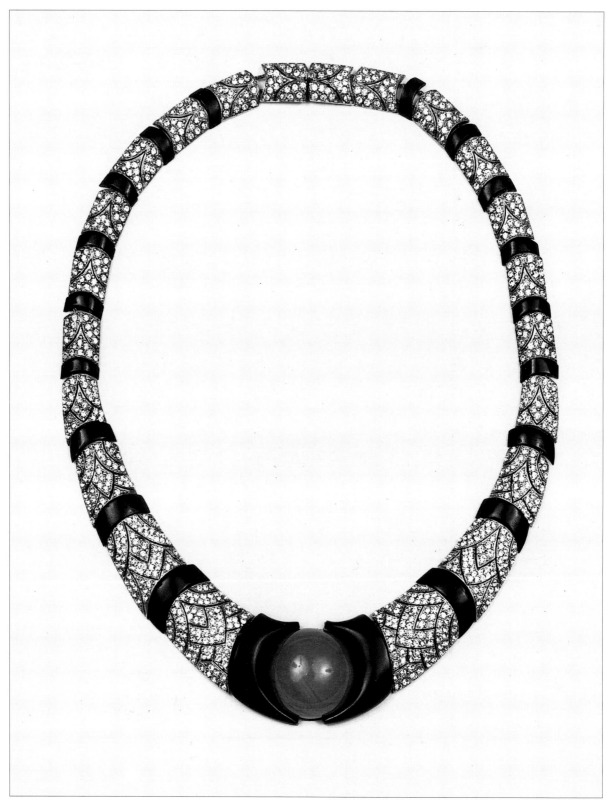

Plate 177.

Art deco white paste, black and yellow plastic necklace backed with silver-plated metal, the sections strung on a silver chain. £500 – £600.

Antiquarius, The Purple Shop

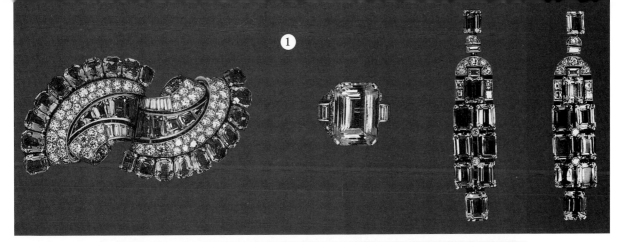

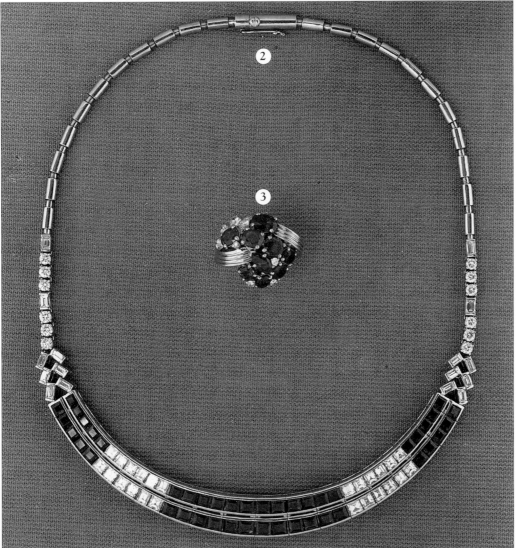

Plate 178.

1. Art deco suite of aquamarine and diamond double clip brooch, ring and earrings, mounted in platinum, c.1925. £15,000 – £20,000.

2. Art deco ruby and diamond necklace, set with calibré cut rubies and diamonds, on a white gold chain, c.1940. £30,000 – £35,000.

3. Ruby and diamond ring set with nine rubies and seven diamonds, in yellow gold, c.1940. £3,000 – £5,000.

Christie's

Plate 179.

20th century diamond and coloured stone jewellery at its best. Each piece is imaginative, and the work of a craftsman.

1. Jardinière brooch set with white and coloured diamonds, rubies, emeralds and sapphires in a baguette-cut diamond vase. £12,000.

2. Stomacher brooch/pendant set with cabochon-cut emeralds, rubies, sapphires and brilliant-cut diamonds, by Van Cleef & Arpels. £30,000.

3. Two diamond, ruby, emerald and sapphire parakeets as a brooch, separating into two clips. £15,000.

4. Diamond, sapphire, carved emerald and ruby jardinière brooch, the vase formed by a large single diamond. £12,000+.

5. Art deco stylised jardinière brooch set with baguette- and brilliant-cut diamonds, ruby and sapphire flowers with carved emerald leaves. £7,500.

6. Diamond buckle brooch with carved emeralds, sapphires and rubies. £6,000.

7. Sapphire, emerald and diamond earrings in gold. £6,000. *S.J. Phillips*

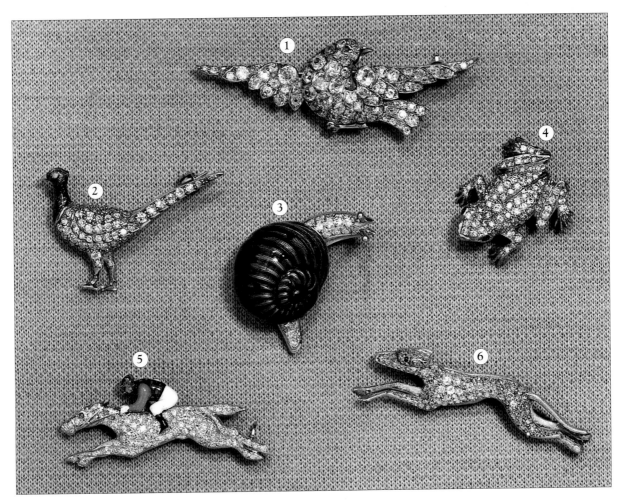

Plate 180.

1. Pavé set diamond bird in flight, set in silver and gold. £3,000 – £3,500.

2. Pavé set diamond pheasant brooch with enamelled head, set in yellow and white gold. £1,800 – £2,500.

3. Diamond snail with blue enamelled shell, set in yellow gold. £2,500 – £3,000.

4. Pavé set diamond frog brooch set in yellow gold. £1,800 – £2,500.

5. Pavé set diamond racehorse with enamelled jockey, set in yellow gold. £1,800 – £2,500.

6. Pavé set diamond greyhound brooch set in yellow and white gold. £2,000 – £2,500.

Tessiers

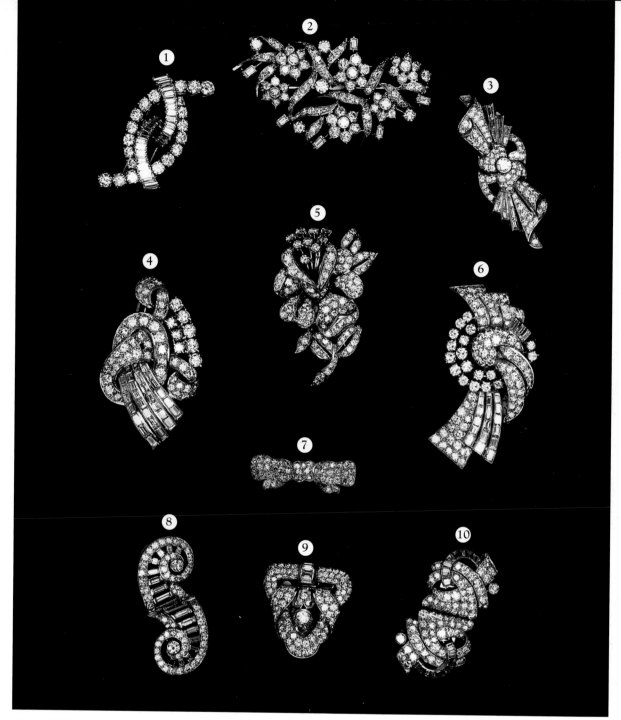

Plate 181.

These brooches of the 1930s, 1940s and 1950s are set in white gold or platinum.

1. Stylised tied knot brooch set with diamonds.   2. Traditional diamond floral cluster brooch.

3. Stylised diamond tied ribbon brooch, pavé set.   4. Diamond knotted 'waterfall' brooch.

5. Diamond flower brooch.   6. Diamond circular 'cascade' brooch.

7. Diamond tied ribbon brooch, c.1930.

8. Diamond S-shaped, double clip brooch. This brooch will separate to form two individual clips of identical design.

9. Half of a diamond double clip brooch.   10. Diamond scrolled double clip brooch.

Varying in price £3,000 – £6,000.   *B. Barnett Ltd.*

210

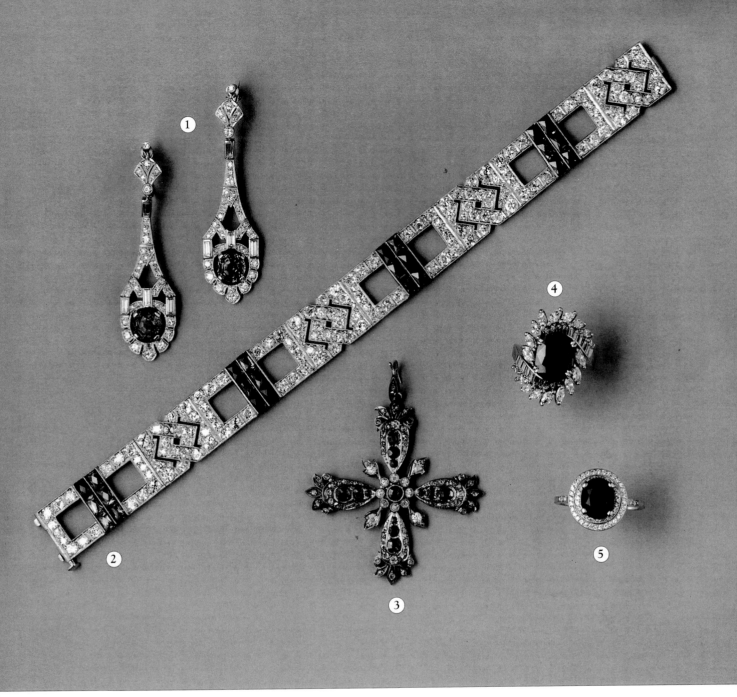

Plate 182.

1. Pair platinum mounted diamond and baguette diamond earrings set with Ceylon sapphires, c.1920. £10,000 – £12,000.

2. Platinum mounted diamond bracelet set with four twin-rows of French-cut Ceylon sapphires, c.1930. £15,000 – £20,000.

3. Edwardian silver and gold-mounted cross pendant set with diamonds and sapphires, c.1900. £3,500 – £4,500.

4. Ring with marquise and baguette diamond swirl mount set with a Burma sapphire estimated 6cts., c.1950. *No quote.*

5. Ring set with Burma sapphire estimated 4cts., twin-row diamond surround, c.1910. £6,000 – £10,000.

N. Bloom

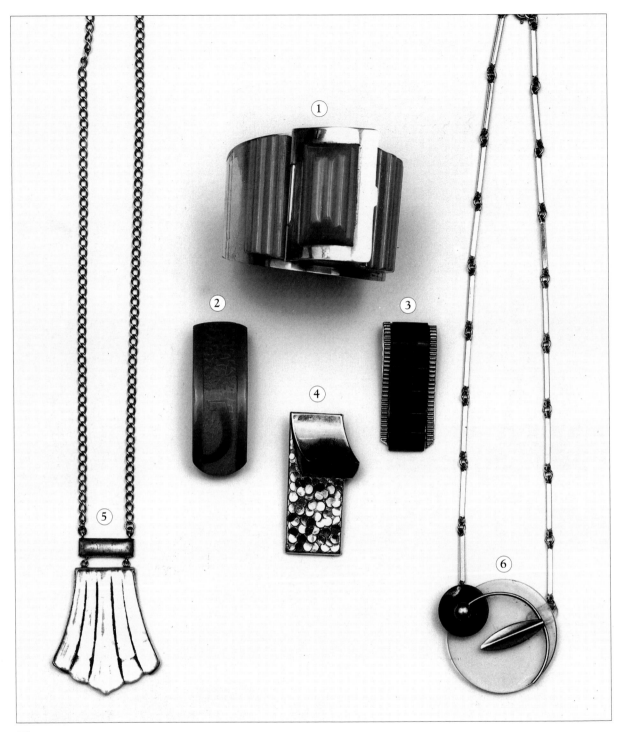

Plate 183.

1. Bangle of green bakelite and lacquered brass, the centre opening as a compact, c.1930. £250.

2. Bakelite dress clip carved with initial 'J'. £40.

3. Wood and chrome dress clip. £40.

4. Silvered glass dress clip. £40.

5. Mirror-backed glass and silver pendant on a chain. £100 – £120.

6. Chrome and bakelite stylised cherry pendant on chain. £100 – £175.   *Antiquarius, Bellamy*

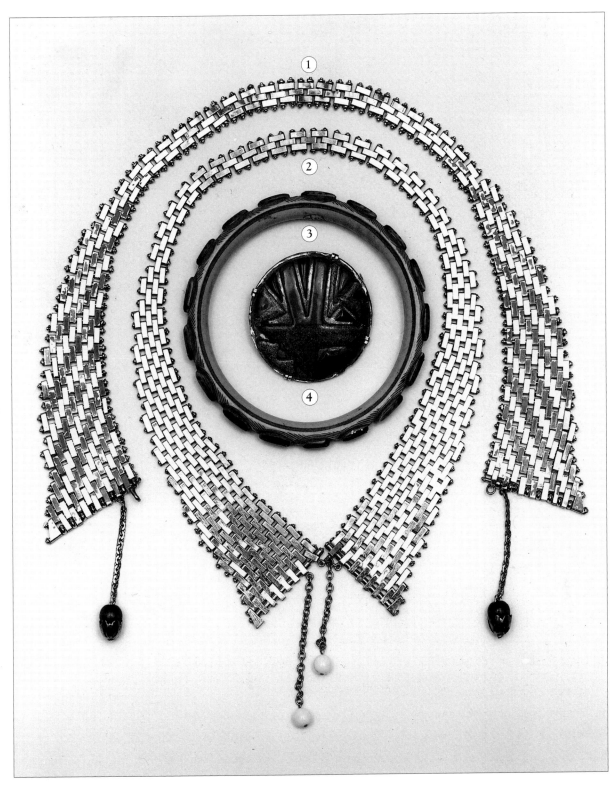

Plate 184.

1/2. Art deco flexible chrome collars, stove enamelled. *£150 each.*

3. Plastic ladybird bangle. *£50.*

4. Art deco Limoges enamel and silver brooch, c.1925 by Fauré. *£1,500.*

Antiquarius, Bellamy, Thesaurus

Plate 185.

1. Pair of diamond earrings set with baguette- and brilliant-cut diamonds in a geometric design. *£1,400.*

2. Large sapphire and diamond flower brooch, the flower composed of an exceptional range of pavé set, calibré-cut sapphires with a brilliant-cut diamond cluster centre, the stem of baguette diamonds with two marquise diamonds designed as buds. *£30,000 – £50,000.*

3. Unusual pendant of pink tourmaline and jade pebbles set with rose diamonds. *£2,500 – £3,000.*

4. Diamond bracelet, each linking section formed of brilliants and baguettes. *£6,500 – £8,500.*

5. Diamond and sapphire brooch set with marquise, brilliant- and baguette-cut diamonds, the sapphires calibré-cut. *£6,000 – £7.000.*

6. Circular, carved emerald set in a diamond rectangular brooch, the emerald forming the flowerhead surrounded by diamond leaves with two small sections of black enamel, in a milled setting. *£4,000+.*

7. Emerald and diamond graduated open oval brooch. *£10,000.*

8. Diamond clip brooch incorporating diamonds of fancy cuts such as trapeze and triangular, and also a half brilliant as well as the more conventional brilliants and baguettes, by Cartier. *£4,000 – £5,000.   S.J. Phillips*

214

Plate 186.

1. Ruby and diamond double clip brooch in white gold. *No quote.*

2. Diamond double clip brooch set with brilliant and baguette-cut diamonds. *£10,000+.*

3. Diamond and sapphire brooch designed as two lilies, pavé set with brilliant- and baguette-cut diamonds, c.1935. *£25,000.*

4. Sapphire and diamond double clip brooch set with marquise, brilliant- and baguette-cut diamonds. *£25,000 – £30,000.* *Christie's*

The quality of stones in clip brooches of this type is frequently mixed, and they are often broken up and the stones reset into more fashionable pieces of jewellery.

Plate 187.

1. Large diamond cluster ring, claw set in yellow gold. £12,000.
2. Diamond cluster ring in yellow gold. £6,000 – £7,000.
3. Diamond cluster ring with diamond shoulders. £2,800.
4. Floral diamond cluster ring in yellow gold. £3,300.
5. Diamond cluster ring, plain shank. £2,500.
6. Edwardian diamond cluster ring in milled setting. £5,000.
7. Traditional diamond cluster ring. £3,200.
8. Spaced diamond cluster ring. £3,500.
9. Diamond cluster ring with spaced outer stones. £2,850.
10. Square shaped diamond cluster ring. £3,300.
11. Ten stone diamond half-hoop ring with white gold, twisted rope sides. £4,500.
12. Five stone diamond half-hoop ring with white gold, twisted rope sides. £5000+.
13. Traditional five stone diamond graduated half-hoop ring. £4,800 – £5,000.
14. Five stone diamond half-hoop ring set in yellow gold. £4,000.
15. Diamond and white gold half-hoop ring, the diamonds set in diagonal bands of three. £3,900 – £4,000.
16. Diamond double row half-hoop ring. £2,500.
17. Five stone diamond ring in yellow gold. £3,500.
18. Large diamond three stone ring. £12,000, *depending on individual quality of diamonds.*
19. Diamond three stone ring in white gold. £8,000.
20. Diamond three stone ring with carved shoulders. £6,000.
21. Diamond three stone ring in white gold. £5,500.
22. Graduated diamond three stone ring in white gold. £6,000.
23. Diamond three stone ring. £5,000.
24. Diamond three stone ring, collet set. £4,500.
25. Five diamond three stone rings with slight variations in setting and price. £3,000 – £5,000.
26. Gold ring set diagonally with three diamonds. £1,800.
27. Small diamond three stone ring. £1,700.
28. Emerald-cut diamond set as a ring with baguette shoulders. £11,500 – £12,000.
29. Single stone cushion-cut diamond ring in open claw mount. £8,000.
30. Trap-cut diamond ring with baguette diamonds on either side. £6,500.
31. Single stone diamond ring. £2,800.
32. Single stone diamond in heavy gold, claw mount. £3,750.
33. Single stone diamond ring in plain gold band. £2,000.
34. Single stone diamond ring in plain gold mount. £1,650.
35. Single stone diamond ring with engraved shoulders. £1,800.
36. Single stone diamond ring with baguette and small brilliants on the shoulders. £3,750.
37. Claw set single stone diamond ring. £1,400.
38. Single stone diamond ring set with four claws in a boat-shaped mount. £1,600.
39. Single stone diamond ring in gold. £1,500.
40. Single stone diamond in a modern gold mount. £1,800.

Richard Ogden Ltd.

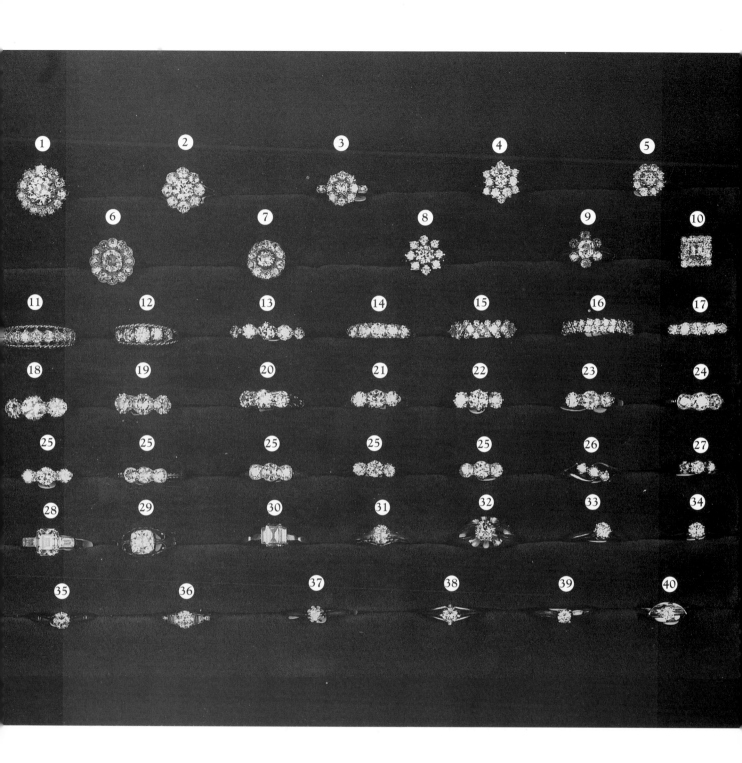

217

A TREASURE TROVE OF JEWELLERY

from necklaces to amulets

NECKLACES

Plate 188.

Late 17th century English necklace set with rubies, table-cut diamonds and emeralds set in a scrolled silver and gold mount, the stones foiled. *£10,000 – £12,000, exceptionally rare.*

Cameo Corner

Plate 189.

18th century Spanish necklace with large pendant attached, emeralds and rose diamonds set in gold. £15,000 – £18,000.   *Christie's*

Plate 190.

Georgian diamond collet necklace with five graduated sapphire and diamond cluster pendants attached, the necklace c.1830, the clusters c.1870. This was presumably 'made up' at some time, and would probably be 'broken up' today to make either earrings or rings, depending on how the individual sapphires matched for colour. *No quote*.   *Christie's*

Plate 191

19th century Berlin ironwork necklace signed 'Deveranne', Berlin, c.1850. £2,000 – £2,750, *extremely rare.*

Christie's South Kensington

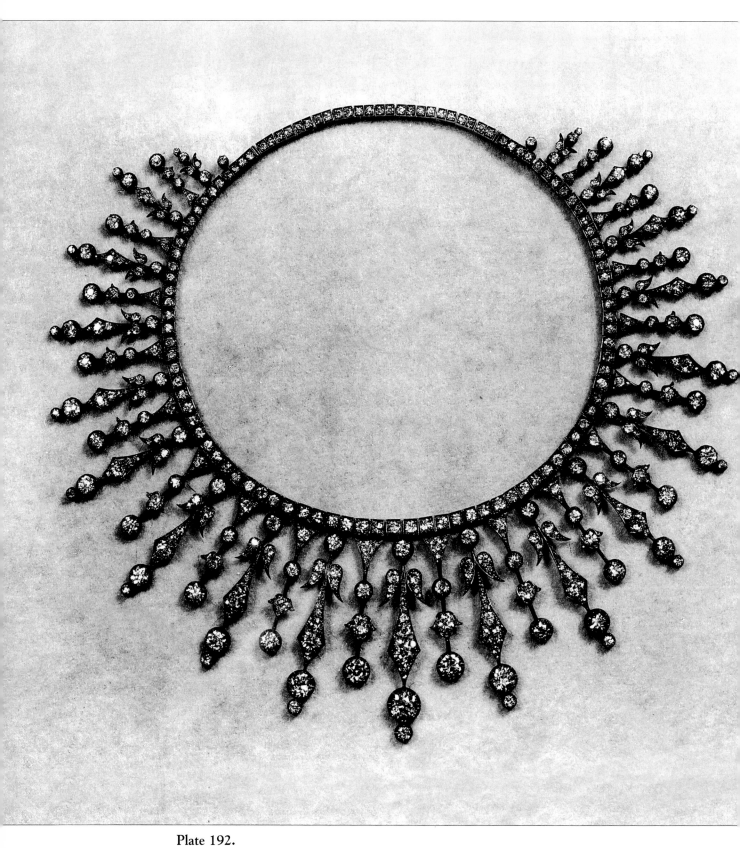

Plate 192.
Mid-Victorian diamond fringe necklace set in silver and gold (can be adapted to form a tiara),
c.1870. £25,000+. *Christie's*

Plate 193.

Late Victorian diamond necklace (can be adapted to form a tiara), c.1895. £25,000+.

Christie's

Plate 194.

Art deco diamond and emerald bead necklace (can be adapted to form two bracelets). *No quote.* *Christie's*

Plate 195.

Art deco diamond flange necklace, set with brilliant-cut diamonds in gold, by Boucheron. *No quote.*   *Christie's*

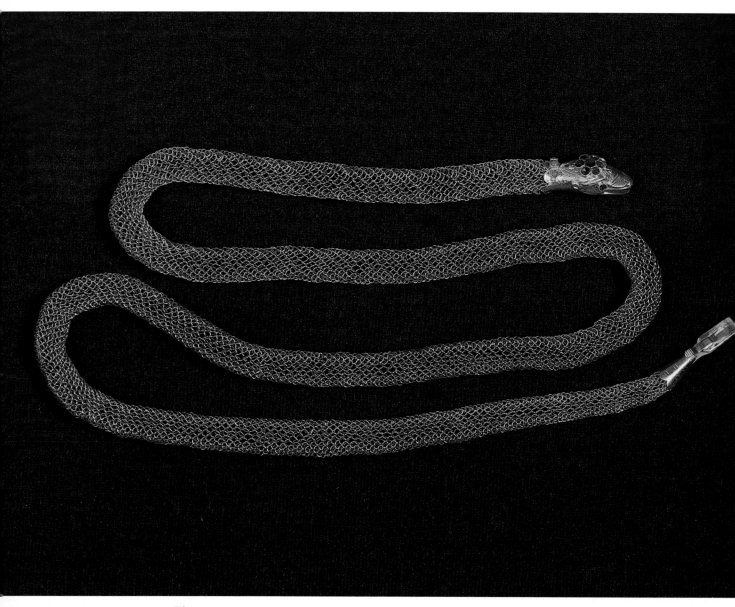

Plate 196

Fine gold mesh necklace with a gold snake clasp set with garnets and turquoises, c.1825. An excellent example of fine Georgian gold-work, adapted to the characteristic movement of the animal it depicts. This type of necklace was made in gold or pinchbeck, but once damaged is difficult to repair. £3,000.   *Harvey & Gore*

Plate 197.

1. String of coral beads, 48in. (120cm). *£150 – £200.*

2. String of green-stained alabaster beads. *£50 – £75.*

3. Carved amethyst and rock-crystal beads. *£300 – £400.*

4. String of variegated agate beads. *£150 – £200.*

5. Graduated ivory beads. *£200.*   6. Tiger's eye beads. *£60 – £100.*

7. Pink coral and seed-pearl necklace. *£150 – £250.*   8. Aventurine quartz beads. *£50 – £100.*

9. Faceted citrine and crystal bead necklace, 24in. (60cm) long. *£150 – £200.*

10. Moonstone beads. *£150.*   11. String of malachite and lapis lazuli beads. *£250 – £300.*

12. String of faceted rose quartz beads. *£200.*

13. Graduated sardonyx beads. 36in. (90cm) long. *£250 – £350.*

14. String of blue-stained quartz beads. *£50.*

Antiquarius, Thesaurus, Tony & Sara, Bellamy, The Purple Shop

Plate 198 (approx. ½ size).

Six-row graduated Oriental pearl necklace. *No quote.*

Graduated Oriental pearl necklace, the pearls of very large size, with a cushion-cut diamond collet clasp. *No quote.*

Christie's

Plate 199.

Georg Jensen jewellery.

Silver and moonstone necklace with a British Import Mark for 1961. (Most jewellery imported into England which is less than one hundred years old normally has to be sent to the Assay Office who will then stamp the appropriate control marks. Therefore, an Import Mark for 1961 means only that the piece entered England at that date and it could have been made some years before.) £2,000.

Silver cloak fastener/brooch, set with moonstones and labradorite. Could be worn as a brooch or cloak-clasp since the fastenings are on each top section. £1,500.

Antiquarius, The Purple Shop, Marie Mills, Private Collection

Plate 200.

Collection of necklace clasps ranging in age from the early 19th century to the present day. Antique clasps are relatively rare and highly desirable.

Varying in price £150 small contemporary clasp; £850+ antique clasp set with gemstones.

Plate 201.

Fine long Georgian gold guard chain, the hand clasp set with a turquoise. This is a particularly fine example of this type of chain, much sought after and always fashionable. The originals were light in weight and either finely granulated or plain-linked. Modern reproductions are heavy and coarse and should be about one-third of the price. Georgian gold clasps were often made in the form of single or clasped hands and were finely tooled. £3,000 – £3,500.

Wartski, London

CHAINS, CROSSES, LOCKETS AND PENDANTS

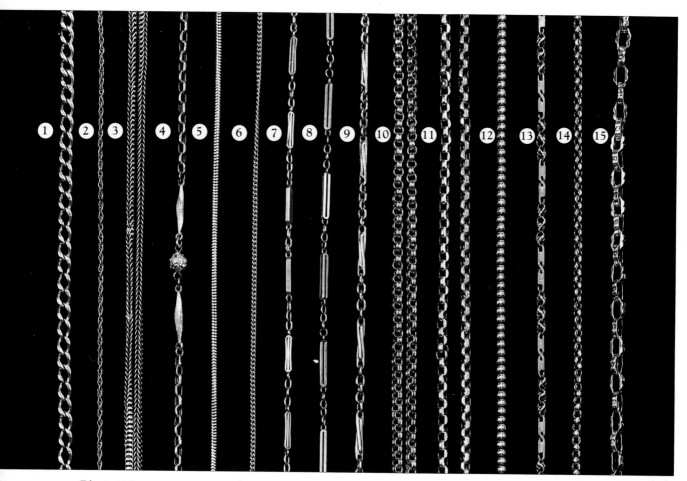

Plate 202.

1. 9ct. gold curb chain, 30in. (48cm) long. £300 – £350.

2. 9ct. gold treble trace chain, 16in. (38.4cm) long. £75.

3. 9ct. gold open snake link chain, 42in. (100.8cm) long. £250, *damaged.*

4. 9ct. gold decorative link chain, 17in. (40.8cm) long. £150 – £200.

5. 9ct. gold snake link chain, 22in. (52.8cm) long. £200.

6. 9ct. gold fine curb chain, 26in. (62.4cm) long. £150.

7. 9ct. gold decorative link chain, 14in. (33.6cm) long. £200 – £250.

8. 9ct. red and white gold decorative link chain, 14in. (33.6cm) long. £200 – £250.

9. 9ct. gold decorative link chain, 14in. (33.6cm) long. £200 – £250.

10. 9ct. gold guard chain, 46in. (110.4cm) long. £650 – £850.

11. 9ct. gold guard chain, 36in. (86.4cm) long. £500 – £600.

12. 9ct. gold decorative link chain, 16in. (38.4cm) long. £150.

13. 9ct. red and white gold decorative link chain, 16in. (38.4cm) long. £200 – £250.

14. 9ct. decorative gold guard chain, 26in. (62.4cm) long. £250 – £300.

15. 9ct. gold decorative open link chain, 15in. (36cm) long. £200 – £250.

Antiquarius, Thesaurus, The Purple Shop

232

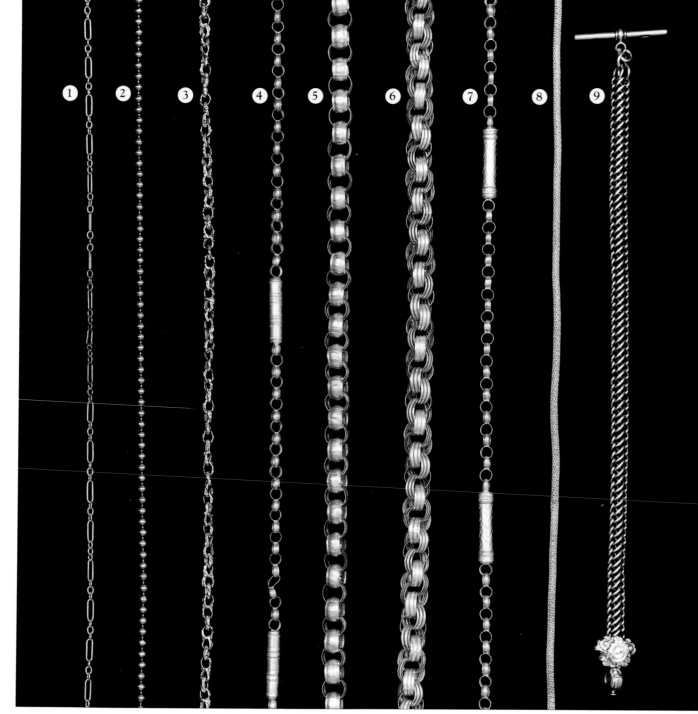

Plate 203.

1. 9ct. white gold long link chain, 32in. (76.8cm) long. *£300.*

2. Victorian 9ct. gold ball chain, 19in. (45.6cm) long. *£270.*

3. 18ct. gold, textured link chain, 30in. (72cm) long. *£1,200.*

4. 18ct. gold barrel and open link chain, 1.1oz., 35in. (84cm) long. *£1,200.*

5. 18ct. gold muff chain, 2.7oz., 33in. (79.2cm) long. *£3,000.*

6. 18ct. gold double link chain, 3.05oz., 26in. (62.4cm) long. *£3,500 – £5,000.*

7. 18ct. gold barrel and open link chain, 37in. (88.8cm) long. *£1,200 – £1,500.*

8. 8ct. gold long, hand-woven mesh chain, 57in. (136.8cm) long. *£1,000.*

9. 18ct. gold fob chain, by McIntosh & McCulloch, Glasgow c.1850, 9½in. (22.8cm) long. *£650.*   *N. Bloom*

Plate 204.

1. Early 20th century peridot, diamond and pearl pendant in 15ct. gold. £400 – £500.

2. Edwardian peridot, pink tourmaline and aquamarine open-work pendant in 9ct. gold. £400.

3. Gold spider's web pendant, with a turquoise and pearl set spider. £300 – £350.

4. Amethyst and pearl open-work pendant in 9ct. gold. £300.

5. Circular 9ct. gold pendant set with a peridot and pearls suspended from a peridot collet. £250 – £300.

6. Opal, ruby and pearl clover leaf pendant set in 18ct. gold. £350 – £400.

7. Opal and ruby set spider and fly pendant in 9ct. gold. £350 – £400.

8. Opal, ruby and diamond set clover leaf pendant in yellow gold. £450.

9. Montana sapphire open-work pendant set with rose diamonds in gold. £700.

10. 9ct. gold scrolled pendant set with a centre amethyst. £300.

11. Circular diamond and open-work pendant in 18ct. gold. £350 – £400.

12. Garnet and pearl set circular floral pendant in 9ct. gold. £250 – £300.

13. Sapphire and pearl open-work pendant in 18ct. gold with a sapphire drop. £350.

14. Aquamarine and pearl pendant in 9ct. gold. £400 – £450.

Allow £50 – £100 for chains.   *Antiquarius, Thesaurus, The Purple Shop, Tony & Sara, Private Collection*

Plate 205.

Necklace and pendant in gold, set with aquamarines and pearls, the pendant set with a plaque of iridescent enamel, c. 1900, designed by C.R. Ashbee. *No quote.*   *Wartski, London*

Plate 206.

1. Sardonyx cross, metal-backed, c.1870. *£100.*

2. Large sardonyx cross set with 9ct. gold, c.1865. *£200 – £250.*

3. Sardonyx cross with 9ct. gold pendant fitting, c.1870. *£150.*

4. Ornate niello cross, c.1880. *£100 – £120.*

5. Mother-of-pearl cross set in silver. *£50.*

6. Carved serpentine cross, mounted with metal. *£50.*

7. Enamelled cross set in metal, made in Birmingham, c.1860. *£50.*

8. Open-work silver cross set with moonstones, c.1910, Arts and Crafts. *£200 – £250.*

9. Plain hollow 9ct. gold cross. *£120 – £150.*

Antiquarius, Tony & Sara, J. Riffel of Thesaurus, The Purple Shop

Plate 207.

1. Georgian cut steel cross, metal backed. *£100 – £150.*

2. Mid-Victorian open-work diamond cross in gold, c.1860. *£1,000 – £1,200.*

3. Mid-Victorian pavé set Bohemian garnet cross in gold, c.1860. *£250 – £300.*

4. Early Victorian Brazilian topaz cross set in 18ct. gold with a locket back, c.1845. *£1,200.*

5. Mid-19th century Hungarian cross set with amethysts, pearls and enamel in silver, c.1860. *£650 – £750.*

6. Early Victorian 15ct. three colour gold cross set with a topaz and four turquoises, dated 1840. *£1,200.*

7. 19th century Italian mosaic cross in the form of a bird with flowers, set in silver. *£250 – £350.*

8. 19th century Hungarian stylised cross set with garnets, turquoises and enamel in silver-gilt. *£350.*

9. Six square-cut amethysts set as a cross in silver-gilt collets. *£300.*

Antiquarius, Thesaurus, Anne Tan, Tony & Sara

Plate 208.

1. Georgian diamond Maltese cross brooch set in silver and backed with gold, c.1790. £4,500 – £5,000. *Michael Poynder*

2. Early 18th century pale emerald and rose diamond bow with pendent cross in silver, the emeralds clear-set. £4,500 – £5,000. *Christie's*

3. Georgian Maltese cross pendant of agate and three-colour gold, made as a gift for Caroline Mary Gardiner, December 1817, with 'From the Prince Leopold' engraved in gold on the reverse centre section, the locket containing a piece of hair. £2,000 – £2,500.
Michael Poynder

4. Mid-Victorian onyx, pearl, turquoise and enamel cross, c.1870. £800 – £1,000. *N. Bloom*

5. Fine early 18th century diamond pendant cross set in silver and gold with a large rectangular-cut centre diamond. £10,000. *Christie's*

6. Victorian lapis lazuli and gold stylised cross, c.1860. £2,000. *N. Bloom*

Plate 209.

Cross in the form of a spray of hawthorn flowers and leaves, designed by Arthur Severn.
No quote. *Wartski, London*

Plate 210.

Collection of traditional Coptic crosses in silver, all early 20th century. The Copts were a sect of early Christians in Egypt and the four birds in the bottom cross are said to represent the four apostles. £50–£100 each.

Antiquarius

Plate 211.

1. Late Georgian gold vinaigrette, c.1830 (open). £800.   **2.** 9ct. gold engraved locket, c.1880. £200 – £250.

3. 15ct. gold, rose diamond and turquoise locket in the Gothic style, c.1865. £500 – £550.

4. Georgian gold locket (open). £600.   **5.** 9ct. gold locket with hairwork centre (open). £300 – £350.

6. 9ct. gold heart locket set with rubies and pearls, c.1880. £200 – £250.

7. 18ct. gold oval locket, engraved and with applied decoration. £500 – £600.

8. 9ct. gold oval 'back and front' locket. (Hinge and other fittings are metal.) £200 – £250.

9. Edwardian 9ct. gold heart locket, engraved surface, c.1905. £200 – £250.

10. 9ct. gold, ruby and pearl locket. £100, *slightly damaged on back.*

11. 9ct. gold 'back and front' locket, c.1880. £200 – £250.   **12.** 9ct. gold engraved locket, c.1880. £300 – £400.

13. 9ct. gold locket with shield, engraved and with applied decoration, c.1880. £300 – £350.

14. Shield-shaped 15ct. gold locket showing classical influence, c.1850. £400 – £500.

Antiquarius, Thesaurus, The Purple Shop

Plate 212 (approx. ¾ size).

1. Oval gold locket containing the original photographs, c.1885. £500 – £600.

2. Pale blue enamel and gold locket, set with pearls, c.1870. £500 – £700.

3. Oval gold locket with applied thread decoration, the centre of turquoise enamel and set with a pearl, c.1875. £500 – £600.

4. Floral gold locket set with an amethyst, pearls and rose diamonds, c.1880. £1,500 – £1,800.

5. Oval 15ct. gold locket with diagonal band of applied decoration, c.1860. £500 – £700.

6. Oval gold locket of fine quality, with a diamond set flower, on a hollow large link chain, c.1875. £2,000 – £2,500.

7. Oval 15ct. gold locket with a vertical band of repoussé decoration, c.1860. £500 – £700. *Cameo Corner*

Plate 213.

1. Late 17th century carved wax reliquary pendant, the gold crown set with garnets and white sapphires or crystals. *£1,400 – £1,600.*

2. Early 18th century English enamel portrait miniature in Flemish ruby and rose diamond-set frame. *£2,000 – £2,500.*

3. Late 17th century Spanish reliquary carved in wax, in a frame of gold and rubies. *£1,400 – £1,600.*

4. Mid-Victorian enamel brooch of cherubs, in a seed pearl frame, c.1870. *£750 – £850.*

5. 19th century cornelian cameo set in a black and white enamel frame of openwork design. *£900 – £1,100.*

6. Late Victorian faceted rock crystal pendant with a beetle of smoky quartz attached, c.1880. *£700 – £800.*

7. Mid-Victorian glass mosaic of birds and flowers in a gold frame, c.1870. *£1,200 – £1,400.*

8. Mid-17th century English wax portrait medallion in a pierced silver pendant frame. *£350 – £450.*

9. Fine mid-Victorian painted ivory miniature in a pearl and gold frame, c.1850. *£900 – £1,100.*

10. Fine mid-19th century French madeira citrine cameo in the classical style, mounted in a blue enamel, diamond and gold frame, c.1850. *£2,500 – £3,000.*

11. Mid-Victorian pietra dura butterfly brooch of malachite, ivory and agates set in an oval gold frame, c.1850. *£1,200 – £1,500.*

12. Mid-19th century sardonyx and enamelled gold pendant of classical influence, c.1850. *£700 – £900.*

Richard Digby

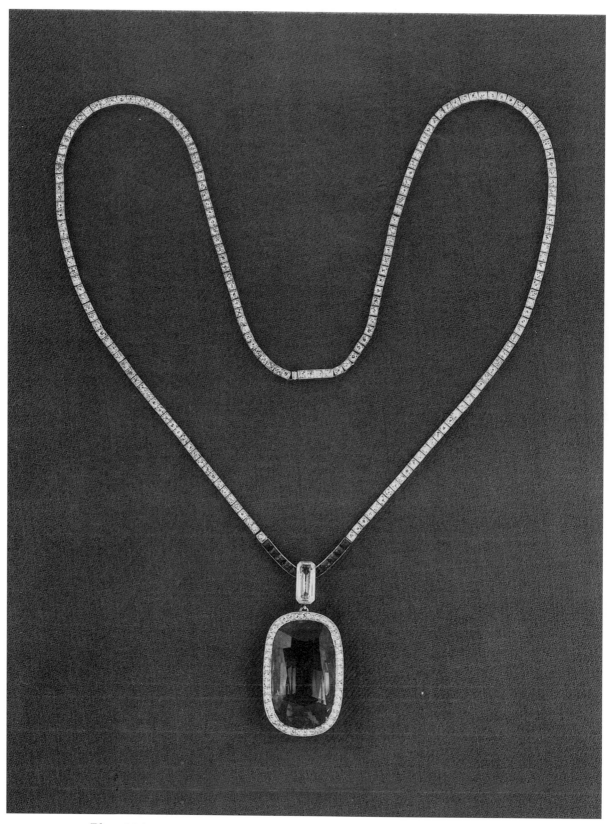

Plate 214.

Fine 20th century sapphire and diamond pendant with line necklace, by Cartier. *No quote.*
Christie's

Plate 215.

Geoffrey Hunt jewellery.

1. Rose quartz, chalcedony, chrysoprase, freshwater pearl and green enamel brooch, unsigned, c.1940. £800.

2. Blue, green and orange enamel pansy brooch set with two freshwater pearls in silver, 1937. £1,000.

3. Pink and blue enamel Cherub pendant in moonstone, rose quartz, amethyst and silver frame, on a chain. £1,500.

4. Green and pink enamel flower, set as a brooch in a silver and pearl frame, 1922. £1,000.

5. Green and orange enamel Poppies pendant set with chalcedony and imitation pearls in silver as a necklace, 1935. £1,800.
   The Purple Shop, Private Collection

Plate 216.

1. Georgian pavé-set diamond six-petalled flower, set in silver with closed back, c.1790. £11,000.

2. Early Victorian diamond flower spray brooch with *en tremblant* flowerhead, mounted in silver and gold, c.1840. £12,000 – £14,000.

3. Georgian diamond oval brooch of open design with four spaced centre collets, set in silver and gold, c.1820. £4,000 – £5,000. *Tessiers*

Plate 217.

Early 19th century English diamond floral spray brooch, the three flowerheads *en tremblant*, surmounted by two wheat ears, set in silver and gold, c.1800. £25,000+.   *Christie's*

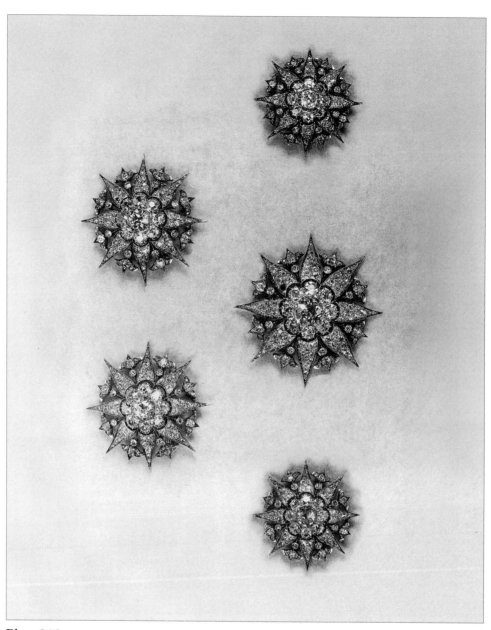

Plate 218.

Set of five eight-pointed diamond stars with fleur-de-lys between the points, probably originally a tiara, c.1860. Top quality mid-Victorian mounting and setting, but it is unlikely that these would be kept as a set today, the wearing of one diamond brooch being considered enough. *£25,000 the set.*

Christie's

Plate 219.

Set of five Victorian flower brooches, the diamonds pavé set in silver and gold, c.1840. £12,000 set.

Victorian diamond-set sunburst brooch in silver, backed with gold, c.1870. £7,000.

Christie's

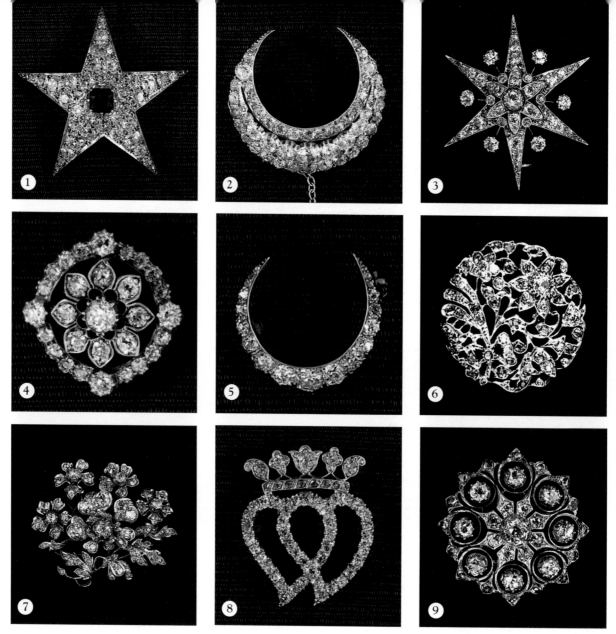

Plate 220.

1. Victorian pavé set diamond and sapphire five-pointed star brooch set in silver and gold, c.1870. £3,500– £4,000.

2. Victorian triple-row diamond crescent brooch, the diamonds cushion-cut, set in silver and gold, c.1870. £3,000 – £3,500.

3. Large Victorian diamond six-pointed star brooch set in silver and gold, with a single diamond collet between each point, c.1875. £2,500 – £3,000.

4. Victorian circular floral diamond brooch, set in silver and gold, c.1870. £4,000 – £5,000.

5. Victorian diamond crescent brooch set in silver and gold, c.1870. £1,500 – £2,000.

6. Georgian diamond and rose diamond circular open-work daisy brooch set in silver and backed with gold, c.1820. £1,500.

7. Early Victorian diamond spray brooch set in silver and gold, c.1840. £2,000 – £2,500.

8. Early Victorian diamond crowned double witch's heart set in silver and gold, c.1855. £2,200 – £2,500.

9. Diamond target brooch set in silver and gold, c.1860. £3,200 – £3,500.   *Michael Poynder*

As illustrated the brooches are not in proportion so do not give a true indication of value size to size.

250

Plate 221.

1. Victorian circular diamond set brooch/pendant of open-work design, c.1860.

2. Victorian diamond target brooch of floral design, c.1855.

3. Late Georgian diamond brooch in the form of an ornamental cross, c.1830.

4. Early Victorian diamond pendant in the design of a floral cross, c.1850.

Varying in price £4,000 – £6,000. *Christie's*

Plate 222.

1. Emerald and pearl circular brooch in gold mount, c.1870. £1,500.

2. Gold marquise-shaped pendant with fringe, set with pearls and turquoise, enamel centre, c.1860. £1,500 – £1,800.

3. Blue enamel target brooch, set with a cabochon amethyst and seven half pearls and applied gold-work scrolled design, c.1870. £750.

4. Citrine and gold brooch, the citrine set in a gold frame, ornamented with birds and flowers, c.1865. £650.

5. Scrolled gold brooch of open-work design set with aquamarines, c.1870. £700.

6. Suite of brooch and earrings, set with cabochon amethysts and pearls, with applied gold decoration, c.1860. £1,500 – £2,000 set.

Cameo Corner

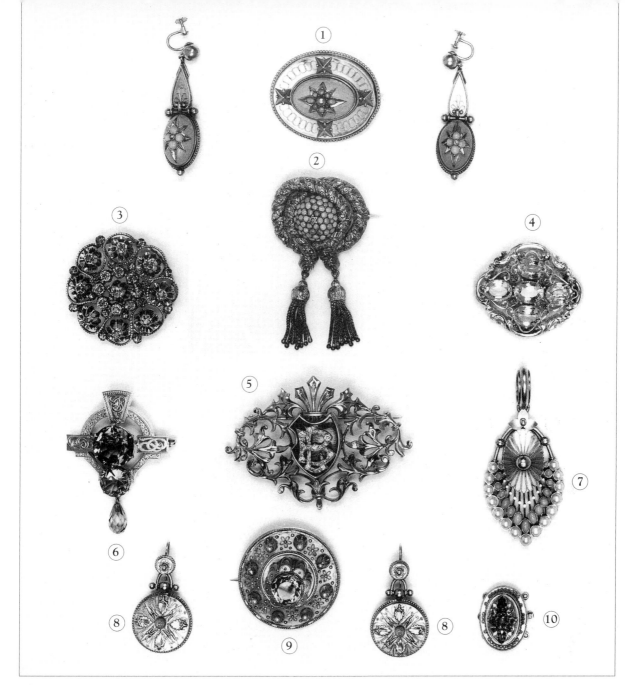

Plate 223.

1. Brooch and earrings of coral, pearls and turquoise enamel, set in an 18ct. gold mount of classical influence, c.1850. *£1,200 – £1,500 set.*

2. Gold knotted rope brooch with a pavé set turquoise centre and gold tassels, c.1845. *£650 – £750.*

3. Green garnet and chrysoberyl target brooch, set in gold, c.1900. *£1,200.*

4. Pink topaz and emerald brooch in scrolled gold setting, c.1845. *£1,100.*

5. Blue enamel and diamond monogrammed shield in an open floral gold mount, c.1880. *£700.*

6. Scottish engraved gold brooch, set with three cairngorms (citrines), c.1870. *£800 – £900.*

7. Coral, pearl and gold long drop pendant, c.1880. *£800-£900.*

8. Pair of circular gold swing earrings of classical style, c.1850. *£650 – £750.*

9. Circular gold brooch with applied thread decoration, set with a citrine and pearls, c.1870. *£550 – £650.*

10. Oval gold and amethyst clasp, c.1850. *£300.*   *B. Barnett Ltd.*

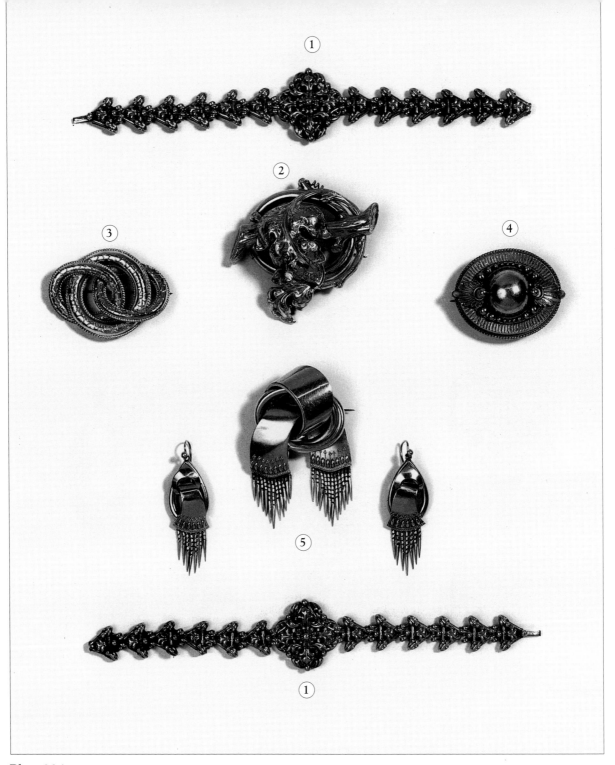

Plate 224.

1. Pair of mid-Victorian gold link bracelets with quatrefoil central motif, c.1860. £2,500 – £3,000 *pair*.

2. Gold brooch of open design in the form of an intertwined ivy spray, c.1870. £650.

3. Gold linked circles brooch with applied thread decoration, c.1865. £500 – £550.

4. Oval gold brooch of classical influence, with a matt finish (achieved by gilding the gold), c.1865. £550 – £650.

5. Gold brooch and earrings *en suite*, a stylised ribbon knot with pendent articulated tassels, c.1855. £1,200 – £1,500.   *Cameo Corner*

Plate 225.

1. 15ct. gold locket set with a carbuncle and a pearl, c.1860.

2. 18ct. gold target brooch, diecast and set with corals, c.1860.

3. 18ct. gold target brooch, cast with applied decoration, set with pearls in a centre star, c.1860.

4. 18ct. gold lozenge-shaped brooch, cast and with applied decoration, set with a diamond, c.1865.

5. 18ct. gold brooch, cast and applied circular motif.

6. 18ct. gold brooch, cast and applied decoration.

7. 18ct. gold brooch with applied oak-leaf decoration.

8. 18ct. gold oval brooch, cast, of good quality.

9. 18ct. gold oval brooch.

Varying in price £275 – £550.   *Antiquarius, Tony & Sara, The Purple Shop, Thesaurus*

Plate 226.

1. Late Victorian diamond swallow brooch set in silver and gold, c.1880. £2,000 – £3,000.

2. 19th century 18ct. gold, ruby and diamond stork brooch, French, c.1860. £2,500 – £3,000.

3. Diamond, emerald and ruby set falcon, standing on a group of Baroque pearls. £1,500 – £2,000.

4. Sapphire, diamond and pearl butterfly brooch, the platinum body made as a spring to allow movement of the wings. £1,800 – £2,300.

5. Diamond butterfly brooch set with white, yellow and cinnamon-coloured diamonds. £8,000 – £12,000.

6. Victorian butterfly brooch, the mother-of-pearl body set with green garnets and rubies in gold, c.1890. £3,000 – £4,000.

7. Victorian fly brooch set with pearls, rubies and rose diamonds in yellow gold, c.1860. £2,000 – £3,000.

8. Victorian lizard brooch set with diamonds and green garnets, with ruby eyes, c.1880. £3,500 – £5,000.

9. Victorian diamond butterfly brooch with ruby eyes and a gold body, c.1880. £1,000 – £1,500. *N. Bloom*

Plate 227.

1. Victorian hardstone (agate) cameo in an 18ct. gold frame, c.1860. £2,000.

2. Mid-Victorian blue enamel and gold scroll brooch set with diamonds. £2,500.

3. Victorian gold piqué and tortoiseshell scallop shell shaped brooch. £650.

4 Victorian turquoise and gold scroll brooch with pendant locket, c.1865. 650 – £750.

5. Oval Roman style brooch of gold and lapis lazuli in 19th century classical revival style. £900 – £1,000

6. Georgian padlock of gold and blue enamel and real half pearls, c.1825. £600 – £700.

7. Art nouveau enamel and gold brooch with pearl drop, *plique-à-jour* technique, c.1900. £3,000 – £4,000.

8. Gold, amethyst and pearl pendant locket, c.1880. £1,500 – £1,800.

9. Garnet and gold necklace, English, c.1820. £2,500 – £3,000.

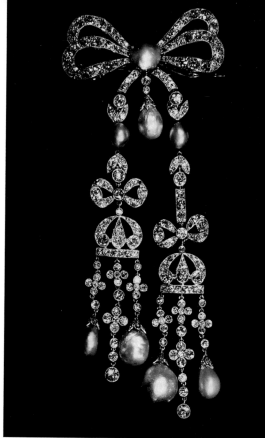

Plate 228 (approx. ½ size).

Pair of late 19th century diamond brooches in the form of trails of wistaria, set in silver and gold, each section hinged for flexibility. Difficult jewellery to wear but typical of the period when it was fashionable to wear as many diamonds as possible. £30,000+.

Christie's

Plate 229.

Edwardian pearl and diamond ribbon bow brooch; the long ribbon pendants are convertible to earrings. The milled setting is typical of the period, c.1910. £30,000+ *real pearls*.

Sotheby's

Plate 230.

1. Silver bird brooch, c.1880.   2. Target brooch with applied decoration, c.1875.

3. Target brooch, c.1880.   4. Silver and gold shamrock brooch, c.1880.

5. Silver and gold 'Le Havre' brooch, c.1915.   6. Silver name brooch, 'Beatie', c.1870.

7. Two love birds brooch , c.1890.

8. Silver and pearl open-work name brooch, 'Annie', c.1880.

9. Shoe, c.1880.   10. Silver name brooch, 'Eliza', c.1890.

11. Silver 'Baby' brooch, c.1880.

12. Silver and two-colour gold brooch set with an agate, c.1885.

13. Silver 'Baby' nappy pin, c.1880.   14. Silver Jubilee brooch, 1887.

15. Late 19th century 'Japanese' fans.   16. Silver dog brooch, 'Pet', c.1900.

17. Silver anchor and enamelled bird brooch, c.1875.   18. Die-cast silver cockerel.

19. French, British, Belgian and Dutch flag brooch, enamelled on metal, c.1914.

20. Double flag brooch, enamelled, c.1914.   21. Single flag brooch, c.1914.

Varying in price £50 – £120.   *Antiquarius, The Purple Shop, Thesaurus, Tony & Sara*

Plate 231.

1. Hand-painted porcelain sentimental miniature in a twisted silver frame, c.1870. £250 – £300.

2. Cherub brooch in a 15ct. gold frame, c.1870. £650.

3. Miniature of a girl in a jet and silver frame, c.1870. £350 – £400.

4. Rectangular brooch of an archer, in a gilt metal frame, c.1870. £200.   *Antiquarius, Thesaurus*

Plate 232.

Gold brooch by John Hardman & Co. of Birmingham, decorated in the medieval taste with champlevé enamel in the form of a vase of Madonna lilies. The six lobes set with clusters of pearls, the borders defined with filigree and gold granules, c.1883. *No quote.*

Wartski, London

Gold broch in the form of a marguerite by Child & Child. The heart-shaped petals are green stained ivory and the centre is set with a citrine. Signed with the monogram of two 'C's and a marigold. *No quote.*

Wartski, London

Plate 233.

1. Blue and green enamel, mother-of-pearl and silver wing brooch. £500 – £700.

2. Amazonite, blue and green enamel and freshwater pearl pendant, set in silver and 18ct. gold. £500 – £700.

3. Amethyst and green enamel wing pendant in silver-gilt. £600 – £800.

4. Opal, blue and greenish enamel and crystal open-wing brooch. £750 – £850.

5. Blue enamel brooch, designed as wings and a staff, set with a pearl and a crystal, the staff intertwined with a pale green and a blue enamel snake. £500 – £700.

All c.1900 by Child & Child.   *Antiquarius, The Purple Shop, Bellamy*

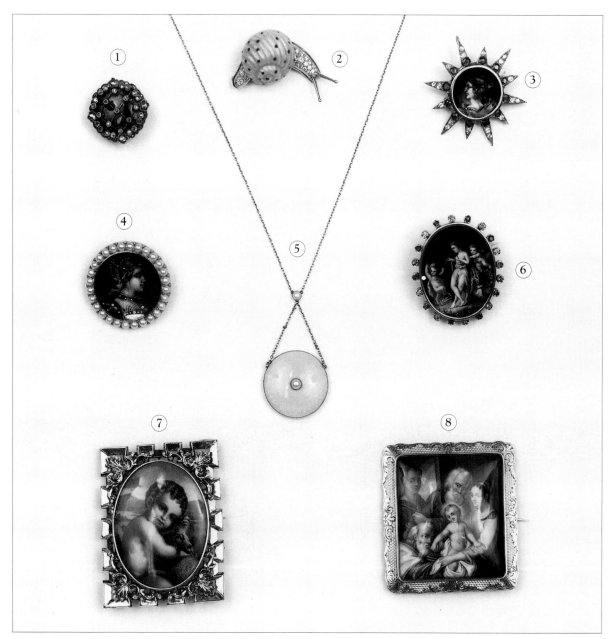

Plate 234.

1. Mid-Victorian green enamel and rose diamond target brooch, c.1860. £1,000.

2. Flesh-coloured enamel snail brooch with diamond body, set in white gold, by Boucheron, c.1950. £2,000 – £2,500.

3. Mid-19th century Limoges enamel profile head in a ruby and diamond star-shaped frame, set in gold, c.1870. £1,600 – £2,200.

4. Mid-19th century Limoges enamel circular brooch with a pearl frame, c.1860. £800 – £1,200.

5. Edwardian pink enamel and pearl pendant on chain, c.1905. £800 – £1,000.

6. Mid-Victorian oval brooch with a painted enamel scene of a nymph with two fauns, in a ruby and diamond frame, c.1850. £1,500 – £2,000.

7. Mid-19th century Swiss enamel brooch in a rectangular gold frame, c.1850. £1,200 – £1,500.

8. Mid-19th century Swiss enamel brooch of 'The Adoration of the Magi', c.1850. £1,200.   *N. Bloom*

BRACELETS AND BANGLES

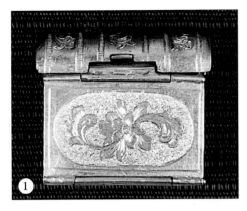

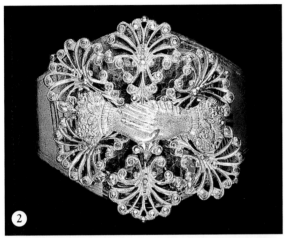

Plate 235.

1. Early Victorian pinchbeck bracelet, the plaques spelling out 'Souvenir', folding back into book form, c.1840 (both forms shown). A typical piece of the sentimental jewellery popular at this time. £400 – £500.

2. Late Georgian 'clasped hands' pinchbeck bangle, c.1835 (one of a pair). £400 – £600 *pair*.

3. Early Victorian pinchbeck bangle of foliage scrolls and trellis pattern, set with a pink paste, c.1845. £300 – £500.

4. Early Victorian pink paste and pinchbeck bracelet of formal *cannetille* work, c.1840. £400 – £600.

1–4 Cameo Corner

5. Fine Georgian gold link bracelet with *cannetille* work clasp, c.1820. The clasp is detachable and may be worn as a pendant with a special fitting (not shown). £1,000 – £1,500. *N. Bloom*

Plate 236.

Gold bracelet decorated with enamel in medieval style and set with carbuncles, pearls and turquoises. Made 1859 by John Hardman & Co. *No quote*.   *Wartski, London*

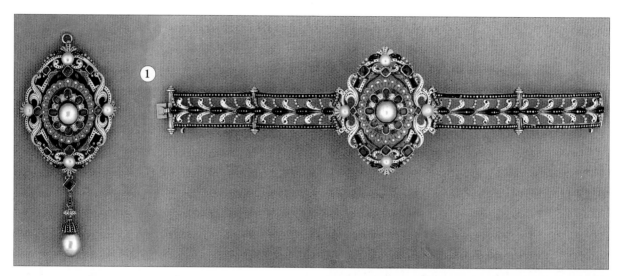

Plate 237.

1. 19th century bracelet and pendant *en suite*, the pearls, rubies and diamonds set in blue and white enamel on gold, by Giuliano, c.1880. £35,000 – £40,000.

2. Good Victorian emerald and diamond hinged bangle set in silver and gold, c.1860; the centre cluster can be detached and used as a brooch. The value of this type of bracelet depends largely on the quality of the emerald as the diamonds are less important. *No quote*.

3. Large Victorian diamond bangle set with three rows of diamonds in silver and gold, c.1850. This triple row mounting is also a typical ring style of the period. *No quote*.   *Christie's*

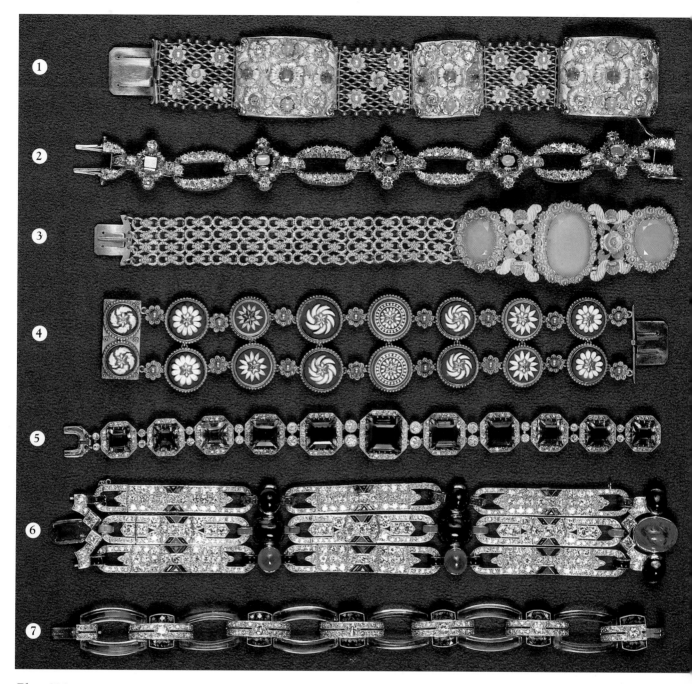

Plate 238.

1. Georgian plaque and gold mesh bracelet set with diamonds, rubies, turquoises and pearls in a floral design, c.1820. £5,000.

2. Late Georgian diamond and sapphire link bracelet set in silver and gold, c.1830. £7,000.

3. Georgian chrysoprase and three-colour gold bracelet, c.1825. £3,000.

4. Early Victorian gold bracelet with Wedgwood medallions, c.1840. £2,750.

5. Victorian amethyst and diamond bracelet, c.1880. £7,000.

6. Art deco wide link bracelet set with diamonds, cabochon sapphires, emeralds, rubies and black enamel, c.1925. £25,000.

7. Art deco diamond, cornflower sapphire and crystal link bracelet, c.1925. £12,000.   *Harvey & Gore*

Plate 239.

Late Victorian silver bangles, some with a gold inlay, or showing Celtic and Oriental influences in design, c.1880, hallmarked usually in Birmingham, Chester or Newcastle. Varying in price £85 – £250.   *Antiquarius, all from Thesaurus*

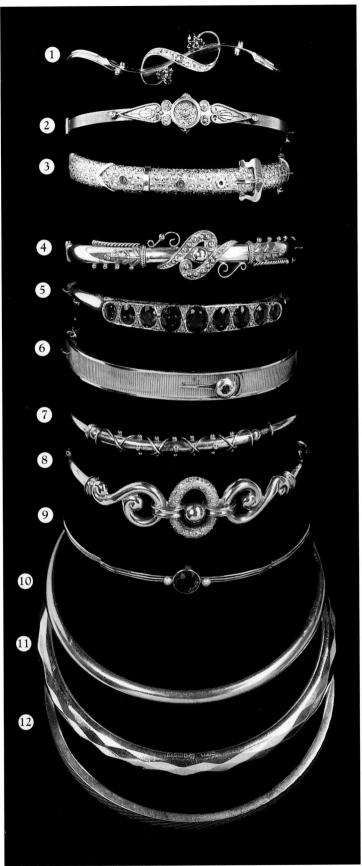

Plate 240.

1. Ruby and rose diamond set 9ct. gold bangle, c.1885. *£350 – £450.*

2. 15ct. gold cast bangle in the Etruscan style, c.1860. *£500 – £600.*

3. 9ct. gold engraved bangle in the form of a belt. *£350.*

4. 15ct. gold bangle with applied decoration, c.1880. *£600 – £650.*

5. Gold bangle, set with almandine garnets and rose diamonds, c.1875. *£750–£1,000.*

6. 9ct. gold bangle set with a garnet. *£300–£400.*

7. 15ct. gold bangle with applied decoration, c.1880. *£400 – £500.*

8. 9ct. gold scrolled bangle, cast. *£450 – £500.*

9. 9ct. gold bangle set with an amethyst and two pearls, c.1885. *£250.*

10. 9ct. gold, slave bangle. *£200 – £250.*

11. 9ct. gold, slave bangle, hall-marked in Chester. *£200 – £250.*

12. 9ct. gold, slave bangle. *£200 – £250.*

Antiquarius, The Purple Shop, Tony & Sara, Thesaurus, Bellamy

Plate 241.

Butterfly bracelet in silver and decorated with blue enamel, c.1900 by Child & Child. *No quote.*

Wartski, London

Plate 242.

1. 9ct. red gold close curb bracelet, late Victorian. *£400 – £500.*

2. 18ct. gold open curb bracelet, c.1950. *£550.*

3. 9ct. gold curb bracelet, the centre set with turquoises and pearls, late Victorian. *£350 – £450.*

4. 14ct. gold snake chain bracelet, c.1930. *£350.*

5. 9ct. gold, link bracelet, set with amethysts and pearls, late Victorian. *£600 – £700.*

6. 9ct. gold decorative open-link bracelet, c.1930. *£350 – £400.*

7. 9ct. red gold decorated hollow-curb link bracelet. *£450 – £650.*

8. 9ct. red gold 'gate' bracelet, padlock clasp. *£350 – £450.*

9. 9ct. gold, hexagonal link bracelet. *£350.*

10. Red and yellow gold circular link bracelet. *£350.*   *Antiquarius, Thesaurus, The Purple Shop, Bellamy*

RINGS

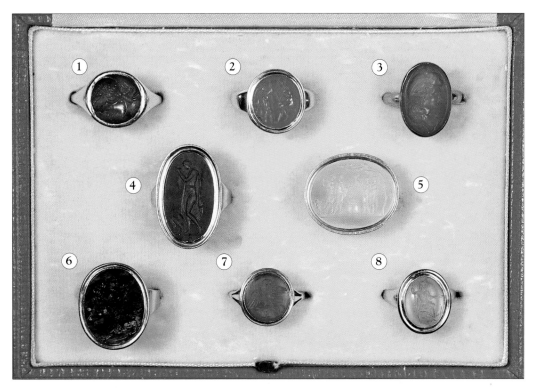

Plate 243

1. 17th century cornelian intaglio of a profile head, set as a ring. £4,000 – £5,000.

2. Classical Greek intaglio in cornelian, two figures, 4th–3rd century B.C. £2,000.

3. Cornelian intaglio ring, profile of a woman. £2,000 – £2,250.

4. Long oval intaglio ring, jasper, mythological figure, 18th century. £2,500 – £3,000.

5. White agate 18th century intaglio ring, group of figures. £2,250 – £2,500.

6. 18th century lapis lazuli intaglio of an angel. (Lapis lazuli intaglios are more commonly found with coats of arms or crests as signet rings.) £2,500 – £3,000.

7. Renaissance cornelian intaglio ring of a falcon. £2,000 – £3,000.

8. Classical white agate intaglio, a sitting figure. £2,000 – £2,250.   *Wartski, London*

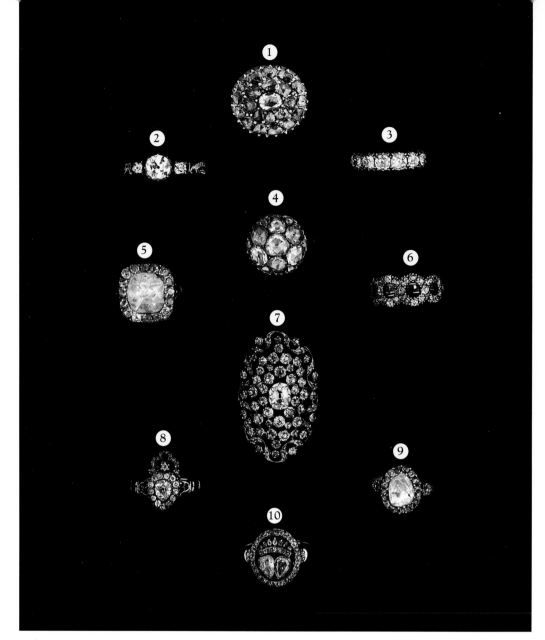

Plate 244.

1. Spanish circular pavé set rose diamond cluster ring. £2,500.

2. English memorial ring, the cushion-cut diamonds set in a white enamelled scrolled hoop. £1,500 – 2,000.

3. Graduated diamond seven stone half-hoop ring. £2,000.

4. English rose diamond seven stone circular cluster ring. £2,500 – £3,000.

5. English diamond cluster ring, the cushion-cut centre diamond (foiled) surrounded by smaller cushion-cut stones. £4,000 – £5,000.

6. French diamond half-hoop ring formed of linked open circles set with diamonds. £2,000.

7. Large French openwork oval diamond ring with a diamond set scrolled border. £2,500 – £3,000.

8. English diamond crowned heart ring. £2,500 – £3,000.

9. English oval rose diamond cluster ring with engraved back. £2,700 – £3,000.

10. English diamond crowned double heart ring on enamel background with a circular diamond border. £3,000 – £3,200.

Christie's

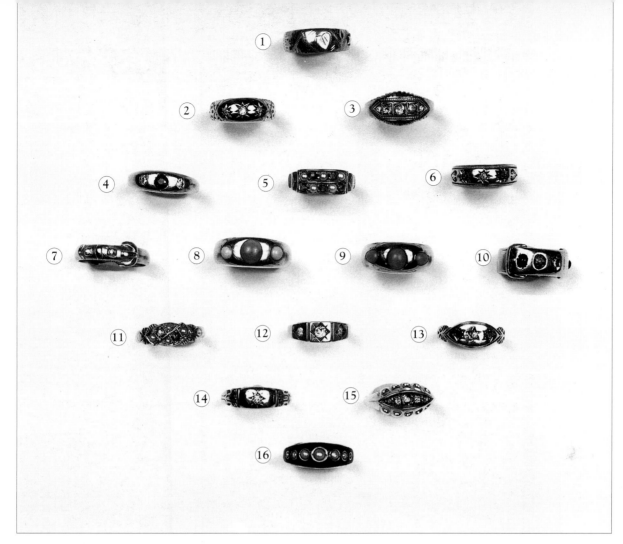

Plate 245.

Victorian gypsy set rings.

1. Red and yellow 18ct. gold ring with applied gold hearts and star. *£150 – £190.*

2. Three stone diamond ring with engraved gold band, c.1890. *£200 – £250.*

3. Five stone diamond ring, the stones set into an elongated hexagonal section, c.1900. *£250 – £300.*

4. Ruby and diamond three stone ring in 18ct. gold, c.1890. *£450 – £500.*

5. Ruby and pearl double banded half-hoop ring in 18ct. yellow gold, c.1900. *£250 – £300.*

6. Sapphire and diamond five stone ring in 18ct. yellow gold, c.1885. *£250 – £300.*

7. 22ct. gold buckle ring set with two rose diamonds. *£250 – £300.*

8. Coral and two turquoises set as a three stone ring in a wide gold band. *£300 – £350.*

9. Three stone coral ring in a wide 18ct. gold band. *£300 – £400.*

10. 18ct. gold, buckle ring set with diamonds and sapphires. *£400 – £450.*

11. Sapphire, ruby and pearl diagonally set ring in 15ct. gold. *£300 – £350.*

12. Three stone diamond ring, c.1890. *£300 – £350.*

13. Ruby and diamond three stone ring in a boat-shaped gold mount. *£300.*

14. Single diamond, in a gold ring. *£250.*

15. Ruby and diamond graduated five stone ring in an ornate gold mount, c.1895. *£250 – £300.*

16. Black enamel ring set with seven pearls in silver. *£200.*   *Antiquarius, Thesaurus, The Purple Shop, Bellamy*

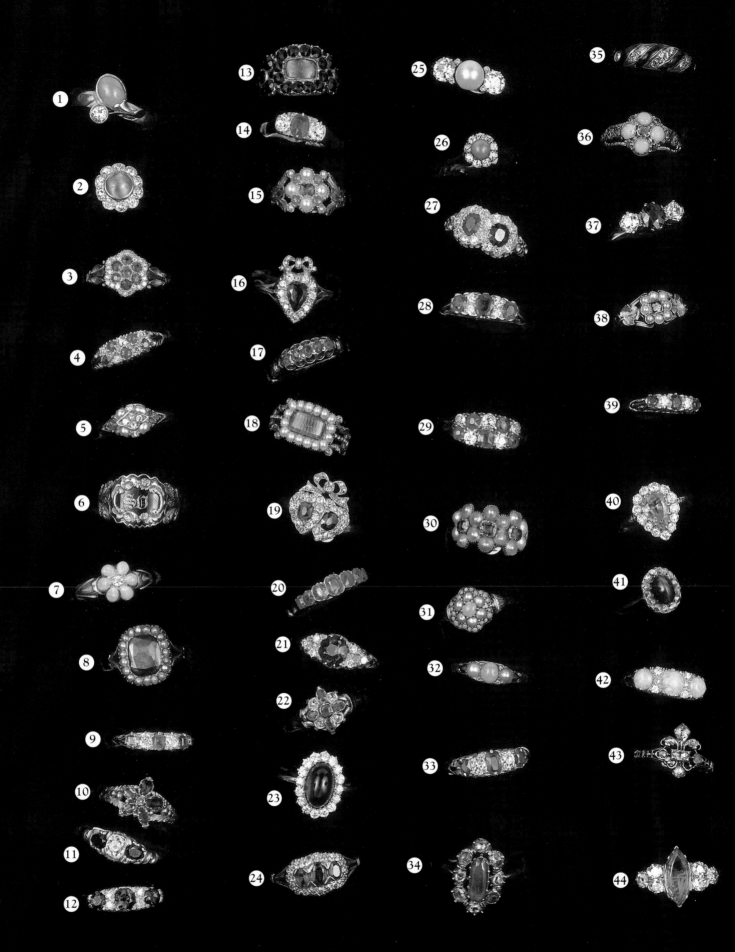

Plate 246.

18th, 19th and 20th century traditional rings with a variety of coloured stones.

1. Turquoise and diamond cross-over ring. £600 – £700.

2. Chrysoberyl, cat's eye and diamond cluster ring. £1,200.

3. Ruby and diamond shaped cluster ring. £1,200.   4. Ruby and diamond double five stone ring. £1,000.

5. Victorian ruby, pearl and diamond ring. £600 – £650.

6. Georgian gold and black enamel, memorial ring, dated 1823. £350 – £400.

7. Opal and diamond flowerhead ring. £550.   8. Garnet and half-pearl cluster ring, c.1820. £550.

9. Emerald and diamond five stone half-hoop ring, c.1870. £2,200.

10. Late Georgian Regard cluster ring, c.1835. £750.

11. Victorian sapphire and diamond three stone ring. £1,500.

12. Blue tourmaline and diamond five stone ring. £500 – £600.

13. Georgian hair-work memorial ring, set with jet, dated 1817. £350.

14. Ruby and diamond three stone ring. £2,200.

15. Georgian emerald, ruby and pearl cluster ring, c.1820. £1,000.

16. Ruby and diamond bow and heart-shaped cluster ring. £1,650.   17. Victorian ruby five stone ring. £800.

18. Georgian memorial ring with hair-work centre surrounded by half pearls. £450.

19. Ruby, sapphire and diamond double-heart ring. £2,400.

20. Victorian ruby seven stone half-hoop ring. £1,800.

21. Peridot and diamond boat-shaped half-hoop ring. £1,100.

22. Early Victorian ruby and rose diamond ring. £650.   23. Carbuncle and diamond oval cluster ring. £1,100.

24. Ruby and diamond shaped cluster ring. £1,400.

25. Oriental pearl and diamond, three stone ring. £3,300.   26. Turquoise and diamond cluster ring. £850.

27. Ruby, sapphire and diamond double-cluster ring. £2,500.

28. Ruby and diamond five stone half-hoop ring. £3,000 – £3,100.

29. Ruby and diamond double five stone half-hoop ring. £3,000.

30. Georgian, emerald and pearl triple cluster ring. £900.   31. Turquoise and half pearl cluster ring. £500.

32. Turquoise and pearl three stone half-hoop ring. £500.

33. Ruby and diamond five stone half-hoop ring. £2,800 – £2,900.

34. Ruby, emerald and rose diamond oval cluster ring. £900 – £1,000.

35. Diamond and blue enamel scrolled half-hoop ring. £750.

36. Georgian opal, emerald and ruby ring, c.1830. £550 – £600.

37. Sapphire and diamond three stone ring. £2,500.

38. Late Georgian ring set with a half pearl cluster in a leaf and scroll mount. £450 – £500.

39. Ruby and diamond five stone half-hoop ring. £1,150.   40. Chrysoberyl and diamond cluster ring. £1,000.

41. Dark cat's eye and rose diamond cluster ring. £975 – £1,000.

42. Opal and diamond half-hoop ring. £1,400.   43. Georgian rose diamond fleur-de-lys ring, c.1780. £750.

44. Marquise-shaped Brazilian topaz and diamond ring. £1,500.

Richard Ogden

Plate 247.

1. Victorian diamond, ruby, emerald and sapphire four-banded ring on gold shank, c.1850. £550 – £750.

2. Early Victorian turquoise and rose diamond ring with scrolled shank. £450 – £500.

3. Late Georgian pearl and ruby memorial ring, the plaited memorial hair removed from the wide gold shank. £300 – £350.

4. Early Victorian garnet and half pearl cluster ring. £350 – £450.

5. Early Victorian cabochon garnet and half pearl cluster ring with scrolled shank. £350 – £450.

6. Mid-Victorian black opal ring with shield-shaped mount. The opal is probably a replacement. £350 – £450.

7. Georgian emerald and rose diamond cluster ring. £1,000 – £1,500.

8. Mid-Victorian pearl and diamond ring, c.1880. £800 – £900.

9. Georgian white paste and carved gold shank ring, c.1810. £350 – £450.

10. Georgian pearl and diamond fancy cluster ring, c.1820. £450 – £550.

11. Georgian rose diamond five stone ring set in silver, c.1760. £1,200 – £1,500.

12. Mid-Victorian emerald and diamond three-stone half-hoop ring with carved shoulders, c.1860. £900 – £1,300.

13. Late Georgian garnet, emerald and pearl cluster ring in scrolled gold mount, c.1830. £400 – £550.

14. Georgian garnet and half pearl ring. £350.

15. Victorian emerald and ruby double horseshoe ring. £400 – £450.

16. Early Victorian pink topaz and half pearl ring. £450.

17. Early Victorian turquoise and diamond cluster ring with a scrolled gold mount, c.1840. £350 – £450.

18. Turquoise enamel and pearl half-hoop ring, c.1870. £350 – £450.

19. Late Georgian Dear ring, set with half pearls and a Diamond, Emerald, Amethyst and Ruby, c.1835. £800 – £1,200.

20. Georgian half-hoop ring in gold, set with half pearls. £500 – £550.

21. Victorian rose diamond fleur-de-lys ring with centre emerald band, possibly made up from a stickpin. £600 – £800.

22. Georgian foiled yellow paste cluster ring with white paste surround, c.1825. £300 – £350.

23. Late Victorian sapphire and diamond five stone half-hoop ring, c.1890. £1,200 – £1,500.

24. Mid-Victorian turquoise and diamond five stone half-hoop ring. £650. *Michael Poynder*

Plate 248.

1. Early Victorian cabochon amethyst and rose diamond cluster ring with twisted gold and black enamelled shank. *£450 – £550.*

2. Georgian single flat-cut garnet ring with narrow twisted gold shank. *£200 – £250.*

3. Georgian graduated five stone rose diamond half-hoop ring, set in silver. *£1,200 – £1,500.*

4. Early Victorian ruby, pearl and emerald ring with carved gold shank, c.1840. *£150, normally more, but damaged.*

5. Georgian garnet and grey pearl cluster ring with carved gold shank, c.1830. *£350 – £450.*

6. Georgian flat-cut garnet and pearl cluster ring with plain gold shank. *£300 – £350.*

7. Georgian crystal ring set in silver and gold. *£700 – £900.*

8. Georgian pearl and emerald ring with scrolled gold shank. *£450.*

9. Georgian pearl cluster half-hoop ring. *£400.*

10. Georgian rose diamond cluster ring set in silver. *£1,000 – £1,500.*

11. Georgian amethyst and pearl cluster ring with amethyst shoulders. *£350 – £450.*

12. Georgian crystal and pearl cluster ring with hair centre and carved gold shank, c.1825. *£350 – £450.*

13. Georgian tourmaline and pearl cluster ring with wide gold shank. *£400 – £450.*

14. Georgian carbuncle and pearl square cluster ring with split gold shank. *£350 – £450.*

15. Georgian ruby cluster ring in filigree setting, 18th century. *£500 – £550.*

16. Georgian foiled citrine ring with hollow scrolled gold setting, c.1820. *£250 – £300.*

Antiquarius, Thesaurus, Bellamy, The Purple Shop

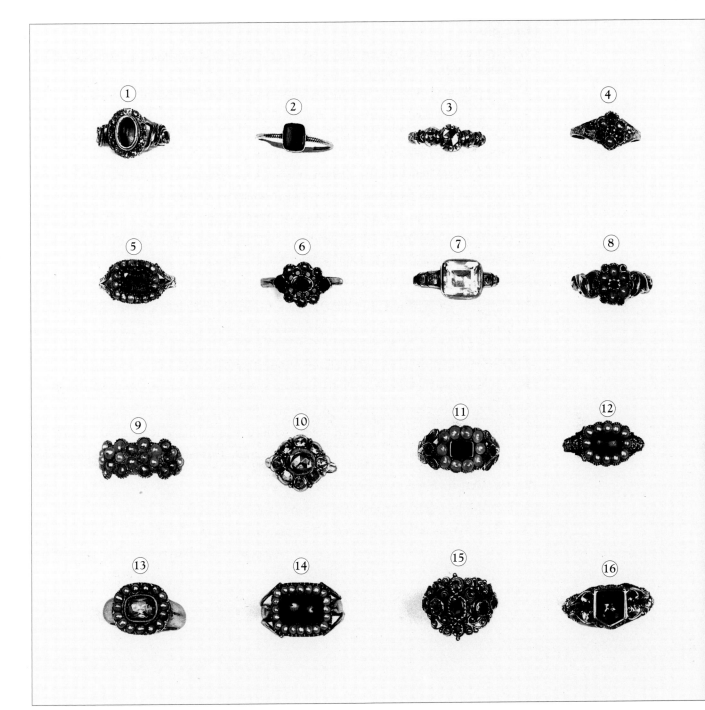

Plate 249.

1. Five stone diamond graduated half-hoop ring in 18ct. yellow gold carved mount, c.1880. £600 – £900.

2. Late Victorian five stone ring set with sapphires, pink and yellow diamonds, in 18ct. gold. £600 – £900.

3. Mid-Victorian five stone coral ring in gold mount. £250 – £300.

4. Late Victorian three stone emerald and diamond ring, c.1880. £800 – £950.

5. Late Victorian turquoise and diamond ring in 18ct. yellow gold mount, c.1890. £250–£300.

6. Edwardian diamond twisted cross-over ring with centre diamond. £300 – £400.

7. Late Victorian, turquoise and rose diamond, cluster ring in yellow gold, c.1880. £200 – £250.

8. Late Victorian emerald and rose diamond cluster ring in wide yellow gold band, c.1890. £500.

9. Victorian ruby and rose diamond marquise-shaped ring in 22ct. gold. £600.

10. Edwardian 18ct. gold, emerald and pearl set ring of elongated form. £350 – £450.

11. Victorian 18ct. gold, pearl, turquoise and rose diamond marquise-shaped ring set in gold, c.1880. £350.

12. Turquoise ring set with four spaced diamonds in gold, c.1860. £400.

13. Edwardian pearl and ruby ring with pearl shoulders in 9ct. gold. £300 – £400.

14. Mid-Victorian emerald and diamond three stone ring in ornate, yellow gold, scrolled setting. £550 – £650.

15. Edwardian pearl and emerald banded half-hoop ring in 18ct. gold. £500 – £550.

16. Mid-Victorian cluster turquoise ring in 18ct. gold. £200.

17. Edwardian garnet and rose diamond cross-over ring. £200.

18. Late Victorian peridot and rose diamond cluster ring in yellow gold, c.1875. £550 – £650.

19. Late Victorian carbuncle and rose diamond cluster ring, set in gold. £550.

20. Opal and diamond three stone cross-over ring in 18ct. gold, c.1910. £400.

Antiquarius, The Purple Shop, Thesaurus, Bellamy

Plate 250.

1. Aquamarine, paste and marcasite octagonal shaped ring, c.1920. *£100 – £150.*
2. Rectangular chrysoprase, marcasite and silver ring, c.1920. *£125.*
3. Cornelian, marcasite and silver rectangular ring, c.1920. *£125.*
4. Square citrine ring mounted with white sapphires. *£125.*
5. Art deco synthetic sapphire and onyx ring in white gold. *£150.*
6. Art deco 9ct. gold and carved coral ring. *£125 – £150.*
7. Oval onyx ring set with diamonds in gold. *£250 – £350.*
8. Smoky quartz and green paste ring in silver. *£75.*
9. Green paste and marcasite ring in silver. *£125.*
10. Oval lapis lazuli and 9ct. gold signet ring. *£200.*
11. Synthetic ruby ring in gold mount. *£125.*
12. Onyx, silver and marcasite ring. *£125.*
13. Three stone citrine ring surrounded with marcasites in silver. *£100.*
14. Jade and white gold oval ring. *£200 – £250.*
15. Synthetic ruby, marcasite, gold and silver mounted ring. *£100.*
16. Art deco synthetic ruby, gold and white gold ring. *£150 – £200.*

Antiquarius, Bellamy, Tony & Sara, Thesaurus, The Purple Shop

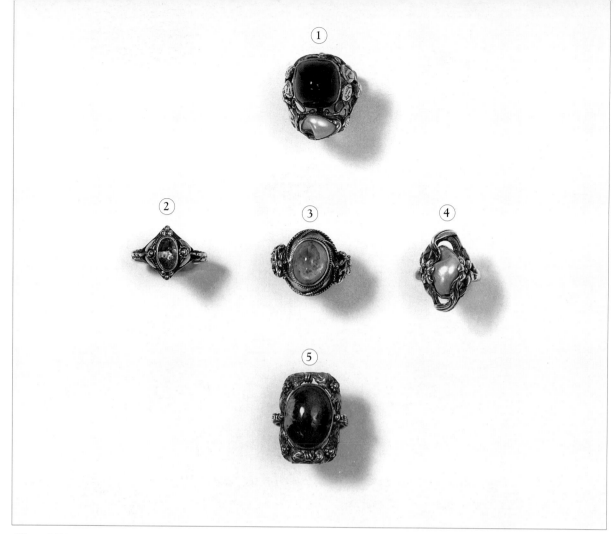

Plate 251

1. Onyx, mother-of-pearl and silver ring in a foliate setting. *£200 – £300.*
2. Sapphire and 18ct. gold ring by Henry Wilson. *£1,000 – £1,500.*
3. Opal and silver ring by Henry Wilson. *£1,000 – £1,500.*
4. Pearl and silver floral ring by de Monville. *£300.*
5. Turquoise and silver rectangular shaped ring. *£250.*   *The Purple Shop, Private Collection*

Plate 252.

1. Trap-cut amethyst, set as a ring in white gold with diamond shoulders. *£1,300 – £1,750.*
2. Mixed-cut amethyst, set as a ring in white gold with diamond shoulders. *£2,000.*
3. Trap-cut aquamarine ring with diamond shoulders. *£3,000 – £3,500.*
4. Oval amethyst and diamond cluster ring with 18ct. gold shank. *£1,200 – £1,600.*
5. Long trap-cut aquamarine ring with diamond shoulders. *£5,000.*
6. Brazilian topaz mounted as a ring in 18ct. gold. *£1,800 – £2,200.*
7. Oval aquamarine and diamond cluster ring. *£1,500.*
8. Green tourmaline ring with diamond trefoil shoulders. *£600 – £850.*
9. Peridot ring with diamond trefoil shoulders. *£1,400 – £1,600.*
10. Star sapphire ring mounted in white gold with diamonds. *£1,500–£2,000.*
11. Opal and diamond half-hoop ring in carved gold setting. *£1,200 – £1,500.*   *Michael Poynder*

282

Plate 253.

9ct. and 18ct. gold wedding rings in white and yellow gold. The top half shows modern designs, cast in various patterns, the lower half traditional settings, from the Victorian era onwards, with plain, engraved or milled settings. The price varies largely according to carat and the weight of gold contained in the ring.

Varying in price £90 – £400.   *Richard Ogden*

Plate 254.

Modern eternity rings.

1. Full eternity, set alternately with two emeralds and two diamonds.
2. Half eternity, set with emeralds and diamonds.
3. Half eternity, set alternately with two sapphires and two diamonds.
4. Full eternity, set alternately with three sapphires and three diamonds.
5. Half eternity, set alternately with three sapphires and three diamonds.
6. Half eternity, set alternately with sapphires and diamonds.
7. Full eternity, set with *calibré*-cut sapphires.
8. Half eternity, set with brilliant-cut diamonds.
9. Full eternity, set with brilliant-cut diamonds.
10. Wide half eternity ring, set with brilliant-cut diamonds.
11. Full eternity, set with brilliant-cut diamonds.
12. Full eternity, set with baguette diamonds.
13. Three row full eternity, the diamond sections hinged to be worn either as a sapphire and diamond three row, or ruby and diamond three row.
14. Half eternity, set alternately with three rubies and three diamonds.
15. Half eternity, set with rubies and diamonds.
16. Full eternity, set alternately with three rubies and three diamonds.
17. Half eternity, set with rubies and diamonds.
18. Half eternity, set with rubies and diamonds.

Full eternity rings £1,800; half hoops £700 – £1,000; triples £2,000 – £2,250.   *Richard Ogden*

Plate 255.

Modern wedding and signet rings.

1. 18ct. gold, 8mm, blue enamel band.   **2.** 18ct. gold, 6mm, 'Fabergé finish'.
3. 18ct. gold, 8mm, open-work circles, double row.   **4.** 18ct. gold, textured ovals.
5. 18ct. yellow and white gold rectangles and squares.   **6.** 18ct. gold, twisted wire.
7. 18ct. gold, four rows of yellow and white gold, twisted rope.
8. 18ct. gold, three row, looped rope twist.
9. 18ct. gold, white stippled band with yellow gold twisted rope.
10. 18ct. white gold plait with frosted finish.   **11.** Gold signet with seal-cut crest.
12. 9ct. gold oval signet with pale blue onyx centre.
13. 9ct. gold signet, set with cushion shaped lapis lazuli.   **14.** 9ct. gold oval signet.
15. 9ct. gold signet, set with cushion-shaped bloodstone.   **16.** 9ct. gold cushion-shaped signet.
17. 9ct. gold, oval signet with textured gold mount.
18. 9ct. gold, oval signet, the textured mount with a bloodstone centre.
19. Lady's 9ct. gold signet with lapis lazuli centre.
20. 9ct. gold signet with broad head, matt finish.   **21.** 9ct. gold signet with broad head.

1–10 *varying in price £120 – £350;* **11–21** *£130 – £280 plus any seal-engraving required.*   *Richard Ogden*

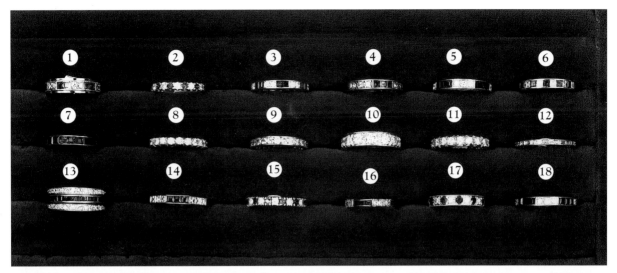

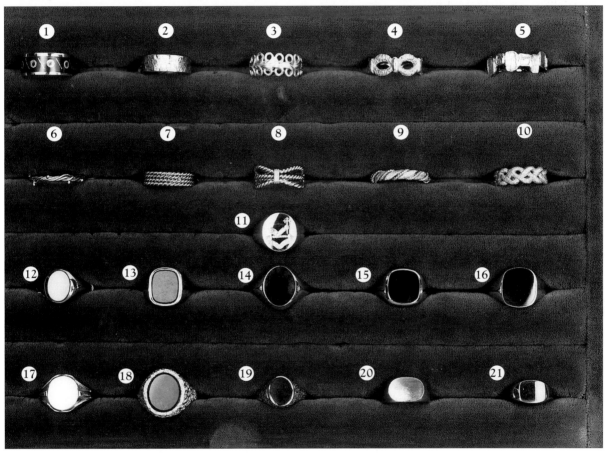

287

EARRINGS

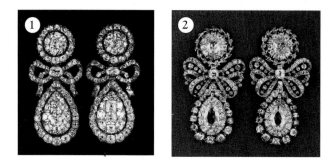

Plate 256.

1. 18th century diamond drop earrings, the stones pavé set in a closed setting, c.1780. £20,000+.

2. Late 18th century diamond pendant earrings. The top clusters of the earrings have been modified at a later date. £25,000+. *Sotheby's*

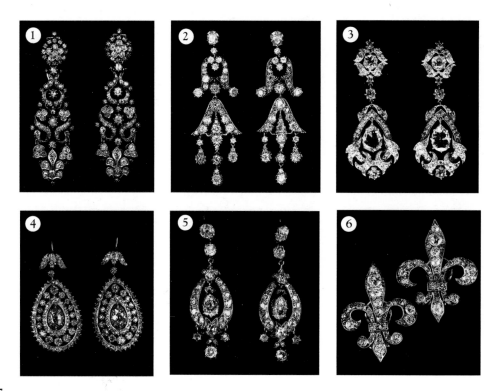

Plate 257.

1. Georgian earrings set with brilliant and rose diamonds. £4,000 – £5,000. *Christie's*

2. Victorian diamond drop earrings with three pendent drops, set in silver and gold. £3,000 – £4,000. *Christie's*

3. Victorian diamond drop earrings, the centre large diamond free-swinging in a scrolled frame, mounted in silver and gold, c.1875. £7,000-£8,000. *Michael Poynder*

4. Georgian diamond pear-shaped drop earrings in a closed back setting, c.1800. £6,000 – £7,000.
N. Bloom

5. Victorian diamond drop earrings with pendent drops, c.1860. £7,000 – £7,500. *N. Bloom*

6. Victorian diamond fleur-de-lys earclips, c.1840. £2,000 – £2,500. *Michael Poynder*

Plate 258.

1. Bohemian garnet earrings set in gold, c.1860. *£350 – £400.*

2. Rosette-shaped gold earrings with drops, of classical inspiration, c.1860. *£550 – £650.*

3. Circular hollow gold earrings with applied thread decoration, c.1870. *£350 – £400.*

4. Silver-gilt drop earrings set with almandine garnets, c.1855. *£250.*

5. Faceted cornelian drop earrings in an oak-leaf designed mount, c.1855. *£300 – £350.*

6. Fine pair of cameo set drop earrings in an ornate scrolled gold mount, c.1850. *£1,200 – £1,500.*

7. Long cornelian drop earrings, c.1860. *£300 – £350.*

8. Coral and gold urn-shaped earrings, c.1860. *£650 – £750.*

9. Gold target earrings with acorn shaped drops, applied thread decoration, c.1860. *£450 – £500.*

10. Reproduction red enamel and gold drop earrings in the mid-Victorian style. *£200 – £250.*

Cameo Corner

Plate 259.

1. Georgian pinchbeck mesh drop earrings, c.1825. £400 – £500.

2. Victorian tortoiseshell piqué-work double loop drop earrings. £850 – £1,000.

3. Georgian coral cameo drop earrings mounted in gold. £350.

4. Mid-Victorian 15ct. gold drop earrings. £650 – £750.

5. Mid-Victorian coral cluster earrings with rose diamonds in gold. £350.

6. Mid-Victorian circular mosaic earrings in silver-gilt, c.1860. £250 – £300.

7. Late 19th century Hungarian coral and pearl earrings in silver-gilt, c.1880. £250 – £300.

8. Pair of tiger's claws mounted in 9ct. gold as earrings, c.1880. £200 – £250.

9. 18ct. gold rosette crescent and tassel drop earrings, c.1880. £350.

10. Anchor earrings, enamelled with pink roses on black, set in base metal. £75 – £100.

Antiquarius, Anne Tan, Thesaurus, The Purple Shop, Tony & Sara

Plate 260.

1. Japanese enamel earrings, c.1900. £75 – £100.

2. Silver earrings set with various semi-precious stones, collet and claw set, c.1940. £100 – £120.

3. Art deco earrings with chalcedony drops, mounted in silver and marcasite. £150.

4. Art deco marcasite and silver drop earrings. £150.

5. Art deco cornelian and marcasite drop earrings, set in silver. £150.

6. Silver-gilt and enamel Egyptian style earrings, c.1920. £120 – £150.

7. Circular stud earrings with a centre pearl surrounded by onyx and marcasites in silver. £50 – £80.

8. Paste drop earrings set in metal, c.1925. £50 – £60.

9. Marcasite and metal earrings, c.1940. £75.

10. Pair of earrings, the drops of real butterfly wings behind painted glass, set and backed in silver, c.1940. £100.

    Antiquarius, Tony & Sara, Bellamy, Thesaurus, The Purple Shop, Lynda Perkin Antiques

Plate 261.

1. Victorian earrings in the form of a hanging basket of flowers, in three-colour gold with pearls and tourmalines, c.1860. £1,200 – £1,500.

2. Georgian filigree gold and chalcedony drop earrings, c.1825. £1,000 – £1,250.

3. Mid-Victorian drop earrings in matt gold, enamelled and set with garnets and diamonds c.1860. £1,250 – £1,550.

4. Victorian urn-shaped drop earrings in banded agate and gold, c.1850. £800 – £900.

5. 18th century Russian gold and pearl drop earrings designed as large bunches of grapes. £750 – £950.

6. Mid-Victorian banded agate (sardonyx), pearl, black enamel and gold drop earrings, c.1860. £700 – £900.

7. Art deco fire opal and diamond drop earrings set in platinum, c.1920. £3,000 – £3,500.

8. 20th century Oriental pearl and diamond earrings, the black and white pearls of large size, c.1930. £10,000.

9. Art deco Oriental pearl and diamond drop earrings, the pearl clusters suspended from an open diamond-set triangle, c.1935. £2,750 – £3,000.

N. Bloom; 7 Michael Poynder

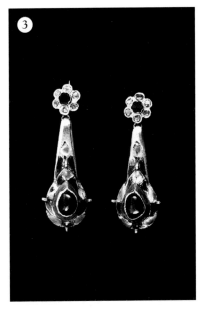

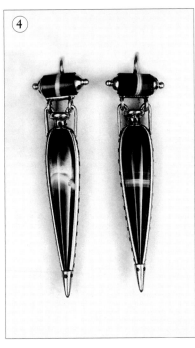

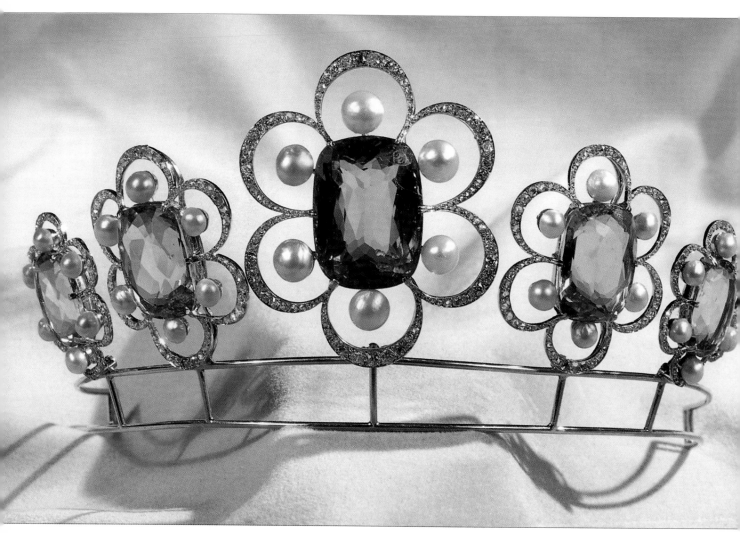

Plate 262.

Five brooches convertible to a tiara, set with aquamarines, pearls and diamonds, c.1908 by Georges Fouquet. *No quote.*

Wartski, London

Plate 263.

Five 19th century paste head ornaments set in metal gilt. All the stones are paste (or glass), imitating pearls, diamonds, turquoises, coral, amethysts, rubies, sapphires and emeralds. One way which helps to differentiate between paste and real stones is to look at the surface lustre. The bright lustre of the 'turquoise' and 'coral' here is too glassy and reflects too much light compared with the real stones, and the 'nacre' of the artificial pearls will peel off, often at the point where they are threaded on to a string, or rub against their setting.

1. £350 – £450. **2.** *In museum.* **3.** £500 – £700. **4.** £500 – £700. **5.** *In museum.*

Richard Digby

Plate 264.

17th century South German gold and enamelled diadem, set with pearls, rubies and emeralds. 4¼in. (10.8 cm) wide.

17th century Hungarian gold and enamel diadem, set with jewels. Note missing star left of centre. 8in. (20.2 cm) wide.

No quote, both exceptionally rare.

Christie's

Plate 265.

Magnificent late 18th century diamond tiara with a detachable ostrich plume of diamonds set in silver and gold. The ostrich plume may also be worn separately as an aigrette, brooch, or corsage ornament. English, c.1800. Formerly in the collection of the 7th Duke of Newcastle. This tiara epitomises the Napoleonic Era. So many portraits and cartoons of the period depict women wearing jewels and plumes like this, but this example must surely be one of the finest for its grandeur and style. *No quote.* *Christie's*

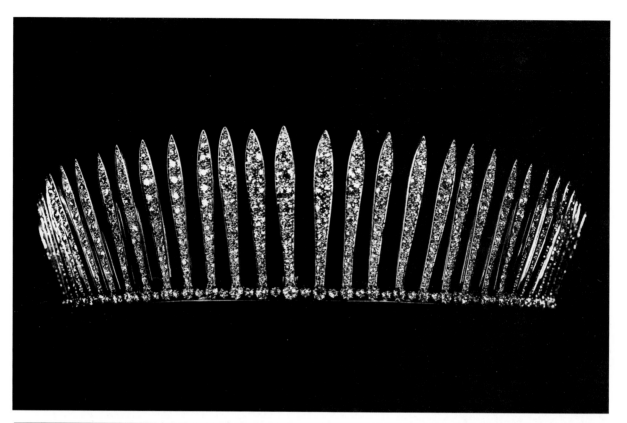

Plate 266.

Early 19th century diamond 'tiara Russe' mounted in silver and gold. It may also be worn as a 'fringe' necklace. *No quote*.

Mid-Victorian diamond tiara set in silver and gold, c.1895. *No quote*.　　　　　*Christie's*

Plate 267.

Tiara by Carlo and Arthur Giuliano in the form of a pair of green enamelled gold wings centering on a star sapphire and supported on two diamond set snakes with ruby set eyes. The wings can be unscrewed to form a brooch. Signed 'C. and A.G.' *No quote*.   *Wartski, London*

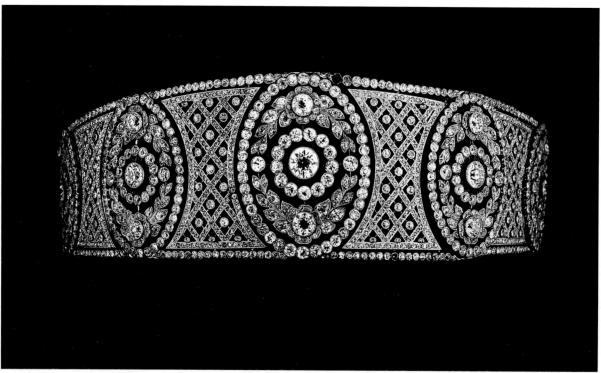

Plate 268.

Edwardian diamond bandeau head ornament formed of open-work floral oval panels linked with fine sections of trellis work, c.1905. £40,000+.   *Christie's*

Plate 269.

1. Mid-19th century French jet and tortoiseshell comb. The lustre is stronger and glassier than real jet. *£500.*

2. Victorian gold hat pin with applied gold-work decoration. *£150 – £200.*

3. Victorian turquoise matrix and gold hat pin. *£150 – £200.*

4. Cabochon amethyst and gold veil pin. *£120.*

5. Peridot and pearl cluster veil pin. *£120.*

6. Assortment of Victorian stickpins for cravats. *£100 – £150 each.*

7. Victorian gold hat pin with applied gold decoration. *£150 – £200.*

8. Art nouveau turquoise, matrix and gold hat pin. *£150 – £200.*   *Richard Digby*

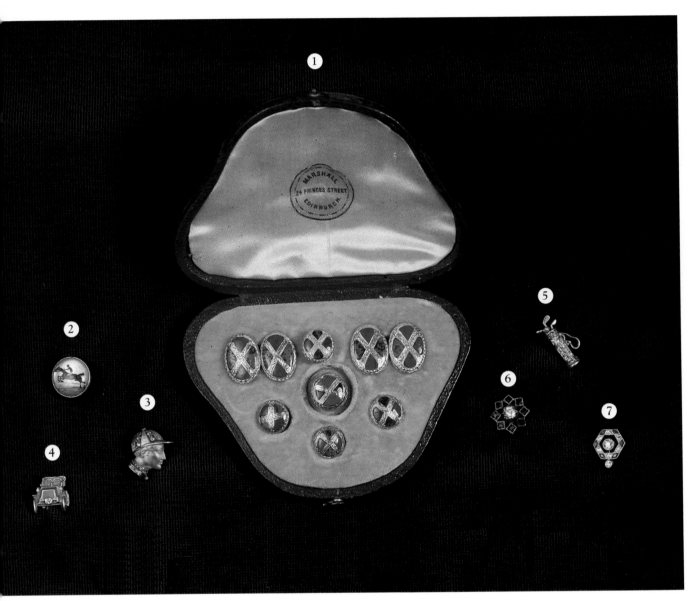

Plate 270.

1. Set of Scottish pebble agate cufflinks and studs set in engraved gold, c.1880. £1,250.

2. Essex crystal race-horse stickpin. £350.

3. Carved moonstone jockey's head stickpin with diamonds and blue enamel in gold, c.1900. £750.

4. Gold vintage car stickpin set with a diamond. £750.

5. Bag of golf-clubs set with diamonds and green garnets as a stickpin. £750.

6. Octagonal diamond and emerald stickpin in gold mount. £750.

7. Art deco ruby and diamond stickpin, set in platinum. £1,250.

Harvey & Gore

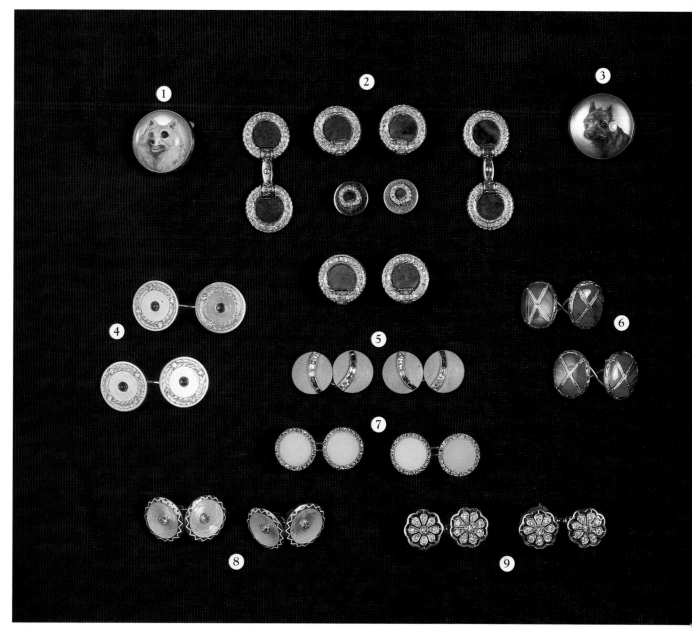

Plate 271.

1. Essex crystal Pomeranian stickpin. £500.

2. Set of lapis lazuli and diamond cufflinks and studs, c.1940. £3,500.

3. Essex crystal cairn stickpin. £500.

4. Cabochon emerald, diamond and engraved platinum cufflinks, c.1925. £1,200+.

5. Art deco sapphire, diamond and platinum cufflinks, with a matt surface, c.1935. £1,500.

6. Scottish pebble cufflinks set in cross-banded gold mount, c.1880. £600.

7. Victorian white agate and diamond cufflinks, c.1870. £500.

8. Edwardian mother-of-pearl, diamond, gold and enamel cufflinks, c.1910. £500.

9. Diamond and enamel cufflinks of floral design, c.1925. £1,000 – £1,400. *Harvey & Gore*

Plate 272.

Early 18th century gold filigree brooch with earrings *en suite*, set with rose diamonds, probably from northern French, c.1700. £2,000.   *Cameo Comer*

Plate 273.

Early 18th century diamond suite of necklace, earrings and brooch, set in silver. Reputedly this suite was offered as ransom by Empress Catherine of Russia after the capture of Peter the Great at the Battle of Rusen in 1711.

Because of its reputed historical connections it is not possible to put a price on this suite.   *Christie's*

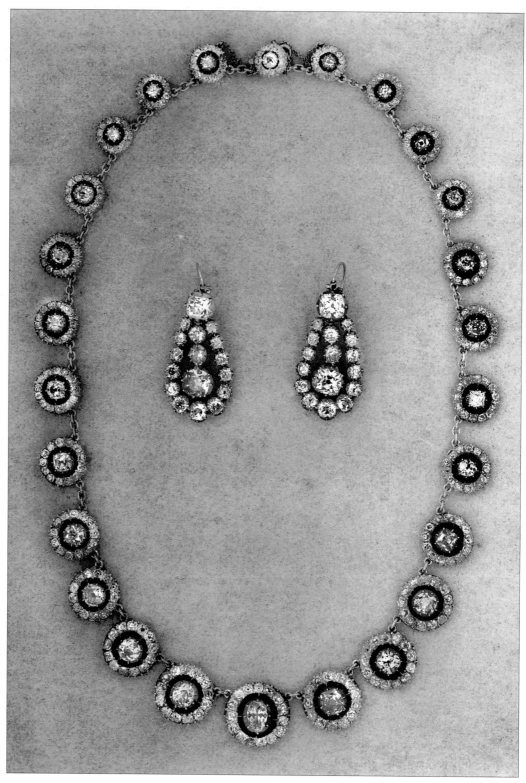

Plate 274.

Late 18th century diamond necklace formed of twenty-five graduated clusters set with cushion-cut diamonds, English, c.1780. *No quote.*

Georgian diamond drop earrings, the cushion-cut diamonds foiled and backed with gold, English, c.1780. £20,000+.

Christie's

Plate 275.

Georgian flat-cut garnet composite suite of necklace, brooch, two pendants and earrings, set and backed with gold, c.1770–1820. All original except the left-hand cross pendant which repeats sections of the necklace and has a modern pendant loop – an 'original' reproduction. Reproduction garnet suites are made today but the workmanship is coarser, the setting thicker and therefore a lot heavier. £5,500 – £6,000. *S.J. Phillips*

Plate 276.

Victorian quartz cat's eye and rose diamond necklace, set in silver, c.1850. These quartz cat's eyes are of particularly good quality showing a clear chatoyancy. £10,000 – £12,000.

Christie's

Plate 277.

Mid-Victorian floral diamond necklace and earrings *en suite*, set in silver and gold, which will also form a tiara, c.1850. £15,000+.   *Christie's*

Plate 278.

19th century Holbeinesque necklace and brooch *en suite*, in blue, white and crimson enamel, set with rubies, diamonds and Baroque pearls, c.1870. *£12,000 – £13,000.*   *Sotheby's*

Plate 279.

19th century ruby and diamond earrings and necklace, the rubies foiled in a closed setting, c.1825. The earrings are made from sections of the necklace. *No quote.* *Christie's*

311

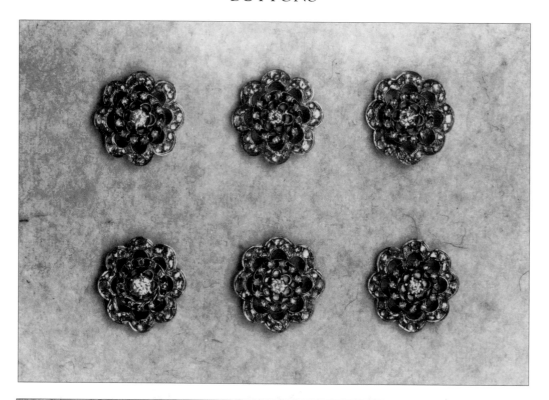

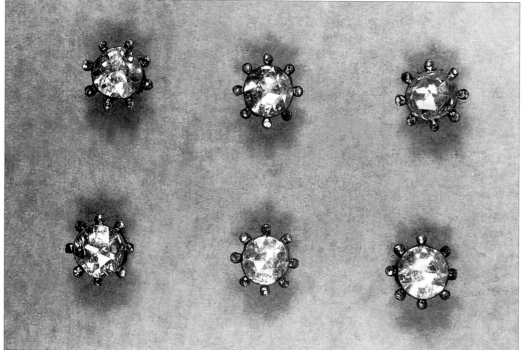

Plate 280.

Set of six 18th century English rose diamond buttons in the form of stylised flowers. This type of work is more often seen in paste. £9,000+.

Set of six 18th century Continental diamond buttons, each large circular rose diamond surrounded by eight smaller ones. £15,000 – £20,000+.   *Christie's*

Plate 281.

19th century emerald and diamond stomacher of openwork design with pendent drop. This is probably a matched-up piece, since there is a difference in the setting of the bow and the centre of the pendant. Top c.1880, the centre of the drop c.1830. This unwearable piece would probably be broken up today, the emeralds re-set as fine, large, cluster rings, the remaining diamonds used by a jeweller as and when needed, and the mounts melted for scrap. *No quote.*

Late Georgian turquoise and rose diamond stomacher, set in silver and gold, c.1810. The flecks of matrix (parent-rock) can be seen in some of the turquoises. £3,750 – £4,500.   *Christie's*

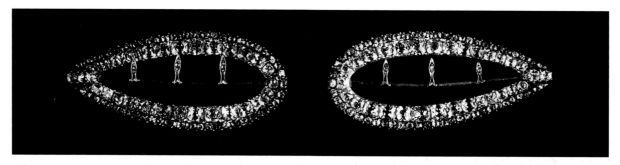

Plate 282.

Georgian diamond pear-shaped pavé set buckles, c.1800. £6,000+, *rare*.   *Christie's*

Plate 283.

Edwardian cut steel, metal and leather belt. £800 – 1,200.   *Antiquarius, Bellamy*

Plate 284.

1. Pair of Georgian metal-gilt bracelet clasps on black velvet, c.1830. £100 – £150.

2. 19th century Chinese enamel buckle set in metal and silver. £75 – £125.

3. Enamelled metal buckle. £50 – £75.

4. Enamelled metal buckle of floral design. £50 – £75.

5. Art nouveau silver and enamelled buckle, the centre enamelled with the figures of Echo and Narcissus. £300 – £400.

6. Late 19th century enamel and metal buckle, silver-backed. £70 – £85.

7. Art nouveau metal bat buckle set with a turquoise coloured paste. £200.

8. Enamel and metal buckle of open-work design. £75 – £100.

9. Art nouveau metal buckle, set with pastes. £100 – £150.

10. Enamel and silver buckle, butterfly design. £150 – £200.

11. Art nouveau silver buckle, with carnation design. £150 – £200.

12. Pair of art deco silver and enamel shoe buckles. £75.

13. Moonstone and silver buckle. £75.

14. Pair of art deco metal and enamel shoe buckles. £50.

Antiquarius, Bellamy, The Purple Shop, John Taylor, Tony & Sara, Thesaurus

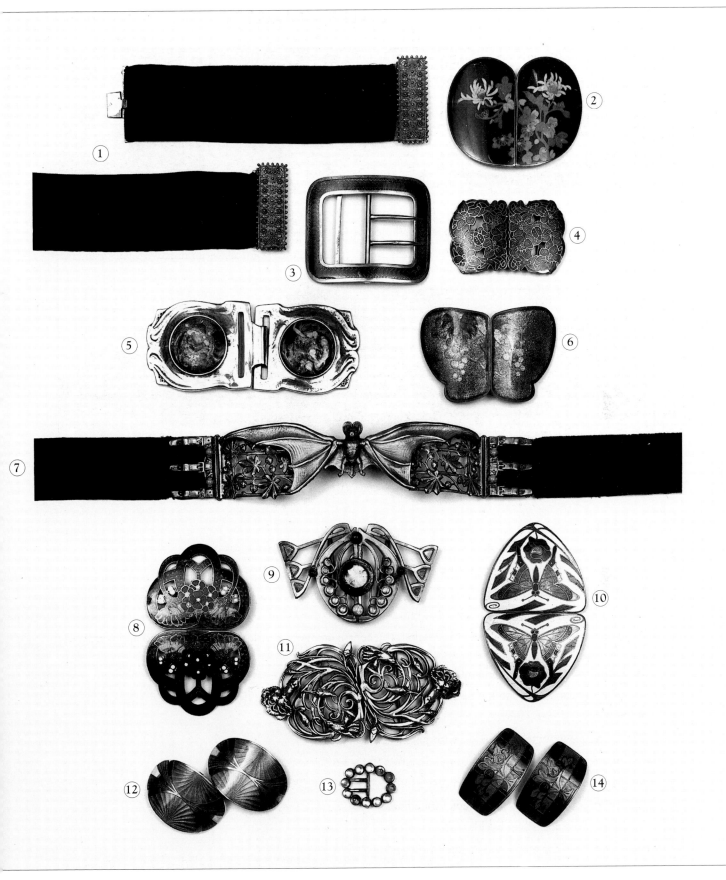

OBJETS D'ART

Plate 285.

1. Cameo of a battle scene, set in a 19th century gold mount. £750 – £850.

2. Shell cameo of an angel in a 9ct. scrolled gold mount. £1,200 – £1,500.

3. Early Victorian cameo of Queen Victoria in a gold mount. £800 – £1,000.

4. Hardstone cameo, set in a pinchbeck mount, with pastes as a pendant brooch. £350 – £400.

5. Mid-Victorian cameo bracelet of mythological scenes set in a 15ct. scrolled gold mount. £2,500.

6. Georgian blue and white Wedgwood double cameo, set in an octagonal, silver frame with a swivel centre. £350 – £400.

7. Pair of mid-Victorian earrings, the cameos set in gold foliage mounts with gold pendant drops, c.1860. £750.

8. Pair of early Victorian earrings, the top cameos of grotesques, the long drop cameos of two Muses, set in 18ct. scrolled gold mounts, c.1845. £1,500 – £1,800.

9. Mid-Victorian lava cameo, the profile of a woman, set in gold. £350 – £400.

10. Hardstone cameo set as a ring in gold. £450 – £500.

11. Mid-Victorian bar brooch of engraved gold set with two portrait cameos. £300.

12. Cameo of two figures in the Roman style, set in 9ct. gold as a brooch. £550 – £600.

13. Hardstone cameo set as a pendant in 9ct. gold. £550.

14. Hardstone cameo, the bust of a lady, set in a rectangular gold frame of leafy design. £550 – £600.

Antiquarius, Anne Tan, Bellamy, The Purple Shop, Thesaurus

Plate 286.

19th century Hungarian enamel jewellery.

1. Pendant of St. George and the Dragon, enamelled and set with garnets and pearls. £500.

2. Silver-gilt and enamelled butterfly set with turquoises and garnets. £500 – £600.

3. Pair of enamel and silver gilt rosette earrings, originally part of a necklace, set with pearls and coral. £250 – £300.

4. Pearl, turquoise and garnet floral pendant set in silver gilt. £175.

5. Hungarian St. George and the Dragon pendant, enamelled and set with a Baroque drop pearl. £400 – £450.

6. Turquoise and pearl brooch in scrolled silver-gilt mount, c.1835. £250.

7. Late 19th century silver-gilt garnet, turquoise and pearl oval pendant. £200.

8. Enamelled silver frame on a chain, set with rubies, a diamond and an aquamarine.

Varying in price £550 – £650.

Antiquarius, Catherine Derry, The Purple Shop, Tony & Sara, Thesaurus

Plate 287.

19th century Hungarian pendant in the 17th century style, the frame of enamelled silver set with pearls and rubies, the centre a cornelian and glass doublet cameo. The spotted appearance of the cameo is a layer of air bubbles trapped between the glass and the cornelian where the glue with which they were stuck together has deteriorated. £700.

Thesaurus at Antiquarius

319

Plate 288.

1. Green enamel, silver and gilt lacquer vanity mirror. £80 – £100.

2. Black enamel and silver Swiss watch. £250.

3. Duck-egg blue enamel and silver-gilt compact, French. £175.

4. Chrome and plastic watch on leather strap. £80 – £120.

5. Marcasite ring watch. £120.

6. Chrome and black leather clip watch. £80 – £100.

7. Turquoise enamel and silver compact, English. £120 – £150.

8. Bakelite vanity mirror. £45 – £60.

9. Purple enamel and silver-gilt powder puff. £90 – £150.

10. Yellow enamel and silver powder puff, with a lipstick case concealed in a yellow tassel. £250 – £300.

11. Diamond and white gold lapel watch. £1,000 – £1,500.

12. 9ct. gold lapel watch, engraved on the reverse '1947', English. £450 – £500.

13. Silver-gilt and enamel 'Egyptian' compact, c.1925. £150 – £200.

14. Silver and enamel compact with a bird and flowers, English. £120 – £150.

Antiquarius, Bellamy, The Purple Shop, Thesaurus

321

Plate 289.

1. Chrome and plastic banded cigarette holder. *£25 – £40.*
2. Circular plastic solid scent jar. *£25 – £40.*
3. Silver and amber cigarette holder with enamelled centre section. *£25 – £40.*
4. Green and red enamel silver cigarette holder. *£25 – £40.*
5. Enamel, silver and plastic cigarette holder. *£25 – £40.*
6. Chrome and plastic étui. *£25 – £40.*
7. Glass scent flask in plastic case, of Japanese influence. *£25 – £40.*
8. Circular plastic solid scent jar. *£25 – £40.*
9. Plastic bamboo cigarette holder. *£25 – £40.*
10. Silver and green enamel lipstick case. *£75 – £100.*
11. Silver and gold rectangular lipstick case with *calibré* ruby catch. *£300 – £400.*
12. Silver, gold and cabochon sapphire lipstick case with floral motif, by Boucheron. *£600 – £750.*
13. Plastic cigarette holder (open). *£25 – £40.*
14. Plastic cigarette holder (closed). *£25 – £40.*
15. Gold, enamel and ivorine cigarette holder. *£75.*
16. Green and white enamelled glass scent flask, with enamelled silver top. *£150 – £200.*

Antiquarius, Bellamy, The Purple Shop

AMULETS AND TALISMANS

Since man first knew fear and learnt to kill, he has worn bits and pieces to give him courage to face the dangers of life, both mystical and practical. These are known as amulets or talismans and take many forms – the claws of a slain animal, the neck bone of a tiger, the hair from an elephant's tail, a piece of coral (particularly thought to ward off disease), or a pure crystal as a protection against pests. Magical qualities have been given to many different stones, hence the development of the zodiacal birth stone charts (see pp.352). Animals, in whom man identifies so many of his own characteristics, are supposed to have special attributes. The Egyptians used the fish as a love symbol; foxes, spiders, ladybirds and even pigs are thought to be lucky in various parts of the world; bats are a symbol of longevity, health and peace to the Chinese. Horseshoes, and anything crescent shaped has a long tradition of magic and good luck and was used as a protection against witches and the plague – hence nailing a shoe to your cottage door. The cross is perhaps the greatest symbolic talisman we wear in the West, for obvious reasons, and medieval confidence tricksters sold pieces of the 'true cross' and bones of the martyrs centuries after the death of Christ to bring the wearer protection from the devil.

The necklace of stones and nuts (Plate 292)was gathered no doubt by a pilgrim, probably a Buddhist or Trappist monk during a pilgrimage, and set to mark attainment of that goal.

Plate 290.

1. Lady's shoe, made of jasper, early 19th century.
2. Late 19th century metal hobnail boot.
3. Edwardian 'Alpha and Omega' pendant, set with rose diamonds in white gold, c.1910.
4. 14ct. gold and enamel ladybird pendant, modern.
5. Mid-19th century Italian mosaic 'Pax' pendant.
6. Early 18th century flat-cut garnet and gold witch's heart brooch.
7. Victorian 9ct. gold whistle.
8. Late Victorian silver and coloured glass bee brooch, c.1880.
9. Nepalese silver female monkey god, traditional, 20th century.
10. Thai composition stone god, set in silver.
11. Early 19th century Chinese carved cornelian 'peach of longevity'.
12. Nepalese silver monkey god, traditional, probably late 19th century.
13. Thai stone god in silver, traditional, probably 20th century.
14. Afghan Koran medal, made in low-grade silver, traditional.
15. Tibetan double tooth pendant, silver-mounted.
16. Victorian silver-gilt mounted otter pad, c.1885.

Varying in price £25 – £200.   *Antiquarius, The Purple Shop, Thesaurus*

Plate 291.

1. Coptic Jimma Jala, traditionally made in the same way as the early Christian silver necklaces, with each section of silver containing charcoal, which the wearers believed to be health-giving. *£350.*

2. Traditional Coptic cross, in silver. *£30 – £50.*

3. Coptic leather prayer-holder. *£30 – £50.*

4. Coptic silver ear-pick. *£50 – £60.*

Antiquarius

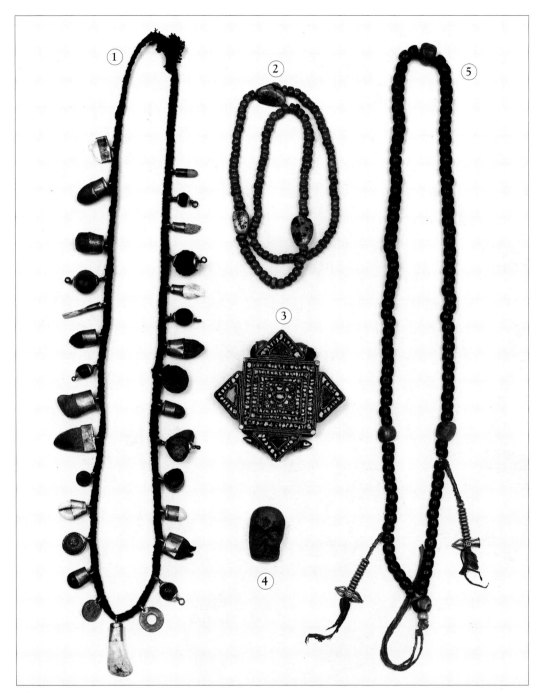

Plate 292.

1. Amulet necklace made up from pieces found on pilgrimage: beads, claws, stones, berries, nuts, coins, shells, etc., 20th century. £200.

2. Bead and turquoise matrix necklace. £150.

3. Low-grade silver prayer box, inlaid with turquoise matrix and glass, stuck in with gutta percha (a natural glutinous resin). £250.

4. Late 19th century skull made from a monkey femur. Earlier ones would probably be made from human skullbone and can be expensive because of their rarity. £100 – £110.

5. Mahla (rosary) made from seeds and cornelian beads, with low-grade silver counting beads, prayer bell and dorje (sacred symbol) forming pendants. £200. *Antiquarius*

Plate 293.

1. Algerian enamelled silver pendant on a hand-moulded resin bead and carved coral necklace. £400.

2. Coral necklace with silver bead pendants, from Goa, south-west India. £400 – £450.

3. Coral necklace with two silver discs and a central silver bead, from northern Africa. £500 – £600.

4. Small coral and silver bead necklace with silver pendant inlaid with gutta percha, from northern Africa. £150.

5. Indian graduated coral bead necklace with a large central bead of paler coral from China. £350.

6. North African coral necklace with four silver ornamental discs. £300.

7. Coral bead necklace with three pieces of turquoise matrix, Tibetan. £500 – £600. *Antiquarius*

APPENDICES

TECHNICAL TERMS

An explanation of the technical terms used in the identification of stones:

Chemical Composition: The chemical make-up of each individual stone, and formula.

Crystal Structure: Gemstones fall into one of seven categories of crystal formation which are referred to as follows, beginning with the most perfect and symmetrical: cubic, tetragonal, orthorhombic, hexagonal, trigonal, monoclinic and triclinic. In some cases stones are referred to as micro-crystalline, or crypto-crystalline, and they are formed by minute crystals packed tightly together. These are opaque stones and normally porous, and they can be stained to improve the colour, e.g. some agates, lapis lazuli and jade. Stones may also be amorphous, i.e. with no identifiable crystal structure.

Hardness: Hardness in gemstones is defined by a scale known as Mohs scale, calculated in 1822 by Friedrich Mohs. He chose ten representative stones and minerals to form the scale, beginning with the hardest substance, diamond, which he graded 10, descending through corundum – 9, topaz – 8, quartz – 7, feldspar – 6, apatite – 5, fluorspar – 4, calcite – 3, gypsum – 2, to talc – 1. Glass varies from 4 to 6, according to its lead content, and steel rates around 6. The scale is uneven and the gap between 9 and 10 is, for instance, much greater than from 8 to 9. Therefore it can only be used as a comparison of hardness from one stone to another, rather than as a regular linear scale. As far as identification is concerned, it is useful in conjunction with other tests, and will give immediate identification of, for example, a diamond, from its simulants, e.g. white sapphire (9), white spinel (8) or strontium titanate (6½).

Refractive Index: When light rays enter a stone they appear to bend. This bending, or refraction, of light happens whenever light passes from one medium to another. This can easily be noticed if a person is observed standing in water up to his waist. His legs will appear to be much shorter than in real life because water refracts light at a different rate from air. Every gemstone will refract light at a different angle and a scale, known as the Refractive Index, expresses this numerically in order to help identification of the stones. Air is considered as 1, and the proportion of the bending of the light ray when it enters the stone expresses the stone's refractive index. It is measured on a refractometer, and together with specific gravity forms a combination of figures, so that two different types of stone will rarely coincide. A refractometer can only be used with cut stones and is an essential part of a jeweller's equipment.

Specific Gravity: Specific gravity means the density or 'heaviness' of an article. A scale has been devised to measure the density of objects and is based on the density of water which is taken to be 1. Equivalent volumes of water and stones are compared and the difference in weight will be the specific gravity figure expressed. Therefore, a stone such as a diamond, with an S.G. of 3.52 will be 3.52 times as dense as the same volume of water. Specific gravity is particularly useful in identifying different gemstones, as every species has its own density, and will help to tell the difference between two stones which appear to be of the same family.

WEIGHTS AND MEASURES

Rough or cut stones are weighed in carats:

1 carat = ⅕ or .200 grammes
1 diamond or pearl grain = ¼ or .250 of a carat

A diamond weighing less than a carat is referred to as having so many points which is the percentage expression, i.e. a ¾ carat diamond is referred to as being 75 points.

Pearls are referred to in grains: 1 grain = ¼ of a carat. However, unlike diamonds, pearls are never referred to as being of so many points if less than a carat.

Metric weight is the expression of grammes:

1000 milligrammes	=	1 gramme
1000 grammes	=	1 kilo
1 gramme	=	5 carats
500 milligrammes	=	2½ carats, etc.

The Troy weight scale is often used in the jewellery, gold and silver trade:

24 grains	=	1 pennyweight (dwt)
20 dwts	=	1 ounce (oz)
12 oz	=	1 pound (lb)

However, the normal domestic Avoirdupois scale is also used, the scale that used to be learnt in the schoolroom:

16 drams	=	1 ounce
16 oz	=	1 lb
14 lbs	=	1 stone

It is therefore vital to know which scale you are using when weighing gold etc., on a spring balance. Here is the conversion between the various scales, which is enough to confuse anyone, but necessary to have available:

Grains to gramme	x	0.0648
Grammes to grains	x	15.4324
Pennyweights to grammes	x	1.5552
Grammes to pennyweights	x	0.6430
Ounces (Troy) to grammes	x	31.1035
Grammes to ounces (Troy)	x	0.03215
Ounces (Troy) to ounces (Avoirdupois)	x	1.09714
Ounces (Avoirdupois) to ounces (Troy)	x	0.91146
Ounces (Avoirdupois) to grammes	x	28.3495
Grammes to ounces (Avoirdupois)	x	0.03527
Pounds (Avoirdupois) to ounces (Troy)	x	14.5833
Ounces (Troy) to metric carats	x	155.517
Ounces (Avoirdupois) to metric carats	x	141.7475
Pennyweights to metric carats	x	7.77
Inches to millimetres	x	25.400
Inches to centimetres	x	2.540

CUTTING

Gemstones are either mined, or found in alluvial deposits. They occur as natural crystals and each species has its own particular crystal structure. The style of cutting stones has developed over the centuries in order to show the maximum amount of beauty from each stone – its colour, clarity, brilliance and shape.

Before the 16th century diamonds were usually left in their natural octahedral shape (two four-sided pyramids base to base) and when set looked rather lifeless. The major source of diamonds in the old world was India, and with the opening of trade between western Europe and the Orient in the 16th and 17th centuries the flow of diamonds and other gemstones from the East increased rapidly and new forms of cutting were devised. At this time, diamonds were flat-cut or table-cut, and coloured stones might be flat-cut or *en cabochon*. However, this increase in the use of diamonds in western jewellery brought about the rose-cut and the brilliant-cut, the latter being the most important and widely used form of cutting in all jewellery. The table-cut was developed into a form now known as the step-, trap- or emerald-cut, and this in turn has been combined with the brilliant to give the mixed-cut – a brilliant-cut crown and step-cut pavilion. In addition, other forms of cutting are used, including the marquise – in principle an elongated brilliant; pendeloque – a pear-shaped brilliant; briolette – a completely faceted drop bead: and baguette – a long trap-cut used for small diamonds in composite pieces of 20th century jewellery.

See the diagrams on the following pages.

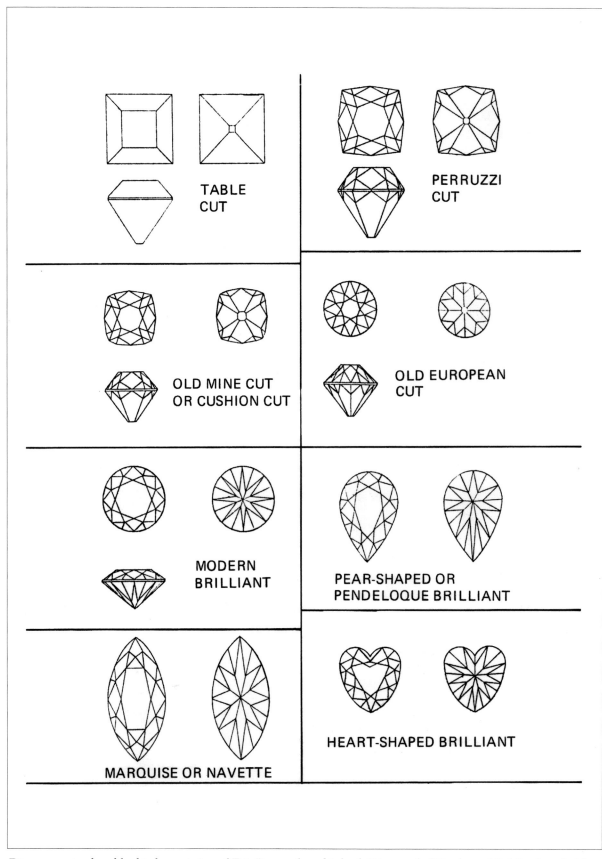

TABLE
CUT

PERRUZZI
CUT

OLD MINE CUT
OR CUSHION CUT

OLD EUROPEAN
CUT

MODERN
BRILLIANT

PEAR-SHAPED OR
PENDELOQUE BRILLIANT

MARQUISE OR NAVETTE

HEART-SHAPED BRILLIANT

Diagrams reproduced by kind permission of Eric Bruton from his book Diamonds *(Northwood Publications Ltd.)*

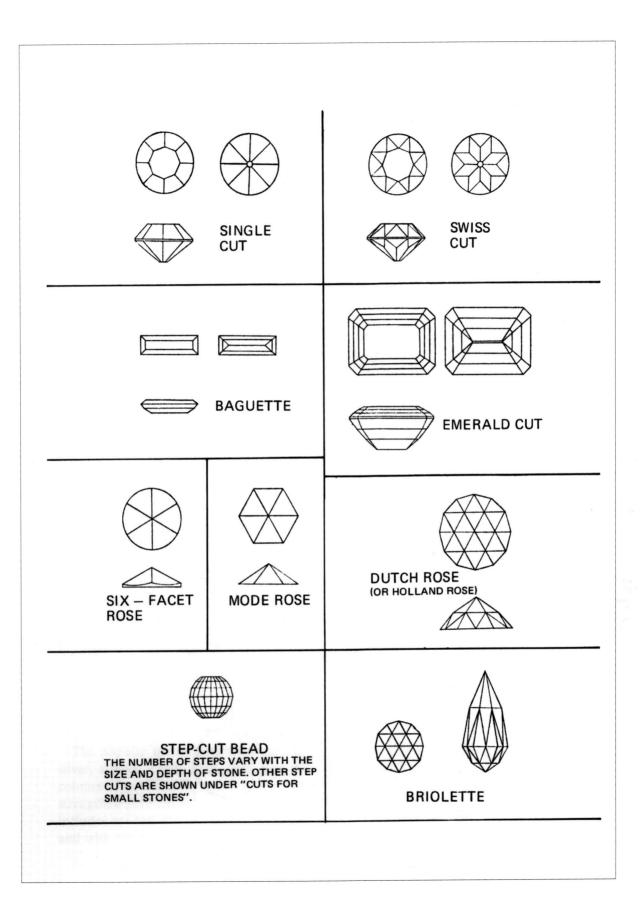

SINGLE
CUT

SWISS
CUT

BAGUETTE

EMERALD CUT

SIX – FACET
ROSE

MODE ROSE

DUTCH ROSE
(OR HOLLAND ROSE)

STEP-CUT BEAD
THE NUMBER OF STEPS VARY WITH THE
SIZE AND DEPTH OF STONE. OTHER STEP
CUTS ARE SHOWN UNDER "CUTS FOR
SMALL STONES".

BRIOLETTE

PARTS AND FACETS OF THE BRILLIANT CUT

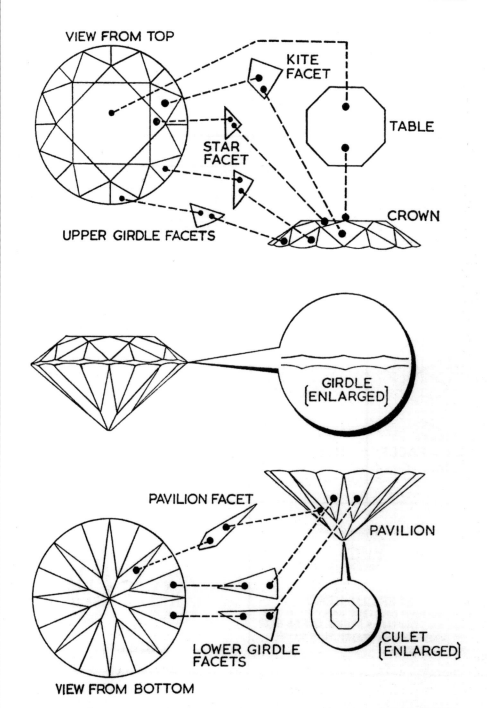

VIEW FROM TOP

KITE FACET

TABLE

STAR FACET

CROWN

UPPER GIRDLE FACETS

GIRDLE [ENLARGED]

PAVILION FACET

PAVILION

LOWER GIRDLE FACETS

CULET [ENLARGED]

VIEW FROM BOTTOM

Parts of the brilliant cut diamond. The names of the facets have been simplified from the old cutters' terms and are generally accepted.

Plate 294.

1. Round brilliant-cut diamond.

2. Marquise-cut diamond.

3. Trap-cut diamond (step-cut or emerald-cut).

4. Pear-shaped brilliant-cut diamond.

The facets of the marquise and pear-shape are of modified proportions to the round brilliant, but follow the same basic design.

De Beers Consolidated Mines Ltd.

Plate 295.

Examples of unmounted circular brilliant-cut diamonds, clearly showing the crown (and table facet), girdle and pavilion of a stone.

De Beers Consolidated Mines Ltd.

MOUNTING AND SETTING

Once a gemstone has been cut it is ready for setting in a mount – so that it can be worn. Within the jeweller's art there are many different individual crafts. For instance, the craftsman who cuts and polishes stones is called a lapidary but he would never make the mounts to take his stones. It is possible for a mounter – the craftsman who designs and cuts out mounts in metal – also to set the stones. But normally a mounter and setter are two different people performing two different crafts.

Mounting is the manufacture of metal cups or frames to hold gemstones so that they can be displayed or worn. The simplest and oldest form of mounting is a cup in which the stone is placed, the metal then being closed over the edge to hold it in. This is referred to as a 'collet' and in this case is 'closed backed'. In early jewellery, when the quality of stones often needed brightening, a layer of foil (tin foil, silver or coloured) was put in the collet before the stone was set. This is referred to as a 'closed backed foiled collet'.

The most important development from this was 'claw' setting, which is self-explanatory. The number, shape and style of the claws and craftsmanship dictate the beauty and simplicity of the finished article. Claw set stones are invariably 'open backed', i.e. there is no metal behind the base of the stone. Hand-made mounts are always better than cast mounts which are used in both antique and modern mass-produced jewellery.

'Collet' and 'claw' are two types of setting used in gem-set jewellery and the many other forms of setting referred to in the book and listed below are only adaptations or embellishments of the two basic styles and are evident in the illustrations:

> Collet (foiled or unfoiled)
> Cut down collet
> Closed back collet
> Open backed collet
> Claw
> Claw with engraved gallery or mount
> Claw with carved gallery or mount
> Filigree
> Gypsy
> Milled grain
> Pavé
> *En tremblant*
> *Cannetille*, etc.

The popular metals used in mounting through the centuries have been: electrum, gold, silver, copper, brass, iron, steel, platinum and various amalgams such as pinchbeck. The colours of gold can be varied by the inclusion of different base metals used to harden and strengthen pure gold, i.e.: white gold includes nickel; yellow gold includes brass; red gold includes copper, etc. All these metals were used extensively as they polish to a high degree and, with the exception of steel, are easy to work.

Plate 296.

Enlargement of an early 18th century cross of table- and rose-cut diamonds in gold showing the mounting and setting. Actual length 3½in (8.4cm).

Plate 297.

Enlargement of a flat-cut garnet brooch in an 18th century mount, actual width of brooch 1⅜in. (3.5cm). (See also Plate 104.)

Plate 298 (front and reverse to show mounting and setting).

1. Late Victorian diamond wing brooch with cluster centre, open-backed and set in silver and gold. *£2,000 – £2,500.*

2. Victorian carved moonstone head of a girl with a rose diamond-set bonnet in a closed silver setting, c.1860. *£2,000.*

3. Rose diamond-set bar brooch designed as three birds on a branch, in a closed setting. *£1,000.*

4. Georgian diamond crescent brooch in a closed back setting, c.1800. *£2,200 – £2,500.*

5. Georgian foiled brown topaz and half pearl cluster brooch, c.1820. *£500.*

6. Diamond daisy brooch with a pearl centre. *£600.*

7. Amethyst and rose diamond sunburst brooch, set in silver and gold, open-backed, c.1900. *£1,000 – £1,200.*

8. Victorian pavé set diamond bird with ruby eyes, open-backed. *£2,000–£2,200.*

9. Blister pearl and diamond cockerel brooch, modern. *£1,000 – £1,200.*

10. Georgian flat-cut garnet brooch-locket with hinged but empty centre compartment, the garnets foiled in a closed setting, c.1820. £200.

11. Late Victorian Essex crystal and pearl pendant, normally closed back, but the back is missing in this case so that it is possible to see the method of reverse painting of the engraved crystal, c.1900. £950 – £1,100.

12. Late Georgian carbuncle set as a brooch in a filigree gold setting with pearls and turquoises, c.1835. £300 – £400.

13. Early Victorian *cannetille* work pendant, showing the coiling of the filigree gold into intricate patterns, forming a pendant/brooch, set with turquoises and pearls, c.1840. £1,300 – £1,600.

14. Mid-Victorian gold bow brooch with a pendent heart locket, set with rubies and pearls, the gold background of the bow stippled to give it a textured look, and the heart engraved, c.1845. £650 – £750.

R. Barnett Ltd.

Plate 299.
The reverse of a Victorian diamond flower spray brooch *en tremblant*, showing the coiled spring to allow independent movement of the flowerhead, c.1850. Although the front of the brooch is mounted in silver, the back is of gold to strengthen the framework. Actual length 2¾in. (6.6cm).

Mid-Victorian rose diamond-set fleur-de-lys pendant, set in silver and gold. The side view shows the claw setting of the centre diamond and the pierced gallery around the outside edge, c.1860. Actual height 2¼in. (5.4cm).
Michael Poynder

Plate 300.

Late 18th century Georgian brooch with various stones set in gold, actual size 2in. (4.8cm) high, enlarged to show details of setting. The reverse shows where pewter has been used at the ends of the basket handle, and a patch which has been put on at the base of the brooch fastening.

Plate 301.

Ring mountings.

1. Mid-18th century, open design shoulders and carved shank.
2. Georgian, carved shoulders and shank.
3. Georgian, carved split-leaf shoulders, c.1830.
4. Georgian, decorative gold, lyre-shaped shoulders, c.1830.
5. Early Victorian, scrolled leaf shank and shoulders.
6. 19th century, split-leaf shank on cluster head.
7. Mid-18th century, wide gold shank.
8. Enamel ring with plain gold band.
9. Early Victorian, scrolled shoulders, c.1840.
10. Mid-Victorian, split shoulders into three leaves.
11. Open shoulders with crowned claw setting.
12. Late Victorian, carved shoulders, c.1880.
13. Late Victorian, carved shoulders, c.1890.
14. Modern, gold band, c.1900.

Plate 302.

Side views of ring galleries.

1. 18th century, closed back setting, engraved on the inside of the shank.
2. 18th century, silver, cut-down collet setting with engraved shoulders. Note the varying height of the old-cut brilliants.
3. Mid-18th century, cut-down collet on a half-hoop ring, open-backed.
4. Mid-Victorian, half-hoop ring, carved gallery and claw-setting.
5. Mid-Victorian, half-hoop ring, carved gallery and claw-setting.
6. Late Victorian, crown claw mount.
7. 20th century, traditional claw mount, plain shank. Note the difference in height compared to 5 or 6.
8. Modern claw mount, plain shank.   *Richard Ogden*

Plate 303.

Side views of eternity ring settings.

1. Half eternity, solid gallery.
2. Full eternity, modern claw setting.
3. Half eternity, anugular plain setting.
4. Full eternity, carved gallery.
5. Full eternity, plain setting.

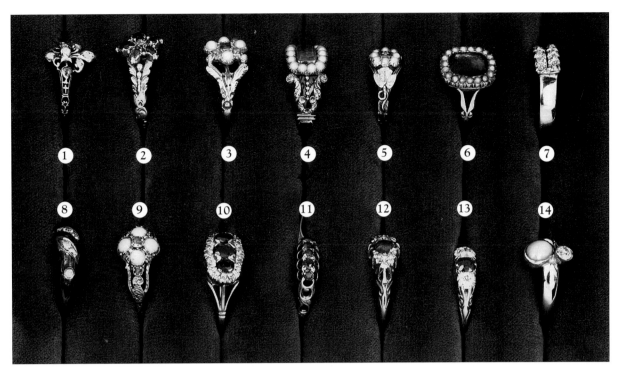

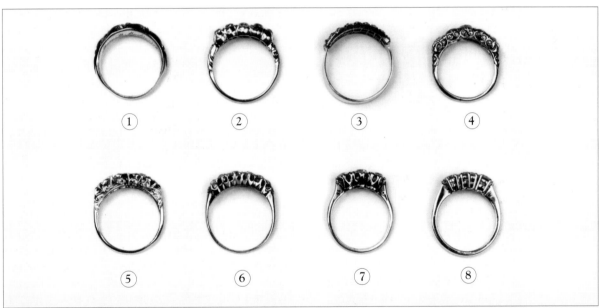

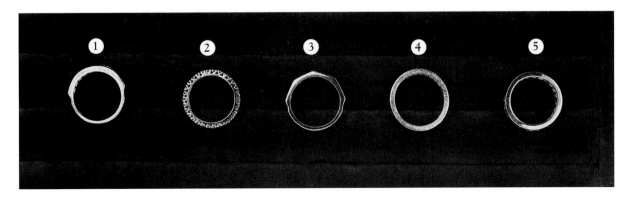

CARING AND REPAIRING

If people took more care of their jewellery and treated it with the respect and attention that hand-made work deserves, then it would not be necessary to pay large sums of money for their own negligence. It is amazing that such valuable articles, with added sentiment and romantic attachment, can be treated so badly. Jewellery should be checked regularly for wear and tear. The following list covers the normal type of repair or break that occurs:

Rings

1. Shanks get thin on the palm side and will eventually break, possibly causing the loss of the ring. A new half shank can be fitted at a fraction of the cost of the whole ring.
2. Galleries: close and constant contact with another ring will wear into a finely pierced gallery – which runs on either side of the body of a half-hoop or cluster ring – particularly when worn next to a wedding ring. This wear is acceptable and unavoidable as wedding rings and engagement rings are traditionally worn side by side, but eventually will necessitate remounting.
3. Claws will gradually rub down or break away if they are caught in strong synthetic fibre such as nylon or terylene, which means that a valuable or sentimental stone could fall out. Re-tipping claws is expensive as the stone must be removed first, but it is necessary.
4. Rubbed stones: although a gemstone is hard, its surface will gradually scratch and chip until it becomes opaque and dull. This can be caused in a variety of ways: by knocking against other hard objects such as car doors, tables, etc., and also by keeping several hardstones jumbled together in a jewel box. However, a stone can easily be removed from its setting, repolished and reset.

Brooches

Brooches are usually lost due to faulty catches, or lack of safety catches and chains. These can be fitted at little extra cost, and are essential. If it does not matter which way up a brooch is worn, then it is safest to wear it with the pin pointing downwards, so that if the catch does come undone, the brooch will not fall out. Brooches are not normally damaged as easily as rings, but probably suffer more damage when put in a jewel box amongst other jewellery than when worn!

Necklaces and beads

1. Pearls and beads: regular restringing is obviously necessary, but it is often left too late. Pearls are usually strung on silk and it is safer to have them strung knotted between each pearl so that if the silk breaks only one pearl will roll away and be lost. Pearls are regularly maltreated by being dropped on dressing-tables and scratched in jewellery boxes. They are not as hard as gemstones and will crack and chip easily. Women should always put on pearls after scent, as scent sprayed from an atomiser directly on to the pearls will eventually discolour them. Beads should be strung in the same way as pearls but with thicker silk.
2. Chains and links: chain links, be they gold or silver, will wear as they constantly rub together, and this cannot be prevented. To strengthen every link in a long-worn chain would be ridiculous, and when links finally become so thin that they break, it is time to replace the chain.

Foiled jewellery

Foiled jewellery should never be allowed to get wet, for if moisture gets behind the stone, the coloured, or silver, tinsel will discolour and the character of the brooch and the stones in it become dull and lifeless.

Seed pearl work

Very little remains in perfect condition since it is very fragile. Regrettably, if it does get broken, there are few jewellers capable or willing to take on this work.

Enamel

Enamel is fragile and, after all, only a form of glass, and therefore will chip, crack and scratch if it is allowed to be in contact with other stones. To touch up enamel is always a patchy job and will be noticeable to the trained eye. The alternative is to remove the enamel completely and start from scratch, but of course this is not practical with early jewellery as its character will inevitably be changed.

Cleaning

A little care and cleaning of your jewellery at home is not only worthwhile but rewarding. Any liquid or spirit that dissolves grease and dirt can be used in conjunction with a soft bristle toothbrush. Mix the spirit with whitening powder, working it into a stiff paste. Methylated spirits is excellent for brightening metal. The powder should be brushed on to the jewellery and left to dry and then brushed off again. Goddards produce a 'Jewellery Care Kit' which consists of a jar of special liquid, an immersible tray and a small stiff brush, and is ideal for cleaning jewellery at home, except, obviously, for foiled jewellery which must never be allowed to get wet. For cleaning the setting of the latter, dry whitening powder brushed over the metal with a soft bristle toothbrush will suffice without damaging the foil in any way.

Repairs reminder

As jewellery repairs are not everyday occurrences, it is only too easy to forget the details of previous repairs, so it is worth keeping some form of 'track record', as suggested below. This will also help as a reminder when an item was last inspected or repaired.

Article	Date and Repair	Repairer	Cost	Remarks

THE JEWELLER'S TOOLS

There are many sophisticated instruments available for identifying gemstones in the laboratory – high-powered microscopes, X-ray equipment, and so on. The working jeweller needs few tools other than his own experienced eye. In the normal course of his day's work he would expect to use: a diamond gauge, which doubles on the reverse as a pearl gauge; a 10 x magnification lens; a magnifying eye-glass 2 x, 4 x or 6 x to choice; a pair of jewellery tongs; a Moe's gauge, diamond weight calculator, consisting of a pair of callipers with a scale and used in conjunction with a table; a Chelsea colour filter, which gives an indication of whether an emerald is genuine; a refractometer and possibly a pair of hand scales.

With these tools an experienced jeweller can get by. When estimating the weight of stones other than brilliant-cut stones, he has to rely on experience and will usually be accurate to within a carat or two for larger specimens. However, when it comes to identifying individual stones, difficulties can arise as many stones appear to be similar. To tell the difference between a spinel, garnet, ruby and tourmaline – or deep pink sapphire – can be difficult. Equally well, the difference between precious topaz, citrine, yellow sapphire or zircon might cause confusion in some cases. Therefore, when jewellers are dealing with each other they will accept without question, and on trust, the seller's description of the stone on the understanding that if it proves to be other than described, it can be returned. A mistake is seldom made, as when a jeweller buys a stone direct from a member of the public he will nearly always buy it subject to test, if it appears to be of sufficient importance. He will probably belong to the London Chamber of Commerce, whose gemmological section is second to none and whose opinion is universally accepted in the jewellery trade.

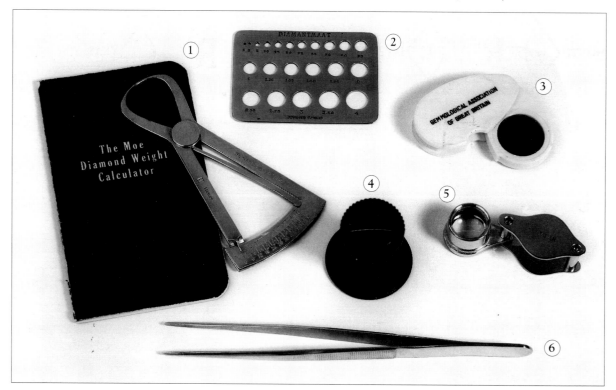

Plate 304.

1. Moe diamond weight calculator.
2. Diamond gauge which doubles on the reverse as a pearl gauge.
3. Chelsea colour filter.
4. Jeweller's eyeglass.
5. Lens with a magnification of ten times.
6. Pair of stone tongs.

REGISTRY MARKS

The British Patent Office used the two styles of Registry Mark shown below on British manufactured goods between 1842 and 1883. By knowing the code one can read the exact day, month and year when the article was registered. The letters were chosen at random, and starting in 1842 run as follows: X, H, C, A, I, F, U, S, V, P, D, Y, J, E, L, K, B, M, Z, R, O, G, N, W, Q, T. In 1868 the mark was changed fractionally, and followed the same sequence from X to K up to 1883 when this mark ceased and was replaced by numbers. The months were indicated by the following letters: C, G, W, H, E, M, I, R, D, B, K, A. R was used for 1–9 September 1857, K for December 1860, and G for 1–6 March 1868, the latter with W for the year.

From 1884 to 1900 serial numbers were used on registered designs. The first numbers in each year were as follows: 1884 – 1, 1885 – 19754, 1886 – 40480, 1887 – 64520, 1888 – 90483, 1889 – 11648, 1890 – 141273, 1891 – 163767, 1892 – 185713, 1893 – 205240, 1894 – 224720, 1895 – 246975, 1896 – 268392, 1897 – 291241, 1898 – 311658, 1899 – 331707, 1900 – 351202.

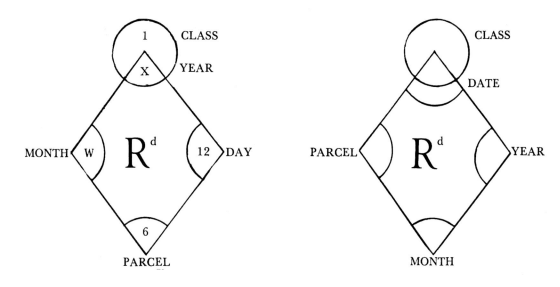

Registry mark used between 1842 and 1867. Example is for 12 March 1842.

Registry mark for 1868–1883.

Plate 305.

Enlargement of the British Registry Mark of the type used on manufactured goods between 1842 and 1883, this particular one is for 18 April 1871. See Plate 124.

HALLMARKS

Reproduced by kind permission of The Assay Offices of Great Britain

British hallmarks have acted as a safeguard to purchasers of gold and silver articles for over six centuries. The designs of individual marks have changed from time to time and new marks have been added, yet despite the many individual marks you may come across, hallmarking is still one of the most important forms of consumer protection. The consumer benefits in many ways under the Hallmarking Act of 1973. For example, it is an offence for any trader to sell or describe an article as gold, silver or platinum unless it has been hallmarked. (There are some exceptions, for example very small articles, certain specific items such as stone set gold rings and platinum articles if made before 1975, and all articles made before 1900.)

Why do I need protection?

Pure gold, silver and platinum are too soft to be used in jewellery or domestic articles and are normally alloyed with other metals. This lowers the intrinsic value and also raises the question of how much other metal has been added. It is impossible to tell what proportion of precious metal there is in any article without the help of chemical analysis. Colour alone is no guide, even brass can look like gold – especially if it has been plated with gold.

How do hallmarks protect me?

Hallmarks on an article show that it has been tested at one of the official Assay Offices which are incorporated by royal charter or by statute and are independent of any trade organisation. They certify that the metal used conforms to one of the legal standards of fineness or purity. The analyses are extremely accurate and are carried out on small samples removed from the articles before they have been finally polished.

What information do hallmarks give?

From 1 January 1999 a hallmark comprises a minimum of three compulsory symbols. These are:

Sponsor's Mark indicates the manufacturer or sponsor of the article. The mark consists of the initials of the person or firm and where two or more sponsors have the same initials there is a variation in the surrounding shield or style of letters.

Metal and Fineness (Purity) Mark guarantees the purity of the metal is at least that indicated by the Fineness Number – in an eight-sided lozenge for gold, oval for silver.

Assay Office Mark identifies the particular office at which the article was tested and marked. There are now four Assay Offices – in London, Birmingham, Sheffield and Edinburgh. Several of the larger provincial cities had Assay Offices which are now closed (see opposite).

In addition two voluntary hallmarks may also be struck:

Traditional Fineness Mark

Date Letter. After 1 January 1975 all four Assay Offices use the same date letter. (Date letters for the existing Assay Offices are given in the booklet *Hallmarks* which can be obtained by sending a stamped, addressed envelope to any Assay Office, see opposite.) To date earlier pieces you first have to identify the Assay Office mark. Earlier cycles of letters, as well as those for Assay Offices which have closed, can be found in various publications (see Bibliography under Bradbury, Culme, Jackson, and Grimwade).

Example of a hallmark showing, from left to right,
the Sponsor's Mark, the Metal and Fineness (Purity) Mark for silver, and
the London Assay Office mark.

Former Assay Office Marks

Of the former Assay Offices now closed, each had its distinctive mark, some of the more important of which are shown below. There is also an Assay Office in Dublin and marks struck there before 1 April 1923 are recognised as approved British hallmarks.

Chester   Dublin   Glasgow

Newcastle   Exeter

Further information

The addresses of the Assay Offices: (please send a stamped, addressed envelope when writing): The Assay Office, Goldsmiths' Hall, Gutter Lane, London EC2V 8AQ; The Assay Office, Newhall Street, Birmingham B3 1SB; The Assay Office, 137 Portobello Street, Sheffield S1 4DS or P.O. Box 187 Sheffield S1 4DS; The Assay Office, Goldsmiths' Hall, 39 Manor Place, Edinburgh EH3 7EB.

BIRTHSTONES RELATING TO THE
SIGNS OF THE ZODIAC

Many different versions are given and this list amalgamates some of them: the leading sign of the Zodiac is considered to be Aries.

Aries	March 21 – April 20	Diamond
Taurus	April 21 – May 20	Emerald and Coral
Gemini	May 21 – June 20	Pearl and Agate
Cancer	June 21 – July 21	Ruby and Moonstone
Leo	July 22 – August 21	Peridot and Amber
Virgo	August 22 – September 21	Sapphire and Jade
Libra	September 22 – October 22	Opal and Lapis Lazuli
Scorpio	October 23 – November 21	Topaz and Bloodstone
Sagittarius	November 22 – December 20	Turquoise
Capricorn	December 21 – January 19	Garnet and Malachite
Aquarius	January 20 – February 18	Amethyst and Jacinth
Pisces	February 19 – March 20	Aquamarine

GLOSSARY

ADULARESCENCE: Term applied to the milky sheen in moonstones.

AGGREGATES: Minerals which form without showing their outer crystal shape.

AIGRETTE: Hair ornament.

ALBERT: Watch chain.

ALEXANDRITE: Type of chrysoberyl, green in daylight and red in artificial light.

ALMANDINE: Purplish-red variety of garnet.

AMAZONITE: Opaque, blue and white coloured feldspar.

AMBROID: Small pieces of amber pressed together.

AMETHYST: Purple quartz.

AMORPHOUS: Without any crystal form.

ANGEL SKIN: Pale pink coral.

AQUAMARINE: Pale blue-green beryl.

ASTERISM: Term applied to the star effect seen in some stones, also known as 'star stones', e.g. star sapphire.

AVENTURINE GLASS: Artificial spangled glass, made to imitate green and golden aventurine quartz, and when golden in colour is known as 'goldstone'.

BAGUETTE: Elongated rectangular cut diamond.

BAKELITE: An artificial resin or plastic dyed in various colours to imitate natural stones.

BALAS RUBY: A term for red spinel, dating back to the Middle Ages.

BAROQUE: Refers to pearls of irregular form.

BASSE TAILLE: Form of engraving rays and two-dimensional designs into the back plate and building up the enamel in translucent layers to produce a shimmering effect.

BI-REFRINGENCE: The splitting of refracted light into two rays which give different readings on a refractometer. All crystals except those of the cubic system are bi-refringent and a measure of a stone's bi-refringence is helpful in identification. See also p.329.

BLISTER: Pearls which form in semi-circular shape, attached to the mantle of the oyster.

BLOODSTONE: Dark green variety of chalcedony (agate); speckled with red jasper.

BOG OAK: Black oak, preserved in peat, used in Victorian mourning jewellery.

BOWENITE: Yellowish-green form of the aggregate serpentine, sometimes confused with jade.

BRILLIANT-CUT: Form of diamond cutting with 58 facets.

BRIOLETTE: Form of cutting used for drop-shaped stones.

CABOCHON: Dome-shaped cut used for opaque and star-stones, and for precious stones of lesser quality.

CAIRNGORM: Name given to the clear brown or 'smoky' quartz crystals found in the Cairngorms in Scotland and used in Scottish jewellery.

CALIBRE-CUT: A method of cutting gemstones so they fit exactly into a tailored setting.

CAMEO: Form of cutting in relief, used particularly with agates and shells where the colour banding is incorporated in the carved design.

CANNETILLE: Form of filigree gold-work used in late 18th and early 19th century jewellery.

CARAT: 1) Method of describing the weight of stones. e.g. 5 carats = 1 gramme; see also p.330. 2) Ratio of precious metal to its alloys, divided into parts of 24, i.e. 18ct. gold is $\frac{2}{3}$ gold, $\frac{1}{3}$ alloy, and anything of 22cts. and over is considered 'fine' or pure gold.

CARBUNCLE: Cabochon-cut almandine garnet (deep purplish-red colour).

CAT'S EYE: Chatoyant variety of chrysoberyl. Other varieties of stones produce cat's eyes, but are normally prefixed by their particular species, e.g. quartz cat's eyes.

CHAMPLEVE: Early type of enamelling where different coloured molten enamel is poured into hollowed-out sections of the metal design.

CHATELAINE: Attachment to a lady's belt from which hung useful objects, e.g. keys, scissors, thimble, etc.

CHATOYANT: Term applied to the sharp band of whitish light which is reflected from the surface of some stones when cut *en cabochon*.

CHELSEA COLOUR FILTER: Filter used for identifying certain gemstones, particularly emeralds.

CHEMICAL COMPOSITION: See p.329.

CHRYSOLITE: Name given to pale yellow chrysoberyls, frequently used in 18th century Spanish and Portuguese jewellery.

CHRYSOPRASE: Pale green translucent variety of chalcedony (agate).

CITRINE: Yellow variety of quartz.

CLASSICAL: Should refer to the Greek and Roman eras, sometimes used loosely to denote 'in the Classical style' when referring to 18th and 19th century craftsmanship.

CLEAN: Stones with no flaws visible under a 10x lens.

CLOISONNE: Early type of enamelling where the design is formed by soldering metal thread to a metal plate and the enamel then applied and polished flat.

CLOSED BACK: Jewellery which is set with stones in 'cups' of metal so that the reverse of the stone is not visible. Stones in closed settings are backed with a layer of coloured foil or painted in order to heighten the colour.

COLLET: Band of metal in which a gemstone is set.

CORNELIAN: Translucent orange variety of chalcedony (agate).

CORSAGE: Jewellery attached to the bodice of a dress, generally fairly large pieces.

CORUNDUM: Gem species of rubies and sapphires.

CROCIDOLITE: Asbestos which has been fossilised into quartz.

CROWN: The top half of a brilliant-cut stone, i.e. the

part above the girdle.

CRYSTAL: A piece of material whose atomic structure is reflected in its outer form, which for definition purposes has been divided into one of seven different crystal formations according to its regularity. See also p.329.

CULET: The bottom facet of a brilliant-cut stone.

CUSHION-CUT: Old form of brilliant-cut, developed in the late 17th century by Peruzzi in Venice.

DEAD PAWN: Unclaimed pieces of American Indian jewellery.

DEAR: See Regard.

DEMANTOID: Bright grass-green coloured garnet.

DOUBLET: Two pieces of stone stuck together in imitation of pieces of better quality or size. In the case of opal, a thin piece of precious opal is backed with opal matrix. Doublets may be 'true doublets', i.e. they are made of the natural stone, or they may be simulants, or even a mixture of both.

ELECTRUM: A natural alloy of gold and silver, used by the Greeks.

EMERALD-CUT: See Step-Cut.

EN TREMBLANT: See Tremblant

EROTES: Greek name for cherubs.

ESSENCE D'ORIENT: Substance made from fish-scales used for coating artificial pearls, simulating the lustre of nacre.

ESSEX CRYSTAL: Rock crystal, cut en cabochon with a design engraved and painted on the reverse, popular in the Victorian era.

FAIENCE: Glazed earthenware, also used for making beads, scarabs, etc. from the Egyptian period onwards.

FANCY-COLOURED: Any colour in a stone other than its expected normal colour, e.g. sapphires other than 'blue' and diamonds other than 'white'.

FANCY-CUTS: Any cut of a stone other than the normal expected cut.

FEDE: Ring formed from two clasped hands; probably a betrothal ring since Roman times when this symbol represented a contract.

FELDSPAR: Gem family, best known in jewellery as moonstones, sunstones, labradorite and amazonite.

FILIGREE: Metal work formed of fine wires twisted into ornate patterns.

FLAT-CUT: Form of cutting a tablet of stone with a large flat top surface.

FLORENTINE WORK: Form of inlay in jewellery using sections of differently coloured hardstone and ivory to create designs.

FOILING: See Closed Back.

FOSSILISED: Objects which have been turned to stone, sometimes used in jewellery, e.g. petrified wood.

FRENCH JET: Black glass jewellery imitating jet.

GALLERY: Strip of pierced metal used to make settings for rings.

GIRANDOLE: A popular 18th century design of jewellery with swinging pear-shaped drops on pendants, brooches and earrings.

GIRDLE: Widest part of a brilliant-cut stone, between the crown and the pavilion, usually partly hidden when the stone is set.

GOLDSTONE: Gold-spangled glass imitating aventurine quartz.

GRISAILLE: See Limoges Enamel.

GROSSULAR GARNET: Type of garnet, the green variety of which is used to simulate jade, known as 'Transvaal jade'.

GUTTA PERCHA: Glutinous resin from trees, used by Indian craftsmen in the manufacture of jewellery.

GYPSY-SET: Stones set deeply into the metal mount.

HALLEY'S COMET: Comet which appears every 76 years, named after Halley in 1759 following its appearance in 1758. It was recorded in 1834, 1910 and 1986 and jewellery in the form of a comet was made, particularly in 1834, in commemoration.

HARDNESS: See p.329.

HARDSTONE: Normally applied to decorative opaque stones used for inlay work or cameos, e.g. lapis lazuli, agates, jades.

HEAT TREATMENT: Some stones when heated change colour or deepen their existing colour which makes them more attractive, and more saleable.

HELIODOR: Golden-coloured beryl.

HOLBEINESQUE: 19th century jewellery in the Renaissance style, after Holbein.

IMITATION: One material simulating another of different substance.

IMPERIAL JADE: Highly prized jadeite of a brilliant translucent green.

INCLUSIONS: Faults in the natural crystal which may take the form of gas bubbles, liquid-filled cavities or small crystals, which help to identify the type and source of the stone.

INTAGLIO: Cutting into stone; reverse of cameo cutting.

IRIDESCENCE: Shimmering effect of rainbow-like colours which change with the light; opals, labradorite, butterflies' wings and oil all show iridescence.

IVORINE: Plastic or bakelite simulating ivory.

JACINTHS: Yellow, orange and red zircons, sometimes also called hyacinths.

JADEITE: Greenish opaque stone varying from a brilliant translucent green to white, usually known as 'jade' and confused with nephrite, which is generally less valuable and varies in colour.

JARDINIERE: In the form of a floral arrangement (from the Italian giardinetto – little garden).

JARGOON: Name for white sapphires and white zircons in Indian jewellery, a term sometimes incorrectly applied to rose-cut diamonds.

JASPER: A form of agate, an opaque rusty-red colour.

LABRADORITE: Type of feldspar first found in Labrador, exhibiting bluish-green iridescence on a grey background, popular in art nouveau jewellery.

351

LAVA: Light, porous volcanic material carved and set in 19th century jewellery.

LIGNUM VITAE: A particularly hard wood.

LIMOGES ENAMEL: Enamels painted in grisaille (black, white and greyish tints), perfected at Limoges, often taking the form of portrait enamels in the Renaissance style.

MABE PEARLS: The cultured pearl version of blister pearls. The hollow semi-circular pearl is filled with wax and backed with mother-of-pearl. Mabé means half in Japanese.

MADEIRA CITRINE: Deep brownish-orange citrine.

MATRIX: Parent rock in which the gemstone is found, occasionally incorporated in pieces of jewellery, particularly with carved turquoise and opal.

MEMENTO MORI: Literally 'Memory of the Dead'. Applied to Medieval and Renaissance memorial jewellery.

METAMORPHOSIS: The changing of one substance into another, associated with volcanic activity on pre-existing rocks or materials, e.g. asbestos fibres underwent metamorphosis to become crocidolite.

MILLED: Type of setting popular in Edwardian jewellery, also known as *millegrain*.

MIXED-CUT: Brilliant-cut crown and step-cut pavilion of a stone, commonly used for semi-precious coloured stones.

MORGANITE: Pink coloured beryl.

MUTTON-FAT JADE: Whitish coloured nephrite.

NACRE: The fine surface layers of a pearl, or mother-of-pearl – the inside layer of the shell.

NATIVE-CUT: Stones cut at source, particularly in India and Sri Lanka.

NEPHRITE: Opaque stone varying from dark green to white to brown, sometimes confused with jadeite as both are termed 'jade'.

NIELLO: Engraved design filled with black metal alloy.

NON-NUCLEATED: Freshwater cultured pearls which apparently have no core, the small piece of mantle originally inserted to start the nacreous process having dissolved before the pearl is formed completely.

OLD-CUT: Diamond cut with a higher crown, a smaller table and a bigger culet than the modern brilliant-cut.

OLIVINE: Mineral name for peridot.

ONYX: Brown and black chalcedony (agate).

OPALESCENCE: Flashes of rainbow colours seen against the milky background of white opals.

OPAQUE: Impervious to light.

OPEN-BACKED: Form of setting jewellery where the stones can be seen from the reverse.

OPEN-WORK: Form of setting jewellery where stones are set in an open design determined by the metal; the opposite of pavé setting.

PARCEL-GILT: Silver partly overlaid with gold.

PARIS JET: Black glass imitating jet.

PARURE: A suite of jewellery designed to be worn at the same time; typically necklace, earrings, brooches and bracelet.

PASTE: Jewellery set with glass instead of real stones.

PATE DE VERRE: Powdered glass, moulded, fired and enamelled lightly, a material used in art nouveau jewellery.

PAVE : Form of setting where the stones are adjacent to one another with the minimum of metal showing on the surface.

PAVILION: Lower part of a cut stone, below the girdle.

PECTORAL: Jewellery worn on the chest, usually associated with ancient jewellery.

PENDELOQUE-CUT: Cutting in the form of a pear or tear; also known as pear-cut.

PINCHBECK: Alloy of zinc and copper developed by Christopher Pinchbeck and used instead of gold in less expensive jewellery of the late 18th and early 19th centuries.

PIQUE WORK: The inlay of tortoiseshell with silver and gold in fine and intricate designs.

PLAQUE-CUT: Cut in flat tablets, for engraving seals, etc.

PLAY OF COLOUR: Synonymous with iridescence and opalescence.

PLIQUE-A-JOUR: Form of enamelling when enamels are set in open metal frames, particularly popular with French art nouveau jewellery.

QUARTZ TOPAZ: Yellow or brown citrine (quartz), and not true topaz.

REFRACTIVE INDEX (R.I.): Method of identifying a gemstone by measuring the angle at which the light rays are optically bent when entering a stone. See also p.329.

REGARD (DEAR): Brooch, ring, etc., made up of stones whose initial letters spell the word, e.g. Ruby, Emerald, Garnet, Amethyst, Ruby, Diamond.

REPOUSSE: Metal which has been pushed into a raised design from the reverse.

(R.I.): See Refractive Index.

ROSE-CUT DIAMONDS: Refers to the cut, not the colour.

RUBELITE: Red coloured tourmaline.

RUTILE: Mineral found in quartz, forming in long strands, when it is known as Venus hairstone.

SAINT ESPRIT: Symbol of the Holy Ghost in the form of a dove holding an olive branch or a sprig of forget-me-nots. Appears in pendant form only.

SARDONYX: Banded form of chalcedony (agate).

SATSUMA: Japanese glazed earthenware, finely over-painted and gilded, particularly associated with the 18th and 19th centuries.

SCARABS: Beetles worn as amulets by the Egyptians, their form imitated in various materials such as faïence and cornelian. Also found in Roman jewellery.

SERPENTINE: An aggregate carved more frequently as *objets d'art* than jewellery, although bowenite is one kind which is used to simulate jade.

(S.G.): See Specific Gravity.

SHOULDERS: The top half of a ring shank, on either side of a cluster or single stone.

SILK: Whitish reflection or inclusion, seen particularly in sapphires and Burma rubies.

SOUDE: Triplet of quartz and green gelatine, usually simulating emerald.

SPECIFIC GRAVITY (S.G.): Measurement of the density of gemstones, helpful as an identification test. See also p.329.

SPINACH JADE: Dark green spinach-coloured nephrite.

STEATITE: Soapstone, sometimes used to imitate pale-coloured jade.

STEP-CUT: Form of cutting in horizontal layered bands, used for coloured stones; identical to emerald- and trap-cut.

STOMACHER: Large brooch worn centrally, usually pinned to the bodice of a dress, often made with detachable pendant sections and drops.

STOVE-ENAMELLED: Enamelling at very low temperature.

STRAPWORK: Formal geometrical banded designs of the Renaissance and 16th century.

STRASS: French jeweller who perfected the manufacture of white glass and developed high quality paste jewellery in the 18th century.

STYLE OF: In the manner of a known craftsman or artist, but unsigned or authenticated.

SUNSTONE: Spangled orange-yellow type of feldspar.

SYNTHETIC: Gemstone of identical chemical composition as the natural stone but produced in the laboratory, whereas an imitation may be made of anything but look like the natural stone at first glance.

TABLE: Flat top facet of a brilliant- or step-cut stone.

TASSIE: 18th century Scottish seal and intaglio moulder making paste medallions in the antique style.

TORQUE: Prehistoric Irish neck or wrist ornament.

TOUR-A-GUILLOCHER: See Basse Taille.

TRANSLUCENT: Allowing light to pass through, but not transparent.

TRANSVAAL JADE: A dark green opaque form of grossular garnet which looks like jade.

TRAP-CUT: See Step-Cut.

TREMBLANT: Parts of a brooch set with a spring behind to give a shimmering effect and movement are said to be *en tremblant*.

TRIPLETS: Three pieces of stone stuck together in layers to imitate a finer stone, e.g. triplet opals are made of a thin surface layer of glass or crystal covering a piece of black opal, and backed with opal matrix.

VAUXHALL GLASS: Black glass imitating jet, or coloured glass with a mirrored back.

VENUS HAIRSTONE: Rock crystal with long hair-like inclusion of reddish-gold rutile.

VERNEUIL: Chemist who developed a process for the synthesis of corundum and spinel.

VERRE EGLOMISE: Glass which is painted from the reverse, usually with gold or black, popular in the Renaissance and 16th century.

VINAIGRETTE: Small container of silver or gold with a sponge soaked in aromatic vinegar to ward off evil smells.

WEDGWOOD: Staffordshire potter whose factory produced jasper-ware, blue, green and black with applied white decoration. In jewellery, popularly made as cameos in the late 18th and early 19th centuries in the neo-classical style.

WINDOWS: Directions of transparency and little colour in coloured stones, particularly sapphires.

BIBLIOGRAPHY

222 Jahre Zeichenakademie Hanau, Stuttgart, 1995.

ACIDINI-LUCHINAT, C., *Treasures of Florence*, Munich, 1997.

ALDRED, CYRIL, *Jewels of the Pharaohs*, London, 1971.

AMAYA, M., *Art Nouveau*, London, 1966.

ANDREWS, C., *Ancient Egyptian Jewellery*, London, 1996.

ANTIQUE COLLECTORS' CLUB, *Guide to the Antique Shops of Britain*, annually.

ANTONOVA, I., TOLSTIKOV, V., AND TREISTER, M., *The Gold of Troy*, London, 1996.

ARMSTRONG, NANCY, *Jewellery, an Historical Survey of British Styles and Jewels*, London, 1973.

BAKER, L., *Hatpins and Hatpin Holders*, Atglen, 1998; *100 Years of Collectible Jewellery*, Paducah, 1983; *20th Century Fashionable Plastic Jewelry*, Collectors Books, 1992; *50 Years of Collectible Fashion Jewelry*, Paducah, 1986.

BALFOUR, I., *Famous Diamonds*, N.A.G. Press, London.

BALL, J., *Costume Jewelers*, Atglen, 1997.

BALL, J., AND TOREM, D., *Masterpieces of Costume Jewelry*, Atglen, 1996.

BALL, S.H., *A Roman Book on Precious Stones*, Los Angeles, 1951.

BARTEN, S., *René Lalique*, Prestel, Munich.

BARTHELEMY, A., *Tazra: Bijoux et Tapis de Quarzazate*, Aix en Provence, 1990.

BATTLE, D., AND LESSER, A., *The Best of Bakelite*, Atglen, 1996.

BAUER, J. AND A., *A Book of Jewels*, London, 1966.

BECK, R.J., REED, A.H., AND REED, A.W., *New Zealand Jade: the Story of Greenstone*, New Zealand, 1971.

BECKER, *Friedrich Becker*, Arnoldsche, Stuttgart, 1988.

BECKER, V., *Antique and Twentieth Century Jewellery*, N.A.G. Press, London; *Art Nouveau Jewellery*, London, 1986; *Fabulous Costume Jewellery*, Schiffer, West Chester; *The Jewellery of René Lalique*, London, 1987.

BECKER, V., ETC., *Jewels of Fantasy*, Abrams, New York.

BENNETT, DAVID, AND MASCETTI, DANIELA, *Understanding Jewellery*, Woodbridge, 1989, rev. ed. 1994.

BENNETT, E.M., *Turquoise and the Indian*, Chicago, 1970.

BLAKEMORE, K., *Collecting Gems and Ornamental Stones*, London, 1966.

BOARDMAN, J., *Engraved Gems*, London, 1968; *Intaglios and Rings*, London, 1975.

BOARDMAN, J., AND SCARISBRICK, D., *The Ralph Harari Collection of Finger Rings*, Thames & Hudson, London.

BOREL, *The Splendour of Ethnic Jewelry*, London, 1995.

BOYER, M., *Mongol Jewellery*, London, 1995.

BRADBURY, *Bradbury's Book of Hallmarks*, J.W. Northend Ltd. Sheffield.

BRADFORD, E., *English Victorian Jewellery*, Feltham, 1967; *Four Centuries of European Jewellery*, Feltham, 1967.

BRAY, W., *The Gold of Eldorado*, London, 1978.

BRUNHAMMER, Y., ET AL., *The Jewels of Lalique*, New York, 1998.

BRUTON, E., *Diamonds*, N.A.G. Press, London; *Legendary Gems or Gems that made History*, N.A.G. Press, London; *The True Book about Diamonds*, London, 1961.

BURKHOLZ, M., *The Bakelite Collection*, Atglen, 1997.

BURKHOLZ, M., AND KAPLAN, L., *Copper Art Jewelry*, Schiffer, West Chester.

BURY, SHIRLEY, *Jewellery 1789–1910 The International Era*, 2 vols., Woodbridge, 1991.

BUTOR, *Adornment*, London, 1995.

BUXBAUM, G., AND WEBER, C., *Fashion and Jewelry 1920–1970*, Stuttgart, 1995.

CARTIER, *Capolavori di Cartier*, Naples, 1988.

CAUNT, P., *Military Sweethearts*, London, 1995.

CAVALCANTI, O., *Ori Antichi di Calabria*, Palermo, 1991.

CERA, DEANNA FARNETI, *Costume Jewellery*, Woodbridge, 1998; *The Jewels of Miriam Haskell*, Woodbridge, 1998.

CHADOUR, A., *Rings: Forty Centuries as viewed by Four Generations*, Leeds, 1995.

CHALMERS, R.O., *Australian Rocks, Minerals and Gemstones*, Sydney, 1966.

CHAUMET, *Chaumet Paris: Deux Siécles de Création*, Paris, 1998.

CLIFFORD, ANNE, *Cut-Steel and Berlin Iron Jewellery*, Bath, 1971.

CLIFFORD, D., *Anne Clifford's Antique Jewellery*, London, 1985.

COLOGNI, F., AND NUSSBAUM, E., *Platinum by Cartier*, New York, 1995.

CONTENT, D., *Islamic Rings and Gems*, London, 1987.

COOPER, C.W., *The Precious Stones of the Bible*, London, 1924.

CRANFORD, A., *By Hammered Hand*, Birmingham, 1984.

CRAWFORD, A., *C.R. Ashbee*, London, 1985.

CULME, JOHN, *The Directory of Gold and Silversmiths, Jewellers and Allied Traders from the London Assay Office Registers*, 2 vols., Woodbridge, 1987.

CUMMINS, GENEVIEVE E., AND TAUNTON, NERYLLA D., *Chatelaines – Utility to Glorious Extravagance*, Woodbridge, 1994.

CURRAN, M., *Jewels and Gems*, London, 1961.

DAVIDOV, C., AND DAWES, G., *The Bakelite Jewelry Book*, New York, 1988; *Victorian Jewelry*, New York, 1993.

DAVIS, M., AND PACK, G., *Mexican Jewelry*, Sustin, 1982.

DAY LEWIS, F., *Enamelling*, London, 1907.

DELAROZIERE, M., *Perles d'Afrique*, Aix en Provence, 1994.

DICKENSON, J.Y., *The Book of Pearls*, New York, 1968.

D'OREY, L., *Five Centuries of Jewellery*, London, 1995.

DORMER, P., AND TURNER, R., *The New Jewelry*, London, 1994.

DOUGHTY, O., *Early Diamond Days: The Opening of the Diamond Fields of South Africa*, London, 1963.

DRUCKER, J., *Georg Jensen*, Atglen, 1997.

DUBBS BALL, J., *Jewelry of the Stars*, Schiffer, West Chester.

DUBIN, L., *The History of Beads*, London, 1984 and 1996.

DUNCAN, ALASTAIR. *The Paris Salons 1895–1914 Vols I & II: Jewellery*, Woodbridge, 1994.

EGGER, G., *Generations of Jewelry*, Schiffer, West Chester.

ENGLISH, H., AND DORMER, P., *Jewelry of our Times*, London, 1995.

ERIKSON, J., *The Universal Bead*, New York, 1993.

ESMERIAN, R., ETC., *Daniel Brush*, New York, 1998.

ETTINGER, R., *Popular Jewelry of the 60s, 70s and 80s*, Atglen, 1997; *Forties and Fifties Popular Jewelry*, Schiffer, West Chester; *Popular Jewelry, 1840–1940*, Schiffer, 1997.

EVANS, JOAN, *English Jewellery from the Fifth Century to 1800*, London, 1921; *Magical Jewels of the Middle Ages and the Renaissance*, Oxford, 1922; *A History of Jewellery, 1100–1870* (full bibliography), London and New York, 1923, rev. ed. London, 1970.

EVANS, I.O., *Rocks, Minerals and Gemstones*, London, 1971.

EYLES, W.C., *The Book of Opals*, U.S.A. and Japan, 1964.

FALES, MARTHA GANDY, *Jewelry in America 1600–1900*, Woodbridge, 1995.

FALKINER, RICHARD, *Investing in Antique Jewellery*, Barrie and Jenkins.

FICHTNER, S., AND RUSSELL, L., *Rainbow of Rhinestone Jewelry*, Atglen, 1996.

FIELD, *The Jewels of Queen Elizabeth II*, Thames & Hudson, London.

FLOWER, MARGARET, *Victorian Jewellery*, London and New York, 1951, rev. ed. London 1967.

FODOR, ETC., *Baroque Splendor*, New York, 1994.

FORBES, C., *Fabergé Eggs*, New York, 1995.

FRANCIS, P., *Beads of the World*, Schiffer, West Chester.

FRANK, J., *The Beauty of Jewellery*, London, 1979.

FREDRIKSON, N., *The Covenant Chain*, Ottawa, 1980.

GABARDI, MELISSA, *Art Deco Jewellery*, Woodbridge, 1985.

GARRARD, T., *Gold of Africa*, Prestel, Munich.

GASKIN, *Arthur and George Gaskin*, Birmingham, 1982.

GAUTIER, G., *Cartier the Legend*, Arlington Press, London, 1983.

GERE, CHARLOTTE, *Victorian Jewellery Design*, London, 1972; *European and American Jewellery, 1830–1914*, London, 1975.

GERE, CHARLOTTE, AND MUNN, GEOFFREY, *Pre-Raphaelite to Arts & Crafts Jewellery*, Woodbridge, 1996.

GERLACH, MARTIN (ED.), *Primitive and Folk Jewellery*, Dover Books (reissue of a German work of 1906).

GOODCHILD, W., *Precious Stones*, London, 1908.

GORDON, A., *Twentieth Century Costume Jewellery*, London, 1990.

GRANDJEAN, S., ASHENGREEN, K., ETC., *The Waddesdon Collection*, Philip Wilson, London.

GRASSO, T., *Bakelite Jewellery*, London, 1995.

GREEN, A., AND DYETT, L., *Secrets of Aromatic Jewelry*, London, 1998.

GREENBAUM, J., *Messengers of Modernism*, London, 1997.

GREGIORETTI, G., *Jewellery through the Ages*, London, 1969.

GREINDL, G., *Gems of Costume Jewelry*, New York, 1994.

GRIMALDI, D., *Amber*, New York, 1996.

GRIMWADE, ARTHUR G., *London Goldsmiths 1697–1837, Their Marks and Their Lives*, Faber & Faber, London.

GUBELIN, E., *The Colour Treasury of Gemstones*, London,

HAERTIG, E., *Antique Combs and Purses*, Gallery Graphics Press, Carmel.

HENIG, M., *The Content Cameos*, Oxford, 1990.

HERMAN, L., *Georg Jensen Silversmith*, Washington D.C., 1980.

HICKLING, J., *Practical Jewellery Repairs*, N.A.G. Press, London.

HIGGINS, R.A., *Greek and Roman Jewellery*, London, 1961.

HO, L.Y., *Collecting Jadeite*, Millbank, London.

HOFFMANN, H., AND DAVIDSON, P.F., *Greek Gold*, Brooklyn Museum, 1965.

HUGHES, G., *Modern Jewelry*, London, 1963, 2nd ed. 1964; *The Art of Jewelry*, London, 1972; *Georg Jensen 1866–1966*, Copenhagen, 1966.

JACKSON, *Jackson's Silver and Gold Marks of Scotland and Ireland*, ed. Ian Pickford, Woodbridge, 1999.

JACKSON, *Pocket Edition Jackson's Hallmarks*, ed. Ian Pickford, Woodbridge, 1999.

JARGSTORF, S., *Glass in Jewelry*, Atglen, 1998; *Baubles, Buttons and Beads*, Schiffer, West Chester; *Glass Beads from Europe*, West Chester, 1995.

JARVIS, C., *Jewellery Manufacture and Repair*, N.A.G. Press, London.

JESSOP, R., *Anglo Saxon Jewellery*, New York, 1953.

JESSUP, RONALD, *Anglo-Saxon Jewellery*, London, 1950.

JEWEL, *The Jewel – Sign and Symbolism*, Antwerp, 1995.

JOANNIS, C., *Bijoux des Régions de France*, Paris, 1992.

JOHNS, K., *The Snettisham Roman Jeweller's Hoard*, London, 1997.

JONAS, S., AND NISSENSON, M., *Cuff Links*, Abrams, New York.

JONES, K., *A Silversmith's Manual*, N.A.G. Press, London.

JOYCE AND ADDISON, *Pearls*, Thames & Hudson, London.

KABYLIE, G., AND FABER, H., *Bijoux Berbères d'Algérie*, Aix en Provence, 1990.

KAGAN, JU, *Western European Cameos in the Hermitage Collection*, Leningrad, 1973.

KALIS, L., *The Nasser Khalili Collection of Islamic Art, Vol. XIII*, London, 1996.

KARLIN, E., *Jewelry and Metalwork*, West Chester, 1994.

KELLEY, L., AND SCHIFFER, N., *Costume Jewelry*, Schiffer, Atglen; *Plastic Jewelry Revised*, Schiffer, West Chester.

KOCH, M., AND POSSEME, E., ETC., *The Belle Epoque of French Jewellery*, London, 1985.

KOCTJUK, O., *Gold of the Tsars*, Stuttgart, 1995.

KONINGIN, F., *Contemporary Belgian Jewellery 1945–1995*, Antwerp, 1997.

KREUZER, K., *Gurtelschliessen des Jugendstils*, Munich, 1988.

LANE, K., AND MILLER, H., *Kenneth Jay Lane*, New York, 1996.

LEECHMAN, F., *The Opal Book*, Sydney, 1975.

LEVIN, *American Art Jewelry Today*, Thames & Hudson, London.

LEWIS, M.D.S., *Antique Paste Jewellery*, London, 1970.

LIETHE-JASPER, M., AND DISTELBERGER, R., *The Kunsthistorisches Museum, Vienna*, Philip Wilson, London.

LIGHTBOWN, R., *Mediaeval European Jewellery*, London, 1992.

LINDENBERG, J., *Collecting Plastic Jewelry*, Atglen, 1996.

LIU, R., *Collectible Beads*, London, 1996.

LYNLEE, J., *All that Glitters*, West Chester, 1984.

MACK, J., *Ethnic Jewellery*, British Museum, London.

MARQUARDT, B., *Schmuck*, Munich, 1983.

MARSHALL, F.H., *Catalogue of the Jewellery, Greek, Etruscan and Roman in the British Museum*, London, 1911; *Catalogue of Finger Rings, Greek, Etruscan and Roman in the British Museum*.

MARTIN, S., ETC., *Archibald Knox*, London, 1995.

MASCETTI, D., AND TRIOSSI, A., *Earrings*, London, 1990; *Bulgari*, New York, 1996.

MASSINELLI, A., AND ELEUTERI, L., *Twentieth Century Jewelry*, New York, 1996.

MATLINS, A., AND BONNANO, A., *Engagement and Wedding Rings*, Woodbridge, 1996; *Jewelry and Gems: The Buying Guide*, Woodbridge, 1996.

MAURIES, P., *Jewelry by Chanel*, London, 1993.

MAXWELL-HYSLOP, K.R., *Western Asiatic Jewellery*, Methuen.

MAZLAUM, C., *Jewellery and Gemstones*, Rome, 1990.

MILLER, A., *Cameos Old and New*, New York, 1991.

MORILL, P., *Silver Masters of Mexico*, Atglen, 1996.

MORILL, P., AND BERK, C., *Mexican Silver*, West Chester, 1994

MORO, G., *European Designer Jewelry*, West Chester, 1995

MOUREY, G., *Art Nouveau Jewellery and Fans*, Dover, New York.

MULVAGH, J., *Costume Jewelry in Vogue*, London, 1988.

MUNN, GEOFFREY, *Castellani and Giuliano*, London, 1984.

MUNN, J., *The Triumph of Love*, London, 1993.

NADELHOFFER, H., *Cartier Jewellers Extraordinary*, London, 1988.

NAYLOR, GILLIAN, *The Arts and Crafts Movement*, London, 1971.

NEUWIRTH, W., *Beads from Gablonz*, Vienna, 1994; *Perlen aus Gablonz. Historismus Jugendstil*, Vienna, 1994.

NEWMAN, H., *An Illustrated History of Jewellery*, London, 1982.

NISSENSON, M., AND JONAS, S., *Snake Charm*, New York, 1995.

NOTT, S.C., *Chinese Jade Throughout the Ages*, London, 1937.

O'DAY, D., *Victorian Jewellery*, London, 1974.

O'DONOGHUE, M., *Identifying Man-made Gems*, N.A.G. Press, London.

OMAN, C.C., *Victoria and Albert Museum Catalogue of Rings, 1930*.

OSBORNE, P., *Button Button*, Schiffer, Atglen; *Fun Buttons*, Schiffer, Atglen.

PERRY, N., AND PERRY, R., *Australian Gemstones in Colour*, Sydney, 1967.

PETER, MARY, *Collecting Victorian Jewellery*, London, 1970.

PFROMMER, M., *Metalwork from the Hellenized East*, Santa Monica, 1993.

PHILLIPS, C., *Jewelry*, 1996.

PIERRES, *Les Pierres Précieuses*, Tardy Paris.

POGUE, J.E., *The Turquoise*, Washington, D.C., 1915; reprinted with additions, New Mexico, 1973.

POINÇONS, *Poinçons d'Or et de Platine*, Tardy Paris.

PRESTON WHYTE & MORRIS, *Speaking with Beads*, Thames & Hudson, London.

PRODDOW, P., AND FASEL, M., *Diamonds*, New York, 1996.

QUICK, L., *The Book of Agates*, London, 1963.

RABATE, J., AND M., *Bijoux Marocains*, Aix en Provence, 1996.

RAINWATER, D., *American Jewelry Manufacturers*, Schiffer, West Chester.

RAULET, S., *Art Deco Jewellery*, London, 1986; *Jewelry of the 1940s and 1950s*, London, 1988.

READ, C.H., *The Waddesdon Bequest. Catalogue of the Works of Art*, London, 1902.

ROSS, M.C., *Fabergé and his Contemporaries*, Cleveland Museum of Art, 1965.

RUDOE, J., *Cartier 1900–1939*, London, 1997.

RUDOLF M., *Naum Slutzky*, Stuttgart, 1989.

RUTLAND, E.H., *An Introduction to the Gemstones of the World*, London and U.S.A., 1974.

SARPELLON, G., *Miniature Masterpieces: Mosaic Glass 1838–1924*, Munich, 1995.

SCARISBRICK, D., *Rings*, Thames & Hudson, London; *Chaumet*, London, 1995; *Tudor and Jacobean Jewellery*, London, 1996; *Jewellery in Britain 1066–1837*, London, 1994.

SCHADT, H., *Goldsmith's Art*, Stuttgart, 1995.

SCHIFFER, N., *The Best of Costume Jewelry*, Schiffer, West Chester; *Costume Jewelry*, Schiffer, Atglen; *The Power of Jewelry*, Schiffer, West Chester; *Silver Jewelry Designs*, Atglen, 1996; *Fun Jewelry*, Schiffer, West Chester; *Handbook of Fine Jewelry*, Schiffer, West Chester; *Rhinestones*, Schiffer, West Chester; *Silver Jewelry Treasures*, Schiffer, West Chester.

SCHIFFER, P., *Indian Jewelry on the Market*, Atglen, 1996.

SCHMUNDT, U., WEBER, C., AND BECKER, I., *Theodor Fahrner Jewelry*, Schiffer, West Chester.

SCHMUTTERMEIER, *Cast Iron from Central Europe 1800–1850*, New York, 1994.

SCHOFIELD, A., AND FAHY, K., *Australian Jewellery*, Woodbridge, 1986.

SCHUMANN, W., *Gemstones of the World*, N.A.G. Press, London.

SETHOM, S., *Le Bijoux traditionnel en Tunisie*, Aix en Provence, 1986.

SHEPHERD, W., *Gold and Silversmithing in New Zealand*, Wellington, 1995.

SINGER, J., *Gold Jewelry from Tibet and Nepal*, London, 1996.

SITWELL, H.D.W., *The Crown Jewels*, London, 1953.

SKELTON, R. *The Nasser Khalili Collection of Islamic Art. Vol. XVIII*, London, 1996.

SNIDER, N., *Sweetheart Jewelry and Collectibles*, West Chester, 1995.

SNOWMAN, K., *The Art of Carl Fabergé*, London, 1953; *Fabergé Lost and Found*, London, 1994; *Eighteenth Century Gold Boxes of Europe*, Woodbridge, 1990.

SOMMERS-COOK, A., AND TRUMAN, C., *Renaissance Jewels, Gold Boxes and Objects de Vertu*, Philip Wilson, London.

SOTHEBY, *Guilhou Collection of Rings*, 9 November, 1937.

SPICE, J., *Ancient Gems and Finger Rings*, Santa Monica, 1994.

STREETER, EDWIN, *Precious Stones and Gems*, London, 1877.

SWARBRICK, J., *Jewellery*, London, 1996.

TABURIAUX, J., *Pearls*, N.A.G. Press, London

TILBROOK, A., *The Designs of Archibald Knox for Liberty & Co.*, Richard Dennis, Shepton Beauchamp.

TILLANDER, H., *Diamond Cuts in Historic Jewellery 1381–1910*, Art Books International, 1996.

TOPHAM, J., *Traditional Crafts of Saudi Arabia*, Stacey Int., London.

TRAINA, J., *The Fabergé Case*, New York, 1998.

TRIOSSI, A., AND MASCETTI, D., *The Necklace*, London, 1997.

TURNBAUGH, W., AND S., *Indian Jewelry of the American Southwest*, Atglen, 1996.

UNTRACHT, O., *Jewelry Concepts and Technology*, N.A.G. Press, London; *Traditional Jewellery of India*, London, 1997.

VAUTRIN, L., AND MAURIES, *Line Vautrin*, Thames & Hudson, London.

VEVER II, *La Bijouterie Française au XIXme Siècle*, Editioni Scolte, Florence.

VON HAPSBERG, G., AND LOPATO, M., *Fabergé Imperial Jeweller*, London, 1993.

VON HASSE, U., *Schmuck in Deutschland und Österreich 1895–1914*, Munich, 1977.

WASSERSTRÖM, D., AND PINA, L., *Bakelite Jewelry*, Atglen, 1997.

WEBER, C., *Schmuck*, Arnoldsche, Stuttgart.

WEBSTER, ROBERT, *Gems*, London, 1975; *Gemologist's Compendium*, N.A.G. Press, London; *Practical Gemology*, N.A.G. Press, London.

WENZEL, M., *The Nasser Khalili Collection of Islamic Art Vol XVI*, London, 1996.

WILKINSON, ALEX, *Ancient Egyptian Jewellery*, Methuen.

WILLIAMS, D., *The Art of the Greek Goldsmith*, London, 1998.

WILLIAMS, D., AND OGDEN, J., *Greek Gold*, London, 1995.

WILLIAMSON, C.G., *The Book of Amber*, London, 1932.

WILSON, H., *Silverwork and Jewellery*, London, 1931.

WITHERS, S., *Fashion Beads*, London, 1996.

ZAPATA, J., *The Jewelry and Enamels of Louis Comfort Tiffany*, London, 1993.

ZUCKER, B., *Gems and Jewels*, London, 1984.

INDEX

The frequency with which some gemstones, materials, styles and types of jewellery occur make it impractical to list all the references. In these cases page numbers are given in bold type for main references only.